Bubble and Spark Chambers

Principles and Use

VOLUME I

PURE AND APPLIED PHYSICS

A SERIES OF MONOGRAPHS AND TEXTBOOKS

CONSULTING EDITORS

H. S. W. MASSEY

University College, London, England

KEITH A. BRUECKNER

*University of California, San Diego
La Jolla, California*

Bubble and Spark Chambers

Principles and Use

Edited by **R. P. SHUTT**

BROOKHAVEN NATIONAL LABORATORY
UPTON, NEW YORK

VOLUME I

ACADEMIC PRESS New York and London 1967

ACADEMIC PRESS INC.
111 Fifth Avenue, New York, New York 10003

United Kingdom Edition published by
ACADEMIC PRESS INC. (LONDON) LTD.
Berkeley Square House, London W.1

LIBRARY OF CONGRESS CATALOG CARD NUMBER: 67-19642

PRINTED IN THE UNITED STATES OF AMERICA

List of Contributors

Numbers in parentheses indicate the pages on which the authors' contributions begin.

James W. Cronin, *Palmer Physical Laboratory, Princeton University, Princeton, New Jersey* (315)

W. B. Fowler, *Brookhaven National Laboratory, Upton, New York* (59)

A. Lagarrigue,* *École Polytechnique, Paris, France* (159)

Ch. Peyrou, *CERN, Geneva, Switzerland* (19)

A. Rousset, *École Polytechnique, Paris, France* (159)

Alan M. Thorndike, *Brookhaven National Laboratory, Upton, New York* (1)

W. T. Welford, *Department of Physics, Imperial College of Science and Technology, London, England* (233)

* *Present address*: Laboratoire de l'Accélérateur Lineaire, Faculté des Sciences, Orsay, France.

v

Preface

With the exception of some research on cosmic radiation, experimentation in high energy (or elementary-particle) physics begins at a particle accelerator's injector and ends at analysis and interpretation of the data obtained at detectors.

Bubble chambers and spark chambers are two of the most widely used detectors. Their principles and uses are described in this book in sufficient detail to meet four objectives: (1) to serve as a reference work for physicists active in the field and as a survey of the present state of the art for those less active; (2) to allow students to become familiar with facilities and methods which, for instance, might furnish data for their graduate research but which, because of their complexity and specialization, might remain rather inaccessible; (3) to introduce engineers to a field which makes use of the most modern concepts of their professions such as cryogenics, optics, instrumentation, materials, measuring devices, electronic techniques, magnet engineering, or high voltage dc and rf engineering; and (4) to introduce applied mathematicians and computer engineers to some applications of their most recent, very powerful tools.

Since bubble chambers and spark chambers are useless without arrangements which produce beams of particles from accelerators, or without scanning and measuring procedures and the extensive use of digital computer facilities, beam techniques and data processing methods are described in corresponding detail.

Because of the multitude of successful approaches to be covered and because of their complexities, this work appears in two volumes. Bubble and spark chambers and the special topics concerned with optics and magnets are treated first, followed by the chapters on data processing which include conventional and on-line-to-computer methods. Logically the chapter on beam production belongs near the beginning of the work, but for the sake of continuity of the subjects treated at that point, it has been placed in Volume II.

Elementary-particle physics is a fast-moving field of research, both in theory and experimentation. The larger accelerators of the future will necessitate further improvements in beam technique. Design and construction of new, very large bubble chambers are already in progress. Application of superconductors to produce stronger magnetic fields in large bubble or spark chambers is within reach. Cathode-ray tube display, on-line programming, and random access mass storage are examples of future applications of data processing methods in the field. This work only briefly mentions such future efforts, descriptions of which still belong in special proposals or reports. It emphasizes general principles and those aspects of the various techniques which are likely to remain applicable for a long time.

The splendid cooperation, effort, and patience of the authors and publishers of this work are very highly appreciated.

September, 1967   R. P. SHUTT

Contents

Chapter I.   **Introduction**

ALAN M. THORNDIKE

Chapter II.   **Bubble Chamber Principles**

CH. PEYROU

Chapter III.   **Cryogenic Bubble Chambers**

W. B. FOWLER

Chapter IV. **Heavy Liquid Bubble Chambers**

A. LAGARRIGUE and A. ROUSSET

Chapter V. **Illumination and Photography of Bubble Chambers**

W. T. WELFORD

Chapter VI. **Spark Chambers**

JAMES W. CRONIN

Contents of Volume II

Bubble and Spark Chambers

Principles and Use

VOLUME I

Chapter I

Introduction

Alan M. Thorndike

Brookhaven National Laboratory
Upton, New York

I. General Features of Bubble Chambers and Spark Chambers

Bubble chambers and spark chambers are instruments for detecting the passage of high energy charged particles, which have proved to be especially effective for studying the complicated interaction and decay processes that occur with particle energies of a billion electron volts (BeV) or more. In recent years, bubble chambers and spark chambers have become the dominant experimental tools in high energy physics, and this situation seems likely to continue for some time to come. Although the technical details of bubble chambers and spark chambers are different in many respects, the chambers have a fundamental similarity in that both give accurate spatial information about the paths followed by charged particles during a well-defined time interval. It is consequently reasonable to describe them together, and an attempt will be made in Volumes 1 and 2 to present information on their construction, operation, and use for physical measurements, so that their role in high energy physics experiments may be accurately assessed.

A. BUBBLE CHAMBERS

The basic principle of operation of the bubble chamber involves a superheated liquid, that is, a liquid at a temperature and pressure such that the actual pressure is lower than the equilibrium vapor pressure of that liquid at that temperature. Such a condition is unstable, but boiling in the interior of the liquid requires the formation of additional liquid surface, which requires energy, and so a superheated condition can be maintained for a short period. If the degree of superheat is great enough, the local disturbance

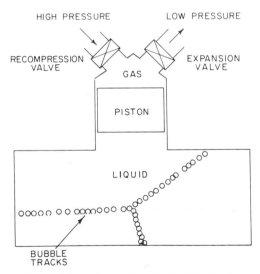

FIG. 1. Schematic drawing of a bubble chamber.

caused by the passage of a single high energy charged particle initiates bubble formation, and a series of bubbles begins to grow along the path of the particle. These bubbles provide a "track" which shows to a high accuracy where the particle went.

To achieve the superheated condition of the liquid, a rapid pressure drop is required, starting from an equilibrium pressure high enough that boiling cannot occur. This pressure drop, or expansion, may be caused by releasing gas pressure or by moving a piston in contact with the liquid, as sketched in Fig. 1. The temperature is held as constant as possible. Soon after the pressure has dropped sufficiently to make the chamber sensitive, the process is reversed and the pressure is brought back to its equilibrium value. A sensitive time of a few milliseconds is typical.

For satisfactory operation, the bubble chamber temperature must be controlled accurately, and the time of sensitivity of the chamber must be synchronized with a pulse of particles from the accelerator which provides the particle beam. The bubbles marking the particle tracks are recorded in stereoscopic photographs using electronic photoflash illumination. The bubble chamber pressure is several atmospheres,[1] and many of the liquids used are inflammable or explosive when mixed with air, so that safety precautions must be carefully provided. A bubble chamber of large size is therefore a complex and costly installation.

B. SPARK CHAMBERS

The basic principle of operation of the spark chamber involves a gas discharge in a gap between two electrodes as shown in Fig. 2. An electric field is applied which is high enough to cause a discharge, or spark, if there are ions and electrons in the gap, such as are left along the path of an

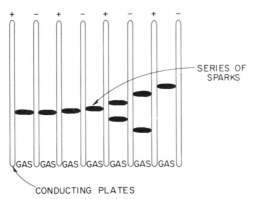

FIG. 2. Schematic drawing of a spark chamber.

energetic charged particle, but not in the absence of such ions and electrons. The exact mechanism is complicated, but the general feature is that the ions and electrons are given enough energy by the electric field that they can

---

[1] This is true of all liquids that are commonly used, except liquid helium.

ionize the gas, making more ions and electrons, and so multiplication occurs to the point that a visible spark is produced. As with the pressure drop in the bubble chamber, the electric field is applied when sensitivity is desired and removed again after the spark has occurred so that equilibrium conditions may be restored. The duration of the electric field is much less, however, than that of the pressure drop: measured in microseconds rather than milliseconds.

This short duration has two important effects. In the first place, it means that the time resolution of the spark chamber is very good—only particles that passed through the chamber just before, or during, the voltage pulse can be recorded, so that background at any other time is eliminated. In the second place, the voltage pulse can be applied fast enough to catch ions and electrons formed by particles that have just passed through previously. The particles can be recorded by scintillation counters which are used to trigger the voltage pulse. If a counter system can be devised to select the desired particles or combinations of them, by triggering the chamber only those particles will be recorded, and undesired particles completely eliminated. In practice the elimination is rarely perfect but is nevertheless extremely useful.

The first spark chambers used stereoscopic photography for recording spark positions in the same general way as that used for bubble chambers. More recently, however, a number of automatic electronic techniques for providing direct digital read-out of spark positions have been introduced. For example, the electrodes may consist of finely-spaced conductors and the spark position determined by recording the conductor in which the discharge current pulse occurs, as described by Fischer (1966). The data obtained by spark chambers are very similar to those obtained by bubble chambers in that both can record track positions for all particles involved in an interaction or decay process. The actual use of spark chambers, however, is often to provide accurate localization for the track of a single particle, in effect as a localizing counter of high spatial resolution.

C. PARTICLE ACCELERATORS

High energy particles occur naturally in cosmic rays, but high energy particle accelerators provide the particle beams for the vast majority of contemporary high energy experiments. Techniques for selection of the secondary beam from the accelerator target are described in Chapter IV, Volume 2. In this book, no attempt is made to discuss the production of the accelerator's primary beam. Accelerator techniques are described, for example, by

Livingston and Blewett (1961). As used for high energy physics experiments, bubble chambers and spark chambers are part of the complex of equipment associated with high energy particle accelerators. Taken together, they have contributed greatly to the progress of modern high energy physics.

II. Previous Track Recording Techniques

While bubble chambers and spark chambers are devices which have come into use during the last decade, they have evolved from precursors that also provided a track recording capability. Many of the methods used in working with bubble chambers and spark chambers have been taken over from the previous techniques without much modification. Many high energy experimenters have transferred their efforts from the older techniques to the newer ones. These factors have made a very rapid growth in bubble chamber and spark chamber use possible.

Among the older track recording techniques, the most widely used was probably the nuclear emulsion, in which the passage of a charged particle is recorded as a track of silver grains that can be observed under a microscope. Positions can be measured very accurately, but there is no time resolution. The emulsion consists of a mixture of elements, and microscopic observation is very tedious.

The most similar of the precursors was the Wilson cloud chamber, in which tracks are marked by droplets condensed on ions in a supersaturated vapor. The sensitive volume is filled at equilibrium with a mixture of non-condensable gas and vapor in equilibrium with a small amount of liquid. A sudden, more or less adiabatic, drop in pressure of the gas-vapor mixture causes a drop in temperature which causes the vapor to become supersaturated. If the volume is sufficiently free of other condensation centers, droplets form along the charged particle tracks. After stereo photography, the filling is recompressed, the equilibrium restored, and the process recycled. The sensitive time is a fraction of a second. The device is, in a sense, the inverse of a bubble chamber, limited in effectiveness by slow cycling rate, low density of the sensitive material, and liability to contamination. Since it operates with a gaseous filling, however, ions have a long enough life time in the chamber that the expansion can be triggered after the passage of the particles. Thus, cloud chambers used in cosmic ray experiments were almost always triggered by counters, a mode of operation that is not possible with bubble chambers but is not needed for experiments with particle beams from accelerators.

A variant of the cloud chamber known as the diffusion chamber used a different way of producing supersaturation. Instead of the temperature drop due to expansion, diffusion of vapor into a cold region is employed to give a sensitive volume. Continuous sensitivity is an advantage; limited sensitive volume and loss of sensitivity in the presence of many charged particles are disadvantages which have led to the diffusion chamber's abandonment today.

These track recording methods are all pictorial in nature. They give a precise record of space relationships from which the significant information is abstracted by later measurement. In a somewhat different sense, a counter hodoscope is also a track recording device. An array of many counters serving as detecting elements is provided, each of which gives a yes–no indication of whether the particle passed through it. If the array is sufficiently extensive that each particle passes through several counters, the particle tracks are defined, and the good time resolution of counters maintained as well. Such counter hodoscopes have been in use for many years. Their practical limitations arise from the fact that many counters are required to give good spatial resolution and the complexity of circuitry becomes formidable. Good accuracy is possible only for particles whose angles and momenta lie within certain limits, and multiparticle processes cannot easily be accommodated.

In general, bubble chambers and spark chambers have proved to be the most versatile and effective of the track recording techniques. Subsequent chapters will provide more details on their design, construction, operation, and use.

III. History of Bubble Chamber Development

A. DISCOVERY BY GLASER

When Glaser began to explore the possibility of a detector for ionizing particles using a superheated liquid, at the University of Michigan in May 1952, he was exploring an idea that seems, in retrospect, simple and almost obvious. It had, in fact, occurred to others previously, but Glaser showed that it could be made to work. Such a device fitted the needs of high energy experiments at large accelerators, and its development and exploitation were soon pushed by many physicists in many laboratories. Within 10 years, the volume of a typical bubble chamber increased by a factor of a million, and the use of bubble chambers spread to every laboratory with a substantial high energy physics program.

Glaser first pictured the formation of a bubble as made easier by the repulsion of like electric charges on its surface, a condition that might be found along the track of a charged particle.[2] He then estimated that diethyl ether might show such supersensitivity if it could be superheated to 140°C, more than 100°C above its normal boiling point of 34.6°C. This seemed a lot to expect, but Glaser found that the literature on superheating of liquids included reports of classic experiments done some 30 years before by Kenrick *et al.* (1924) in which highly superheated liquids had been produced in clean glass tubes. The ether reached a temperature of 140°C, and Kenrick *et al.* found that after an irregular "waiting time" of many seconds the liquid would erupt violently. Glaser noted that the waiting times were understandable if eruption was boiling triggered by the passage of cosmic ray particles. He then repeated the experiment and showed that he could get comparable superheats at which boiling could be caused immediately by bringing up a radioactive source.

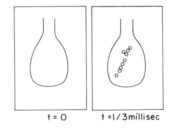

t = 0   t = 1/3 millisec

FIG. 3. Sketch of a cosmic ray track in Glaser's early ether-filled glass chamber, recorded at 3000 frames per second. The two successive frames are before and after passage of the particle.

These results made it reasonably certain that the superheated liquid was sensitive to radiation. A somewhat larger glass bulb was prepared with a more convenient way of reducing the pressure. High speed movies taken at 3000 frames per second showed the clearly defined track sketched in Fig. 3. From this point on, the history of bubble chamber development has been one of technical refinement and elaboration, which has progressed at an overwhelming pace.

The most crucial technical development was the elimination of the all glass construction and introduction of what has been called the "dirty" chamber. The original glass bulbs had scrupulously clean surfaces. In them, the unstable superheated state could be maintained for many seconds. In a "dirty" chamber, many points on the walls provide nuclei at which boiling

[2] This model for bubble formation now seems unlikely. See Chapter II, this volume.

can occur and this boiling tends to restore the pressure to its equilibrium value. If the expansion that provides the pressure drop is fast enough, however, a brief period of sensitivity can be achieved in the presence of boiling at the walls. This means that there are no special limitations on the materials that may be used in bubble chamber construction, and whatever metal structure with glass windows, gaskets, and other parts is suitable from an engineering point of view can reasonably be expected to function as a "dirty" bubble chamber. This mode of operation, first reported by Wood (1954), made it possible to construct bubble chambers of large size, not merely glass bulbs a few centimeters in size. Chambers with dimensions ~ 10 cm were built at once, and within a few years construction was started on ones with dimensions ~ 100 cm.

B. Liquid Hydrogen Chambers

Since the hydrogen nucleus is a single proton, it provides the simplest possible target for nuclear interactions, and a bubble chamber operating with liquid hydrogen has great advantages for high energy nuclear physics. Hildebrand and Nagle soon showed that a superheated condition that was radiation sensitive could be maintained in liquid hydrogen. The pioneering work on liquid hydrogen bubble chambers was done by a group at the University of California under the direction of Alvarez. The $1\frac{1}{2}$-in. chamber described by Wood (1954) began a series which went rapidly to diameters of 4, 10, and 15 in. The larger chambers were provided with a magnetic field, stereoscopic photography, and other features necessary for routine operation. They were used for an extensive series of experiments over a period of several years. Already by 1955, however, plans were being made for a larger chamber, rectangular in shape, with a length of 72 in. This chamber, substantially larger than any other at that time, was assembled and first expanded in March 1959, not quite seven years after Glaser's initial discovery. These seven years were a period of explosive growth which has, since then, continued somewhat more slowly.

The technical problems of building and operating a bubble chamber at liquid hydrogen temperature are numerous: materials, seals, insulation, refrigeration, expansion mechanisms, photography, safety, to name a few. The methods developed are described in Chapter III, this volume. Large scale cryogenic techniques are a basic necessity, and the hydrogen bubble chamber developments drew heavily on cryogenic information and facilities that were part of the hydrogen bomb and rocket propulsion efforts.

Concurrently with the University of California program, liquid hydrogen bubble chambers were built at many other laboratories, both in the United States and in Europe. Variations in design were introduced, particularly in mode of expansion and illumination, and both the quality of photographs and accuracy of data improved. In the analysis of bubble chamber data, large general purpose digital computers came to play a central role. Chambers, such as the Brookhaven 80 in. chamber and CERN 2 meter chamber, were built that had substantially greater volume than the Berkeley 72 in. chamber. Detailed feasibility studies have been made for a chamber volume of 62,000 liters described by Fowler (1966) and construction has begun at Argonne on a somewhat smaller chamber with cooldown expected in the summer of 1969 according to Pewitt (1966). A 7500 liter chamber is nearing completion at Saclay, according to a review of recent developments by Derrick (1966).

C. HEAVY LIQUID CHAMBERS

Chambers filled with a liquid of higher molecular weight than hydrogen have a number of desirable features which, for some purposes, are more important than the simplicity of the hydrogen nucleus. The greater density provides more interactions per unit volume, greater stopping power, and a very much greater effectiveness for the conversion of γ rays to electron pairs. These properties are discussed in Chapter IV, this volume. Heavy liquid chambers have, therefore, been developed along with those employing liquid hydrogen and have been almost as extensively used.

After Glaser's initial experiments, ether was soon abandoned as a bubble chamber liquid, and its place taken by propane, which had a lower operating temperature and other practical advantages. Propane chambers were in use for high energy physics experiments by early 1956. A 30 in. chamber was in operation 2 years later (Powell et al., 1958) and a number of larger ones have been completed since. Their use has been widespread, and a number of individuals and groups have contributed to their development.

Propane is not actually a very heavy liquid. Its operating density is 0.43, and the highest atomic charge contained is 6. Efforts to go further in this direction have been made by a number of people. Perhaps the most dramatic result has been the successful operation of a bubble chamber with liquid xenon filling (density 2.3, atomic number 54), which utilized a substantial fraction of the world's available supply of xenon. A somewhat more practical approach for most purposes has been the introduction of halogen compounds, such as freon CF_3Br and methyl iodide CH_3I. Mixtures of such liquids also operate satisfactorily for bubble chamber fillings as a rule, so that liquids with a wide variety of properties are available. A number of chambers have been built with lengths of about a meter and volumes of several hundred liters. A considerably larger heavy liquid chamber is under construction in France. Known as "Gargamelle," it is 4.8 meters long and 1.9 meters in diameter (Ohayon and Petiau, 1966).

Even liquid helium has been used as a sensitive liquid in a bubble chamber. Mixtures of liquid hydrogen and neon also prove to be suitable for use in cryogenic chambers.

Subsequent chapters will give details of operating characteristics, techniques, and applications to experiments in high energy physics of the many possibilities.

IV. History of Spark Chamber Development

A. EARLY DEVELOPMENTS

Spark chambers have been used extensively only during the last several years, but the conditions under which ionizing particles could cause sparks between parallel plates had been investigated in some detail more than 15 years ago. In the late 1940's, a great deal of effort was devoted to techniques that would provide a charged particle counter with a more rapid operation than the Geiger counter. The scintillation counter has become the accepted solution to this problem, but one alternative solution was the parallel plate counter. Very clean parallel plates could be charged to a voltage such that an ionizing particle would trigger a discharge, that is, a spark. Such counters, investigated by Keuffel (1948) and by Pidd and Madansky (1949), would have been spark chambers if they had been photographed to show the spark position, but the physicists concerned were seeking counters, not track localizing chambers, and concentrated their attention on the electrical signal due to the spark. The possibility of photographing sparks was recognized but not pursued actively at that time.

The early spark counters had voltage on the plates continuously and a discharge could occur at any time. They were difficult to operate and subject to spurious discharges that did not represent particles. A crucial step in making a practical spark chamber was the introduction of a pulsed voltage, triggered by scintillation counters so that voltage was applied only when a particle of potential interest was present. This step, however, was not made universally at first. During the 1950's, a number of investigators used discharges between parallel plates to record particle trajectories. Sparks were photographed by Bella *et al.* (1953), and stereo pairs were used by Henning (1955). His work at Hamburg was followed by an extensive investigation there. Conversi and Gozzini (1955) used a pulsed voltage on a device having many neon filled glass tubes stacked between parallel electrodes. Tubes through which a charged particle had passed glowed, others did not. Cranshaw and deBeer (1957) applied the pulsed voltage to parallel plates, without the tubes, in the way that has since come into general use. They used air instead of a noble gas for filling, and, for reasons explained in Chapter VI, this volume, their chamber would record only a single track. This would be of limited use for experiments.

By this time, there was considerable interest in the spark chamber for use in experiments with high energy accelerators. A chamber sensitive to α particles was reported by Charpak (1957). The first really practical spark chamber design was that reported by Fukui and Miyamoto (1959) which used a neon gas filling. This was a big improvement; the chamber had better efficiency, lower operating voltage, and the ability to record several simultaneous particle tracks in a given gap. Such a device was clearly useful for high energy physics experiments, and a number of groups built spark chambers to use in conjunction with arrays of scintillation counters that selected events to be recorded and triggered the spark chamber. By the summer of 1960, a number of groups had chambers in operation essentially like that of Fukui and Miyamoto. (For a more detailed review of early work see Roberts, 1961.)

B. Spark Chambers Used in High Energy Experiments

Most of the larger bubble chambers that have been built have been used over and over again for a series of many different experiments. A bubble chamber is a general purpose device which can be operated in many different particle beams. Photographs are taken without selection, and a given set of photographs often provides data concerning several different phenomena. The mode of operation of spark chambers is quite different in that the events recorded by the spark chamber are selected by a counter coincidence arrangement. From one viewpoint, the counters are accessories of the spark chamber that provide pictures with a higher proportion of interesting events. From another viewpoint, the chamber is an accessory of the counters, providing more detailed information on the positions of particles taking part in the event counted. Spark chambers have correspondingly tended to be built for a particular experiment, with the geometry of spark chamber and counters fitted to the requirements of a particular experiment.[3] Consequently, a discussion of spark chambers, as they have been used for experiments, can be done most realistically in terms of specific examples. The four following give some idea of the varied uses and types of spark chambers.

1. *Spark Chambers for an Elastic Cross Section Measurement*

The differential cross section for K^+-p elastic scattering was studied by Cook *et al.* (1963) using a liquid hydrogen target largely surrounded by spark chambers. Time-of-flight and Čerenkov counters selected K^+ mesons. Each spark chamber had 6 gaps 10 in. wide by 28 in. long, with $\frac{3}{8}$ in. spacing. The "plates" were hollow, made by stretching 0.003 in. aluminum foil over a frame of aluminum tubing, so that a chamber of low stopping power was available. Three chambers were placed about the hydrogen target as shown in Fig. 4. The spark chambers covered a large solid angle and gave an identification of the event since both scattered K^+ and recoil proton tracks were recorded. (A different arrangement was used for small angle scattering.)

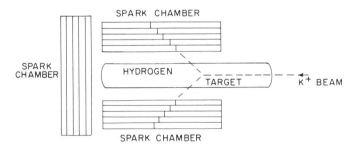

Fig. 4. Spark chambers for detecting elastic K^+-p scattering.

2. *Spark Chambers Used in Measurement of the Λ^0 Magnetic Moment*

The use by Cool *et al.* (1962) of the apparatus shown in Fig. 5 was, in qualitative terms, as follows. The beam consisted of π^+ mesons and protons; interactions in the target of the type $\pi^+ + n \rightarrow K^+ + \Lambda^0$ were selected by requiring a count in Čerenkov counter B sensitive to π^+ but not p, counts in the telescope $S_1 C_1 S_2 S_3$ that was sensitive to K^+, an anticoincidence in counter A, a coincidence in counter T, and tracks observed in the two spark

---

[3] The fact that spark chambers are simpler mechanically, requiring less time and money to assemble than a large bubble chamber, makes this type of operation possible.

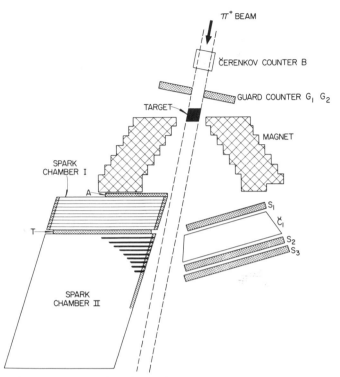

FIG. 5. Schematic diagram of spark chambers, counters, and magnet used for measurement of the angle of precession of the Λ^0 magnetic moment.

chambers that were consistent with a Λ^0 decay occurring in spark chamber I. The Λ^0 decay is asymmetrical since the Λ^0 is polarized in the production process and parity is not conserved in the decay. The magnet was operated with field first parallel and then antiparallel to the general beam direction. In passing through the magnet, the Λ^0 spin precesses, and thus the two field orientations give different Λ^0 decay distributions. The difference measures the Λ^0 magnetic moment.

Spark chamber I was made of 0.008 in. stainless steel plates to have a low probability for interaction of photons and neutrons. The gaps were 0.25 in. Spark chamber II, on the other hand, had 0.125 in. brass plates so that the proton from the Λ^0 decay (and sometimes also the π^-) would stop in the chamber. The angle and range measurements provided a satisfactory identification of the Λ^0 decays in the presence of background consisting of electron pairs and neutron interactions.

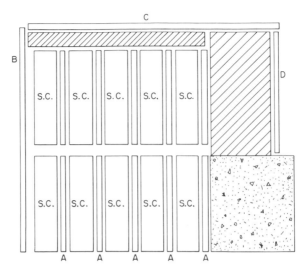

Fig. 6. Spark chamber and counter arrangement used for detection of neutrino interactions. A marks the triggering counters; B, C, and D mark anticoincidence counters. This is the front view seen by the four camera stereo system.

3. Spark Chambers Used to Detect Neutrino Interactions

The spark chambers used by Danby *et al.* (1962) were quite different from the thin-plate chambers just described. They were designed to provide a large mass in which the interactions could occur. The description is taken from their report.

"The spark chamber detector consists of an array of 10 one-ton modules. Each unit has 9 aluminum plates $44 \times 44 \times 1$ in. thick, separated by $\frac{3}{8}$ in. Lucite spacers. Each module is driven by a specially designed high pressure spark gap and the entire assembly triggered as described below ... Fig. 6 illustrates the arrangement of coincidence and anticoincidence counters. Top, back, and front anticoincidence sheets (a total of 50 counters, each $48 \times 11 \times \frac{1}{2}$ in.) are provided to reduce the effect of cosmic rays and AGS-produced muons which penetrate the shield. The top slab is shielded against neutrino events by 6 in. of steel and the back slab by 3 ft of steel and lead.

"Triggering counters were inserted between adjacent chambers and at the end.... These consist of pairs of counters, $48 \times 11 \times \frac{1}{2}$ in., separated by $\frac{3}{4}$ in. of aluminum, and in fast coincidence. Four such pairs cover a chamber; 40 are employed in all."

4. *Wire Spark Chambers Used in a High Energy Particle Spectrometer*

The particle spectrometer shown in Fig. 7 was used by Anderson *et al.* (1966) to obtain precision momentum measurements of protons with momenta from 6 to 30 BeV/c. It is typical of a number of recent experiments in which high resolution and high data acquisition rates are obtained by the use of directly-digitized spark chambers. One may think of the telescope $S_1 S_2 S_3 S_4 \check{C}$ as selecting scattered protons in a given range of angle and momentum. The wire spark chambers give a precise measurement of angle and momentum, with a momentum resolution (including $\pm 0.25\%$ spread in the incident beam) of from $\pm 0.45\%$ at 6 BeV/c to $\pm 0.3\%$ at 30 BeV/c. Data rates in the experiment ranged from 1 to 150 events per AGS pulse.

The information from the chambers was coded and sent to a Digital Equipment Corp. PDP-6 computer which calculated the angle and moment-um for each proton. At the end of each run a summary was printed out which included histograms of differential cross sections, beam characteristics, and information on performance of the wire chambers.

V. Analyzing Large Numbers of Events

Both bubble chambers and spark chambers have the capacity for recording rather detailed information about individual events and recording large numbers of events.[4] The data are usually recorded photographically. The photographs, often numbering 100,000 to 1,000,000 for a given experiment, must be "scanned" to find events and these events measured to extract the necessary data. Bubble chamber pictures require high accuracy of measure-ment; spark chamber pictures are usually less demanding. As a rule, scanning and measurement are performed by specially trained, but nonscientific, personnel. The resulting data are then processed by large scale digital computers to extract the desired information. The methods are described in Chapters II and III, Volume 2.

The growth of bubble chamber and spark chamber techniques has been intimately related to the growth of high speed computers. The availability of computers has made clear the desirability of automation of scanning and measuring methods to provide greater speed, reproducibility, and accuracy. Such automation is obviously possible in principle, as described in Chapter III, Volume 2, but its introduction has proved to be difficult in practice.

[4] The neutrino experiment just referred to was exceptional in that the number of events recorded was ~ 100.

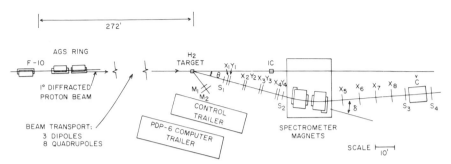

FIG. 7. High energy particle spectrometer used by Anderson *et al.* (1966). $X_i Y_i$ are wire spark chambers used to measure horizontal and vertical coordinates along a scattered proton trajectory. $\check{C}$ is a Čerenkov counter and the S_i are trigger counters such that a scattered proton event is registered as $S_1 S_2 S_3 S_4 - \check{C}$. $M_1 M_2$ form a beam monitor telescope (not to scale). IC is an ion chamber used to monitor the incident beam. The scattering angle θ was adjustable from $0°$ to $15°$ and the deflection angle δ was varied from $2°$ to $12°$.

While the physicist today has many automatic procedures at his disposal, complete automation of the analysis of photographically recorded data is by no means an accomplished fact, at the time of writing.

In the case of spark chambers with direct digital recording the number of individual events in an experiment may well be 10^7 or 10^8, although the number of bits of information per event is usually less than when photographic recording is employed. Data processing procedures are highly automatic and are often carried out to some degree in "real time" during accelerator operation with an on-line computer. As a rule the data are also recorded subsequently for more detailed analysis. These procedures all rely heavily on large scale high-speed electronic computers, and their utilization is vital to high-energy physics experiments employing bubble chambers and spark chambers.

REFERENCES

ANDERSON, E. W. *et al.* (1966). *Phys. Rev. Letters* **16**, 855 (1966).

BELLA, F., FRANZINETTI, C., and LEE, D. W. (1953). *Nuovo Cimento* **10**, 1338.

CHARPAK, G. (1957). *J. Phys. Radium* **18**, 539.

CONVERSI, M., and GOZZINI, A. (1955). *Nuovo Cimento* **2**, 189.

COOK, V., KEEFE, D., KERTH, L. T., MURPHY, P. G., WENZEL, W. A., and ZIPF, T. F. (1963). *Phys. Rev.* **129**, 2743.

COOL, R. L., JENKINS, E. W., KYCIA, T. F., HILL, D. A., MARSHALL, L., and SCHLUTER, R. A. (1962). *Phys. Rev.* **127**, 2223.

CRANSHAW, T. E., and deBEER, J. F. (1957). *Nuovo Cimento* [10] **5**, 1107.

DANBY, G., GAILLARD, J. M., GOULIANOS, K., LEDERMAN, L. M., MISTRY, N., SCHWARTZ, M., and STEINBERGER, J. (1962). *Phys. Rev. Letters* **9**, 36.

DEMARS, P. (1958). "Ionographie, les émulsions nucleaires, principles et applications." Univ. of Montreal Press, Montreal.

DERRICK, M. (1966). Bubble chambers, *Proc. Intern. Conf. Instrumentation High Energy Phys., Stanford, 1966*, p. 431. National Bureau of Standards, U.S. Dept. Commerce, Springfield, Virginia.

FISCHER, J. (1966). Digitized spark chambers at BNL, *Proc. Intern. Conf. Instrumentation High Energy Phys., Stanford, 1966*, p. 31. National Bureau of Standards, U.S. Dept. Commerce, Springfield, Virginia.

FOWLER, W. B. (1966). BNL's large bubble chamber program, *Proc. Intern. Conf. Instrumentation High Energy Phys., Stanford, 1966*, p. 87. National Bureau of Standards, U.S. Dept. Commerce, Springfield, Virginia.

FUKUI, S., and MIYAMOTO, S. (1959). *Nuovo Cimento* [10] **11**, 113.

GLASER, D. A. (1955). The bubble chamber, *Sci. Am.* **192** (Feb.), 46.

GLASER, D. A. (1958). The bubble chamber, *in* "Encyclopedia of Physics," Vol. XLV, p. 314. Springer, Berlin.

GOW, J. D., and ROSENFELD, A. H. (1959). Berkeley 72-in. hydrogen bubble chamber, *in Intern. Conf. High Energy Accelerators Instrumentation, CERN, Geneva* (L. Kowarski, ed.), p. 435.

HENNING, P. G. (1955). Thesis, Hamburg (quoted in Roberts (1961)).

KENRICK, F. B., GILBERT, C. S., and WISMER, K. L. (1924). *J. Phys. Chem.* **28**, 1927.

KEUFFEL, J. W. (1948). *Phys. Rev.* **73**, 531.

LIVINGSTON, M. S., and BLEWETT, J. P. (1961). "Particle Accelerators," McGraw-Hill, New York.

LOFGREN, E. J. (Ed.) (1960). *Proc. Intern. Conf. Instrumentation High Energy Phys., Lawrence Radiation Lab., Sept. 1960*.

OHAYON, M., and PETIAU, P. (1966). The large heavy liquid chamber "Gargamelle," *Proc. Intern. Conf. Instrumentation High Energy Phys., Stanford, 1966*, p. 100. National Bureau of Standards, U.S. Dept. Commerce, Springfield, Virginia.

O'NEILL, G. K. (1962). The spark chamber, *Sci. Am.* **207** (Aug.), 37.

PARMENTIER, D., and SCHWEMIN, A. J. (1955). *Rev. Sci. Instr.* **26**, 954.

PEWITT, E. G. (1966). Design status of ANL 12-foot hydrogen bubble chamber, *Proc. Intern. Conf. Instrumentation High Energy Phys., Stanford, 1966*, p. 104. National Bureau of Standards, U.S. Dept. Commerce, Springfield, Virginia.

PIDD, R. W., and MADANSKY, L. (1949). *Phys. Rev.* **75**, 1175.

POWELL, W. M., FOWLER, W. B., and OSWALD, L. O. (1958). *Rev. Sci. Instr.* **29**, 874.

POWELL, C. F., FOWLER, P. H., and PERKINS, D. H. (1959). "The Study of Elementary Particles by the Photographic Method." Pergamon Press, Oxford.

ROBERTS, A. (1961). *Rev. Sci. Instr.* **32**, 482. (See also pp. 486–531 reporting on the Symp. on Spark Chambers, Argonne Natl. Lab., Feb. 7, 1961.)

WOOD, J. G. (1954). *Phys. Rev.* **94**, 731.

Chapter II

Bubble Chamber Principles[1]

Ch. Peyrou

CERN, Geneva, Switzerland

[1] *Author's note:* The author of this chapter is a nuclear physicist. Thermodynamic considerations may be elementary, old-fashioned, and sometimes, not even quite correct. For most of the

I. Phases in Metastable States

A. INTRODUCTION

It is well known in elementary classical physics that a phase can be brought into a state of temperature and pressure well inside the stability region of another phase of the same substance and remain nevertheless stable. A vapor can be supercooled without condensing into liquid. A liquid can be superheated without boiling or supercooled without crystallizing.

It is also well known that if minute amounts of energy are brought to the substance, phase transition will take place immediately and at the beginning is localized around the points where the excitation was applied. This fact has been used successfully to form tracks of high energy ionizing particles in the cloud chamber and in the bubble chamber. From a broad thermodynamic point of view, the photographic emulsion technique makes use of the same effect. In the presence of a developer, silver should be precipitated from silver bromide, but it does so only where some excitation energy has been applied in advance and stored.

Why such phenomena are so general is not well known, and the subject is probably not so classical since books were written on the subject not long ago. The most comprehensive and complete study on this topic has been given by Volmer (1939), but he himself quotes Gibbs (1878) as having stated the essential point.

Since there is no pre-existing surface of separation, the new phase should start to be formed somewhere in the mass of the old one. (We suppose, of course, that the walls have no catalytic effect since otherwise the metastable state could not be obtained.) If the new phase is a liquid or gas, the surface will take the form of a sphere in order to minimize the surface energy. It can be shown that there is a critical radius for such a sphere. The definition of this critical radius is the following: If the actual radius is smaller than the critical one, it is in fact the new phase which is unstable. If the radius is larger, the new phase (droplet of liquid or bubble of gas) will develop and the metastable state of the old phase will disappear.

Furthermore, it can be shown that the formation of the sphere of critical radius always requires that a certain amount of work must be done on the system. Therefore, in the absence of a mechanism to provide that work, the

---

quantities computed in this chapter the important feature is their order of magnitude. Discrepancies with values reported elsewhere or even internal discrepancies are of no great importance if they do not exceed a factor of 1.5 or 2.

critical radius will never be reached, and the old phase will remain indefinitely stable.

We shall study this theory in more detail for the case of interest here: the vapor bubble in a superheated liquid.

B. THE CRITICAL BUBBLE

If a liquid has been expanded to a pressure p_e, lower than p_∞ (p_∞ = equilibrium vapor pressure at the temperature T, the surface of separation from the liquid being a plane), a vapor bubble of radius r_c will be in mechanical equilibrium if

$$p_c - p_e = \frac{2\sigma}{r_c}, \tag{1}$$

where p_c is the pressure of the vapor inside the bubble and σ the surface tension of the liquid.

This, however, does not define the critical radius r_c since p_c, the pressure of the vapor in equilibrium with the liquid at a spherical surface of separation, is not equal to p_∞; p_c is defined rather by the equilibrium condition, which is best expressed by the equality of the Gibbs potentials, for the liquid and the vapor phases.

On the other hand, when both liquid and vapor are at p_∞, there is equilibrium (at a plane separation surface) and the Gibbs potentials are equal. For an isothermal transformation the variation of the Gibbs potentials is given by $\int v \, dp$. If we consider (Fig. 1) a p, v diagram where I and II are

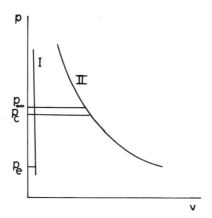

FIG. 1. Isotherms for liquid (I) and vapor (II).

the isotherms for the liquid and the vapor, respectively, p_c is a pressure
defined in such a way that the area determined by the ordinates p_c, p_∞,
and curve II is equal to the area determined by the ordinate, $p_c = $ const.,
$p_\infty = $ const., and curve I. p_c is smaller than p_∞, and one has the equation

$$\frac{RT}{M} \ln \frac{p_\infty}{p_c} = \frac{p_\infty - p_e}{\rho}, \tag{2}$$

where M is the molecular weight of the substance and ρ the density of the
liquid. It is assumed that the liquid is incompressible. If one is not too close
to the critical point, the specific volumes of liquid and vapor are very
different, and therefore p_c is not very different from p_∞ unless the difference
$p_\infty - p_e$ is very large, which can only occur if the pressure p_e is negative.

There are other methods to arrive at Eq. (2). One can, for instance, define
the critical equilibrium bubble in the following way. The radius of the
bubble is such that the evaporation of a minute amount of liquid with a
corresponding increase of radius dr will deliver to the outside of the system
the same amount of work as if this minute increase was achieved by some
other reversible manner. Now, when the radius of the bubble increases by
an amount dr, the volume of the system, vapor-liquid, increases by
$4\pi r^2 \, dr(1 - \rho'/\rho)(\rho' = $ density of the vapor at the pressure p_e) and therefore
the work delivered is $4\pi r^2 \, dr(1 - \rho'/\rho)p_e$. The reversible cycle for evaporation can be the following.

(1) Isolation of a small volume of liquid equal to $4\pi r^2 \, dr(\rho'/\rho)$; this
represents the amount of substance to be evaporated.

(2) Compression of the liquid from p_e to p_∞; this does not require any
work if the liquid is incompressible.

(3) Evaporation of the liquid at p_∞; this does an amount of work
$4\pi r^2 \, dr(\rho/\rho'' - \rho'/\rho)p_\infty$ (ρ'' is the density of the vapor at pressure p_∞).

(4) Isothermal expansion of the vapor from p_∞ to p_c; the work delivered
is $4\pi r^2 \, dr\rho' RT/M \ln p_\infty/p_c$.

(5) Injection of the vapor into the bubble; then on the system one does
the work $4\pi r^2 \, drp_c$, but at the same time the work delivered to the outside
is $4\pi r^2 \, drp_e$.

So we must have the equality:

$$4\pi r^2 \, dr\left(\frac{\rho'}{\rho''} - \frac{\rho'}{\rho}\right)p_\infty + 4\pi r^2 \, dr \, \rho'\frac{RT}{M} \ln \frac{p_\infty}{p_c} - 4\pi r^2 \, dr \, p_c + 4\pi r^2 \, dr \, p_e$$

$$= 4\pi r^2 \, dr\left(1 - \frac{\rho'}{\rho}\right)p_e$$

or

$$p_\infty \frac{\rho'}{\rho''} - p_\infty \frac{\rho'}{\rho} + \frac{RT}{M} \rho' \ln \frac{p_\infty}{p_c} - p_c = - p_e \frac{\rho'}{\rho}. \tag{3}$$

We have $\rho'/\rho'' = p_c/p_\infty$ since we are at the same temperature, and we find again the same equation as previously, $(p_\infty - p_e)/\rho = RT/M \ln p_\infty/p_c$, which together with $p_c - p_e = 2\sigma/r_c$ defines p_c and r_c.

This derivation is of interest because it shows clearly that the critical bubble cannot be formed without work being done on the system. Indeed, we can extend this reasoning to the reversible increase of a bubble of any radius r. Here, however, if r is smaller than r_c, $2\sigma/r$ is larger than $p_c - p_e$, and the pressure p_c cannot do the work necessary for the increase. It has to be helped by some external effect that does on the system the additional work $4\pi r^2 dr[2\sigma/r - (p_c - p_e)]$, which, integrated from $r = 0$ to $r = r_c$, is

$$4\pi r_c^2 \sigma - \tfrac{4}{3}\pi r_c^3(p_c - p_e) = \tfrac{4}{3}\pi r_c^2 \sigma = W_m. \tag{4}$$

Thus, the minimum work W_m necessary to form the critical bubble is equal to one third of the surface energy of this bubble.

With the use of Eq. (1), this formation energy can also be expressed as $W_m = 16\pi\sigma^3/3(p_c - p_e)^2$, which for all practical purposes is not very different from $16\pi\sigma^3/3(p_\infty - p_e)^2$.

As stated at the beginning, in the absence of a source producing this extra energy, the liquid will remain stable for an indefinite time.

It is interesting to see that the minimum nucleation energy varies very rapidly with temperature. Indeed, if one assumes that the best one can do in practical cases is to expand to $p_e = 0$, one has $W_m = 16\pi\sigma^3/3p_\infty^2$. But σ diminishes with temperature to become zero at the critical point, and p_∞ increases with temperature. Therefore, in a relatively narrow range of temperature, the minimum energy required to form the critical bubble will change from hundreds of electron volts, and more, to 0.1 eV, and less; that is, from a region where it will be impossible to obtain the formation energy from ionization to a region where this formation energy is comparable to the binding energies of molecules in the liquid and where therefore small statistical fluctuations will be able to form the critical bubble. For this temperature, the liquid will fizz immediately after expansion.

Of course, we do not intend to imply here that the energy actually required to form a critical bubble in a bubble chamber is as small as the minimum work computed for reversible formation. In fact, the task of a correct theory of bubble formation is to find the detailed mechanism by which ionization energy is used to form a bubble and to find therefore the energy actually used in bubble formation. Whatever this energy is, it will be more or less proportional to the minimum work; and since this work varies by orders of magnitude in a short range of temperatures, the fact that a detailed theory will predict fairly well the operating conditions for a bubble chamber will be a very poor check of its validity, because, as we have seen, these operating conditions are quite accurately predicted by energetic considerations only. This is the reason why the first theory of Glaser, which later was abandoned by Glaser himself, was able to predict successfully the correct temperature conditions for production of tracks in a bubble chamber.

II. Bubble Formation—The Theory of Glaser, or the Electrostatic Theory

A. GENERALITIES

There are in fact only two theories because there are only two ways in which energy can be extracted from ions to produce a bubble. Either it is the energy of the electric field due to the charges of the ions, which is converted into the work of formation of bubbles, or it is the recombination energy of the ions, i.e. heat, which produces thermal spikes and finally bubbles. These theories, however, must have one feature in common; they must explain why only such a very small fraction of the energy given by the particle to the fluid in the form of ionization is useful in bubble formation. Indeed, a particle of relativistic velocity will lose in a bubble chamber between 0.2 and 1 MeV per centimeter of path, depending on the fluid of the chamber. Operation of the chamber is adjusted so as to give 15 to 20 bubbles per centimeter along a track of minimum ionization; therefore, the average energy lost per bubble is at least 10,000 eV in hydrogen and is larger in heavy liquids.

B. ELECTROSTATIC REPULSION AS A SOURCE OF ENERGY

Glaser (1954), in the work he did before any bubble chamber had ever operated and which finally led him to his brilliant invention, tried to find the source of work for bubble formation in the electrostatic energy of the ions. Before we expose his idea, we shall give a brief resume of the situation at that time. Cloud chambers had been operative for about 40 years and the theory of cloud chambers was well established. Here, one had to deal with a phase (the vapor) in a supersaturated state. Here too, this state could last indefinitely since the formation of a critical droplet requires work.[2] However, here the formation of tracks was well understood; ions could start the nucleation of a droplet, and the reason why this happened had been explained by the classical theory of J. J. Thompson. In this theory, it was demonstrated that an ion in a vapor will always condense around it a droplet of very small radius. If the vapor was supersaturated so that the radius of the critical droplet was smaller than or equal to the radius of the droplets around the ions, then these would grow spontaneously. Why ions condense droplets of liquid can be understood in a simple manner. In a charged droplet, the energy of the electrostatic field is less than in the corresponding volume of vapor. Therefore, the work of formation of the surface of the liquid can be taken from the electrostatic energy.

If one applies the same reasoning to bubbles, the result is obvious. A singly charged bubble will collapse even more easily than a neutral one of the same radius, or, in other words, the work of formation for a charged bubble is larger than for a neutral one. This, however, is only true for a unit electrostatic charge, that is, for a point charge somewhere on the surface of the bubble. If there are several ions of the same charge on the surface of the bubble, they will repel each other, which will tend to increase the surface of the bubble.

If the charge on the bubble surface is ne, the force can be represented by an electrostatic pressure, $p = n^2 e^2 / 8\pi r^4 \varepsilon$ (ε is dielectric constant of the liquid).

The expression $(2\sigma/r) - (n^2 e^2/8\pi r^4 \varepsilon)$ has a maximum for $r = (n^2 e^2/4\pi\varepsilon\sigma)^{1/3}$, and the value of the maximum is $\frac{3}{2}(4\pi/n^2 e^2)^{1/3}\sigma^{4/3}\varepsilon^{1/3}$. If, therefore, the expansion of the chamber is such that $p_\infty - p_e$ is larger than this value, every bubble carrying a charge at least equal to ne will grow indefinitely.

---

[2] Incidentally, it might be interesting here to notice an important difference between cloud and bubble chambers (in spite of the fact that this difference has only academic interest and does not concern the comparison we are making). Both chambers operate by expansion. But, in cloud chambers, the reduction of pressure (which is small) goes in the opposite direction to that which one tries to achieve: condensation of the vapor. It is the resulting reduction of the temperature that creates the supersaturated or supercooled state.

In bubble chambers, it is the expansion which achieves directly the formation of the metastable superheated state. The resulting change in temperature (which is small since liquids are not very compressible) is a cooling which also goes in the direction opposite to that which one tries to achieve.

In other words, in first approximation (neglecting the small changes of pressure in cloud chambers and of temperature in bubble chambers), the two kinds of chambers follow orthogonal lines (on a p, T diagram) to pass the equilibrium vapor-liquid line: A line $p \approx$ constant for the cloud chamber, a line $T \approx$ constant for the bubble chamber. Nevertheless, to a superficial observer, the two operations look very similar (a piston moves).

(We have equated p_c to p_∞.) For a given expansion, the minimum excess number of ions of the same charge concentrated on a bubble is

$$n_{min} = \frac{\sigma^2}{(p_\infty - p_e)^{3/2}} \left(\frac{27\pi\varepsilon}{2}\right)^{1/2} \frac{1}{e}. \tag{5}$$

The theory, therefore, relies on statistical fluctuations in the distribution of the ions to form the critical bubbles. As already mentioned, the theory met with considerable success in predicting the operating conditions of bubble chambers. However, as we have seen, this can be well understood on purely energetic grounds. The work developed by the repulsive forces of a moderate number of ions to expand a bubble from a radius of the order of molecular dimensions to the critical radius cannot fail to be in the range from 10 to 1000 eV, and this defines fairly well the temperature and expansion conditions. Therefore, it was necessary to find other more sensitive tests to check the theory.

C. Experimental Checks

A first possibility is to check the sensitivity of a chamber to particles producing very high ionization density. Indeed, the theory requires that there is, in a small subcritical volume of liquid (whose size is such that it contains about the same number of molecules as will be contained in the critical bubble), an excess of n ions of the same charge, n being proportional to $\sigma^2/(p_\infty - p_e)^{3/2}$.

In other theories of bubble formation, one will require inside the same subcritical volume, a certain amount of heat more or less proportional to the minimum work for bubble formation, i.e., to the quantity $\sigma^3/(p_\infty - p_e)^2$.

Therefore in both theories we have two critical quantities:

(a) The minimum excess number of ions of the same charge, and
(b) The minimum heat for bubble formation.

The two quantities depend on temperature in a similar way but (a) varies a little more slowly than (b). On the other hand, the amount of heat released in a given volume will be proportional to the density of ionization. The excess number of ions of a given charge in the same volume will depend on fluctuations and therefore vary more or less as the square root of the ionization density, and even more slowly if correlations of ions are taken into account. Therefore, if both kinds of theories give similarly good fits to experiments at a given value of the ionization density, it is expected that they will give different results for another value. One sees, however, that the required changes in ionization densities must be very large since the slow variation of the fluctuations in the ion density is nearly, but not quite, compensated for by the fact that the critical excess charge varies more slowly than the critical energy.

Therefore, to perform such an experiment, one should study the threshold of radiation sensitivity versus the ionization density. If the heat theory is correct, for very large ionization density, the sensitivity will extend to a region of temperature and expansion where the electrostatic mechanism of bubble formation will be almost inconceivable. An experiment was performed by Glaser using α particles, with the result that sensitivity was found in a region of temperature and pressure where the electrostatic mechanism would have required $n \approx 900$, which is a very unlikely number indeed. In an experiment, reported later in this article, on the sensitivity of bubble chambers to recoil nuclei of α radioactive substances, Riepe and Hahn (1961) arrived at a similar conclusion. Bubble chambers can be made sensitive to events of very high energy densities at temperatures so low, or with an expansion so small, that the corresponding values of n in the electrostatic theories are completely unrealistic, especially if one remembers that a large fraction of the energy of recoil nuclei is not transformed into ionization.

A better and more intuitive proof against the electrostatic mechanism was also found by Glaser and his collaborators (Brown et al., 1956), when they tried to make a liquid xenon bubble chamber. At first these attempts were unsuccessful, until it was noticed that, liquid xenon being a scintillator, the energy of ion recombination might be dispersed in the form of radiation instead of being released locally as heat. The experimenters added to the xenon a small amount of ethylene, which is known to be an efficient radiation quenching agent, and bubble formation was obtained. This result can be understood perfectly if local heat spikes are responsible for bubble formation. On the other hand, the electrostatic mechanism would have to be as efficient in pure xenon as in any other liquid, and the situation could not have been improved by the presence of ethylene. Therefore, it is now universally agreed that bubble formation is due to the heat developed by the recombination of the ions.

III. The Theory of Seitz, or the Heat Spike Theory

The theory of Seitz (1958) assumes that bubbles are formed by thermal spikes produced by the heat released in ion recombination at the end of δ rays. Before giving any details of the theory, let us recall some experimental facts. Bubble chambers are normally operated at bubble densities varying from 10 to 20 bubbles per centimeter for particles giving the minimum ionization. This is done as a practical convenience, but it is perfectly possible to operate a chamber with densities as low as 1 bubble per centimeter or as high as 100 per centimeter. Therefore, statements to the effect that it takes "so many electron volts" to make a bubble in a given liquid have no absolute meaning. They are always to be taken as associated with the phrase "under normal operating conditions." In particular, the difference in formation energy between hydrogen and heavy liquid is not fundamental. If heavy liquids were operated under thermodynamic conditions corresponding to those for hydrogen, they would simply give too many bubbles.

The fact that the bubble density can be adjusted relatively easily probably indicates that several pairs of recombining ions act collectively to form a bubble. Otherwise the sensitivity would drop abruptly to zero as soon as the energy necessary to form a bubble becomes larger than the recombination energy of a single ion pair. We have seen that the energy released in a length of 1 cm in liquid is of the order of 200 keV, which is equivalent to about 7000 ion pairs per centimeter. Therefore, the phenomenon which produces a bubble must be something which happens much more rarely than the recombination of a simple ion pair. Here one could follow two different lines of thought: either one assumes that one or a few recombinations might produce a bubble, but that the probability for it is very small; or one assumes that such a simple recombination is totally inefficient and that as soon as a certain minimum heat is produced (by many recombinations) inside a small volume a bubble is always produced. The latter hypothesis is, of course, much more logical since it is well known that a particle will produce along its path many relatively low energy δ rays which will remain practically very close to the track and produce clusters of ions in a very small volume. Therefore, the task of the theory is the following:

(a) by comparison between the bubble density and the classical formula for δ ray density, to evaluate the energy of bubble producing δ rays;

(b) to check, by the range energy relation, whether or not the energy is in fact released in a small enough volume; and

(c) to evaluate in a realistic fashion, by thermodynamics, the energy necessary to create a bubble and compare the result with that of (a).

In all that follows, we will call W (without index) the true energy necessary to form the critical bubbles in the liquid. It is an unknown quantity. All that is known is that it must be larger than the minimum work $W = 16\pi\sigma^3/3(p_\infty - p_e)^2$, discussed at the beginning of this chapter. W with indices will represent estimates of W, or partial terms whose sum will be an estimate of W.

A. Bubble Density, δ Ray Density

The first task, (a), is extremely easy if one makes the simple hypothesis that there is a threshold energy W_i such that a δ ray with an energy smaller than W_i will never produce a bubble and with an energy larger than W_i will always produce one. The number of δ electrons per centimeter with energy greater than W_i, along a track with minimum ionization, is given by

$$n = 0.150\rho\frac{Z}{A}\frac{m_e c^2}{W_i},\tag{6}$$

where $m_e c^2$ is the rest energy of the electron, and $\rho\, Z/A$ is proportional to the electronic density of the fluid.

Equating the number n to 15 (a typical bubble density) gives $W_i = 600$ eV in hydrogen, 2800 in propane, and 6000 in heavier liquids of density ρ slightly greater than 1. Electrons of the energy W_i will have a range of about 400 Å in hydrogen and 4000 Å in heavy liquids. However, we must remember that on electrons of such an energy the effect of Coulomb scattering is very large indeed. The trajectory will be coiled, and therefore the whole energy of the electron will be transformed into ionization inside a sphere with diameter considerably smaller than the range of the electron.

B. The Range of δ Rays

We assume now, with Seitz, that in order to be efficient, the energy has to be delivered inside a sphere having the radius of the critical bubble. This is, of course, an upper limit since most of the molecules contained in the sphere will not form the vapor in the bubble. One could, for instance, assume that the energy for the formation of the bubble must be in that volume which contains a number of molecules equal to that in the vapor of the critical bubbles. Since under typical bubble chamber conditions there is only a factor of 8 to 12 between the density of liquid and saturated vapor, this will make the radius of the sphere smaller by a factor of 2. However, this seems too drastic an hypothesis; heat produced around that sphere will certainly not be completely lost to the process of bubble formation (for instance, it will heat the liquid and therefore reduce considerably the surface tension).

Under all bubble chamber operating conditions, it turns out (see Table I) that the diameter of the critical bubble varies surprisingly little for different liquids and lies between 120 and 180 Å. We see, therefore, that the range of δ rays having the threshold energy W_i is 2.5 times too large in hydrogen and

22 times too large in heavy liquids. This, however, is not as bad as it looks at first glance. The range-energy relation is quadratic in energy. Therefore a slight modification of the hypothesis on the threshold energy of δ rays is sufficient to explain the discrepancy. Indeed, if we assume that the δ rays above a certain energy do not have an efficiency equal to unity to form bubbles, but only an efficiency x, the critical energy W_i will be correspondingly reduced by the factor x and the corresponding range by the factor x^2. It is enough to take $x = 0.7$ in hydrogen and 0.2 in heavy liquid to have agreement. It is not even necessary to take x as low as that. We have already mentioned the effect of Coulomb scattering. An electron of 3000 eV will turn, on the average, more than $90°$ in 150 Å in a heavy liquid. Therefore, at this stage (it will be shown later that this hypothesis is not acceptable) there would seem nothing wrong in assuming that bubbles are formed with high efficiency by δ rays having an energy greater than a certain minimum W_i which is of the order of 400 eV for hydrogen and 3000 for heavy liquids. We have, of course, to assume that the efficiency drops very quickly for δ rays of lower energy (otherwise there would be many more bubbles along a track). It is also clear that efficiency cannot increase very much for higher energies since in this case the energy is spent over too long a path and since only the end of the range is efficient for bubble formation.

Therefore, the only crucial test of the theory is to see if indeed an energy as high as the one previously mentioned is required to make a bubble. There is, of course, an enormous difference between these energies and the minimum work W_m, which is only a few electron volts. Seitz tried to find the bubble formation energy in two ways:

(1) by purely energetic considerations, and
(2) by dynamic considerations.

C. Energetic Evaluation of the Bubble Formation Energy

The fundamental assumption is that all the excess energy contained in the bubble (compared with the same amount of substance in the liquid phase) has to come from the ionization energy. This contrasts with the calculation of the minimum work for the formation of the critical bubble, where it was assumed that the energy of evaporation was taken freely from the heat reserve of the liquid. The minimum work was the difference between the surface energy $4\pi r_c^2 \sigma$ and the work developed spontaneously by the evaporation, $\frac{4}{3}\pi r_c^3 p_\infty = \frac{8}{3}\pi r_c^2 \sigma$ (when the liquid is expanded to a pressure $p_e = 0$).

The energy of the bubble can be decomposed into three terms which have to be added together:

(1) the surface energy,
(2) the evaporation energy of the matter contained in the bubble, and
(3) the work done against the pressure p_e of the liquid.

Therefore Seitz, following Pless and Plano (1956), wrote the necessary energy to form the bubble in the form

$$4\pi r_c^2 \sigma + \tfrac{4}{3}\pi r_c^3 (\rho'/M)H + \tfrac{4}{3}\pi r_c^3 p_e,$$

$$\qquad W_{s_1} \qquad\qquad W_v \qquad\qquad W_e$$

where H is latent heat of vaporization per mole, M is molecular weight of the liquid, and ρ' is density of the vapor in the bubble. If we take into account the relation $r_c = 2\sigma/(p_\infty - p_e)$ we can write this as

$$W_g = \frac{16\pi\sigma^3}{(p_\infty - p_e)^2}\left[1 + \frac{2\rho'H}{3M(p_\infty - p_e)} + \frac{2}{3}\frac{p_e}{p_\infty - p_e}\right]$$

$$= W_m\left[3 + \frac{2\rho'H}{M(p_\infty - p_e)} + \frac{2p_e}{p_\infty - p_e}\right], \tag{7}$$

where W_g is a guess for the value of W. In this expression, W_v, the vaporization energy, is normally the leading term.

Bugg (1959), Tenner (1963), and Hugentobler et al. (1963), introduced a modification for the first term. They pointed out that the classical expression for the bubble surface energy is in fact the free energy of the bubble and that, the process of formation being adiabatic, one should consider the internal energy as being the true surface energy necessary to form the bubble. The internal energy is given by the classical equation of thermodynamics

$$U = F - \frac{T\,\partial F}{\partial T}$$

or

$$U = 4\pi r^2 \sigma - 4\pi r^2 T\,\partial\sigma/\partial T,$$

$$\qquad W_{s_1} \qquad\qquad W_{s_2}$$

which gives a new expression

$$W_g' = W_m\left(3 - \frac{T}{\sigma}\frac{\partial\sigma}{\partial T} + \frac{2\rho'H}{M(p_\infty - p_e)} + \frac{2p_e}{p_\infty - p_e}\right). \tag{8}$$

TABLE I

BUBBLE CHAMBER OPERATING CONDITIONS FOR DIFFERENT LIQUIDS AND
ESTIMATION OF THE BUBBLE FORMATION ENERGY[a]

Liquids	H_2	He	C_3H_8	$CBrF_3$	SF_6	C_3F_8
Operating temperature T	26.5°K	4.2°K	60°C	37°C	21°C	42°C
Saturated vapor pressure at temperature T, p_∞(atm)	4.5	1.0	22	21.4	22.2	13.6
Expansion pressure drop $(p_\infty - p_e)$(atm)(p_e is the pressure of the expanded fluid)	2.5	0.28	10	8.4	6.6	4.8
Surface tension at temperature T, σ(dyn/cm)	0.9	0.10	3.6	2.6	2.05	2.16
Radius of critical bubble $r_c = 2\sigma/(p_\infty - p_e)$(Å)	72	83	73	63	62	90
Surface free energy $W_{s_1} = 4\pi r_c^2 \sigma$ (eV)	3.7	0.54	15	8	6	13.5
$W_{s_2} = - 4\pi r_c^2 \dfrac{T \, \partial\sigma}{\partial T}$ (eV)	19.5	2.2	140	96	96	178
Vaporization energy $W_v = \frac{4}{3}\pi r_c^3 (H/M)\rho'$ (eV)	9	4.5	90	73	88	180
Expansion energy $W_e = \frac{4}{3}\pi r_c^3 p_e$ (eV)	2	0.94	11	8	10	17
Bubble formation energy (first estimate) $W_g = W_{s_1} + W_v + W_e$ (eV)	14.7	6	116	89	104	211
Bubble formation energy (second estimate) $W_g' = W_{s_1} + W_{s_2} + W_v + W_e$ (eV)	34.2	8.2	256	185	200	390

[a] The minimum work for bubble formation W_m is always given by the equation $W_m = \frac{1}{3} W_{s_1}$. Data for H_2, He, and C_3H_8 are taken from Tenner (1963), but the parameters for operating conditions in H_2 have been modified according to the author's own experience. The data for $CBrF_3$, SF_6, C_3F_8 have been taken from Hugentobler et al. (1963); detailed information not contained in that paper has been kindly provided by Dr. Hugentobler. As in the text, the quantity $(H/M)\rho'$ used in the calculation of W_v is the vaporization heat for 1 cm³ of vapor at the temperature T and the pressure p_∞.

Table I gives the value of the different energy terms and their sum for different fluids.

As one can see, the term $4\pi r^2 \, \partial\sigma/\partial T$ is of great importance since it is even greater than the vaporization energy whereas the term $4\pi r^2\sigma$ is smaller. The author, not being a specialist in thermodynamics, must confess that he is somewhat puzzled by this term. Let us, for instance, choose a definite model for the mechanism of bubble formation; one would assume that (a) all the molecules are evaporated in a first stage in a very small volume and (b) the volume then expands adiabatically to the critical volume. One would find indeed that the internal energy of the vapor in its initial stage is larger than just W_v, the difference being bigger than $W_{s_1} = 4\pi r_c^2\sigma$, but the difference will depend on the ratio of the initial volume to the final volume and on the law of adiabatic expansion of the vapor, not on the properties of the surface of the bubble.[3]

At any rate, one sees from Table I that the energies of formation of the bubble that one obtains are of the order of 10 to 40 eV for hydrogen and helium and of 200 eV for heavier liquids. This kind of energy can be lost by a δ ray in a volume which is indeed much smaller than the critical volume. Therefore, if no more energy were required to form a bubble than W_g or W_g', the bubble density should be roughly 50 times larger than that observed, if the efficiency were of the order of 100%. Therefore we must look for some inefficiency in the mechanism of conversion of ionization energy into bubble formation.

D. Evaluation of the Energy Required for Bubble Formation by Dynamic Consideration

Seitz pointed out that the energy of recombination appears primarily as heat which will immediately diffuse and be lost for bubble formation unless the bubble is formed quickly enough. The relaxation time for the dissipation of the heat contained in a sphere of radius r is $\tau = r^2/D$. D is the diffusion coefficient of heat related to the thermal conductivity λ by the equation $D = \lambda/\rho c$, where ρ is density and c is specific heat. This time τ is of the order of 10^{-11} sec for hydrogen and 10^{-10} sec for propane if r is taken equal to r_c.

---

[3] Since this paper was written, it has become clear to the author that, indeed, the adiabaticity of the process inside the bubble has nothing to do with the adiabaticity of surface formation; that is why extra energy is needed to take this fact into account. However, since heat diffusion is very fast around a little spherical surface (see Section III, D) it is still not clear that the surface formation is indeed an adiabatic process.

If the bubble is not formed in a time more or less equal to τ, most of the heat will have diffused out of the critical volume and will not be available for bubble formation. We therefore have to calculate how much energy is needed to form a bubble, displacing the liquid in the time τ.

To perform the calculation, we must

(a) decide what is the initial volume V_0 of the bubble before it expands,

(b) adopt a certain law for the variation of pressure inside the bubble when the volume changes, and

(c) write the equation of motion of the surface of the bubble.

When these equations are solved, the condition that the expansion is completed in a time τ will give the initial pressure p_0 when the bubble starts to expand. $p_0 V_0$, multiplied by a suitable coefficient (taking into account the number of internal degrees of freedom), will give the initial energy contained in the bubble.

The size of the initial volume of the bubble before expansion was chosen by Seitz to be equal to that of a cylinder having as length the diameter of the critical bubble, the radius of the cylinder being equal to the mean intermolecular distance. There is, of course, no absolute justification of this choice but it is quite logical. It could not be chosen much smaller in any case since it does not contain many molecules. The number of molecules contained in the critical volume of the bubble when it is still filled with liquid is of the order of 15,000; the number of molecules in the critical bubble is, as was mentioned, about 10 times smaller, namely, ≈ 1500; the number of molecules in the Seitz initial volume is roughly 40. Seitz assumed further that the initial volume is a sphere of radius r_0; this is more or less justified by the fact that the trajectory of the δ ray is coiled by Coulomb scattering.

The law of expansion for the vapor is of course the adiabatic law $pv^\gamma =$ const or $pr^{3\gamma} =$ const. A difficulty lies in choosing the proper γ. One can either treat the vapor inside the bubble as an ideal gas or take the specific heat at the boiling point, assuming that one has $c_p - c_v = R$ (R is the constant in the ideal gas law, $pv = RT$). The difference between the two sets of values is not large, and one cannot be very wrong in choosing for γ, as Seitz did, an intermediate value of 1.4 for hydrogen and 1.05 for propane.

To go further into the calculation, Seitz assumed that the equations of motion of the liquid are those of an incompressible fluid. This is likely to be a good approximation since the average velocity of the bubble surface r_c/τ has to be 5×10^4 cm/sec in hydrogen and less in propane, and is certainly subsonic in both cases.

The equation of motion is

$$\frac{\partial u}{\partial t} + u\frac{\partial u}{\partial r} = -\frac{1}{\rho}\frac{\partial p}{\partial r} \tag{9}$$

and the equation of continuity is

$$\frac{\partial(r^2 u)}{\partial r} = 0. \tag{10}$$

Here r is the radial coordinate of a point in the liquid and p the pressure at the same point; therefore the radius of the bubble and its internal pressure will be noted as r_b and p_b, respectively. u is the velocity of a liquid element at the point r, ρ is the density of the liquid. The equation of continuity is satisfied by a solution of the type

$$u = \frac{\dot{r}_b r_b^2}{r^2}. \tag{11}$$

Substituting (11) in (9) and integrating over r, assuming the pressure at infinity, p_e, is 0, one finds

$$\frac{p}{\rho} = (r_b^2 \ddot{r}_b + 2r_b \dot{r}_b^2)/r - r_b^4 \dot{r}_b^2/2r^4. \tag{12}$$

The pressure at the surface of the bubble is therefore given by

$$\frac{p_b}{\rho} = r_b \ddot{r}_b + \frac{3}{2}\dot{r}_b^2. \tag{13}$$

and, if we set $p_b = p_0(r_0/r_b)^{3\gamma}$ (p_0 and r_0 are the pressure and radius of the initial bubble before expansion), a first integral of the equation can be found:

$$\dot{r}_b^2 = \frac{2p_0}{\rho}\left[\left(\frac{r_0}{r_b}\right)^3 - \left(\frac{r_0}{r_b}\right)^{3\gamma}\right]\bigg/3(\gamma - 1). \tag{14}$$

This equation can be further integrated if $\gamma = 4/3$, a value not too far from the one assumed for hydrogen. In the case of a heavy liquid, where γ is very close to 1, Eq. (14) can be approximated by

$$\dot{r}_b^2 = \frac{2p_0}{\rho}\left(\frac{r_0}{r_b}\right)^3 \ln\frac{r_b}{r_0}. \tag{15}$$

The time for the bubble to grow from the radius r_0 to the radius r_c will be given by the integral

$$\int_{r_o}^{r_c} \frac{dr_b}{\dot{r}_b}.$$

Equating this time to τ gives then a value of $p_0 V_0$ for the initial bubble. To obtain the internal energy of the initial bubble, one has to multiply $p_0 V_0$ by a certain coefficient. If the gas is monatomic, the coefficient will be $\frac{3}{2}$. If, on the contrary, the gas is polyatomic, the coefficient will be $\frac{7}{2}$ for hydrogen and 30 for propane on the assumption that all the degrees of freedom are equally excited. Somewhat arbitrarily, Seitz chose smaller values for this coefficient: 2.5 for hydrogen and 15 for propane. His justification is that, if the heat is distributed to the 15,000 molecules included in the critical volume, the temperature rise is not very large (100 degrees).

The calculation gives a very small number for the initial energy contained in the bubble: 2.5 eV for hydrogen, 30 eV for propane, a value hardly greater than the surface energy of the bubble and much smaller than the total value W_g quoted in Table I. (The values of the critical radius adopted by Seitz were not exactly the same as those quoted in Table I, and the values of W_{s_1} ($= 4\pi r_c^2 \sigma$) were 1 eV for hydrogen and 27 eV for propane.)

It is interesting to consider the reason for this rather surprising result. In the energetic considerations, we had assumed that the latent heat of vaporization of the vapor inside the bubble should be supplied by the δ ray. In the last calculation, this assumption has been, in fact, implicitly dropped. All that is asked of the heated region of the liquid is to create the bubble more or less as a cavity without actually requiring that energy is given to the liquid to evaporate the molecules which will fill the bubble with the right number of molecules. It is, therefore, not as surprising as one might think, that the energy required to do this work is not many times larger than the surface energy of the bubble. All that the calculation shows is that, given enough energy (small compared to W_v), the process occurs in a time which can be as short as the heat dissipation relaxation time. We wish to point out that apart from the fact that there is a flagrant contradiction between the final result and the observed density of bubbles, there was nothing especially naive in the hypothesis. The basis of the energetic calculation, "the vaporization heat is to be supplied by the δ ray energy," is also arbitrary. If, indeed, a bubble could be created as a cavity in the way described above, enough molecules could then be evaporated spontaneously from the liquid to fill it.

Since, however, the postulated mechanism will give too many bubbles, the hypothesis must again be revised. Seitz pointed out that if in Eq. (13)

the term in $r_b \ddot{r}_b$ were dropped, the law of expansion of the bubble would be

$$\dot{r}_b{}^2 = \frac{2}{3} \frac{p_0}{\rho} \left(\frac{r_0}{r_b}\right)^{3\gamma}$$ (16)

which gives a rate of growth much smaller than the one previously obtained and therefore a larger $p_0 V_0$ if the critical radius is to be reached in the time τ. The initial energy in the bubble turns out to be 25 eV for hydrogen, 227 eV for propane, which is of the order of magnitude of the energies W_g obtained by purely energetic considerations, and therefore still too small. The change in going from Eq. (14) to Eq. (16) is characterized by the fact that the velocity of expansion is much smaller at the end of expansion, an effect which can be obtained if, for instance, viscosity tends to decrease the high velocity obtained at the initial stage of the expansion.

E. EFFECT OF VISCOSITY

We have seen (Eq. 11) that the velocity of the fluid is given by $u = r_b{}^2 \dot{r}_b / r^2$. Therefore the gradient of velocity is $-2r_b{}^2 \dot{r}_b / r^3$. If viscosity exists, this will result in a pressure opposing the flow, equal to $4\eta (r_b{}^2 \dot{r}_b / r^3)$, and therefore at the surface of the bubble this counter pressure will be equal to

$$p_v = 4\eta \frac{\dot{r}_b}{r_b}.$$ (17)

η is the viscosity constant.

This term can be introduced in the equations, which can then be solved with suitable approximations. The result is that the effect is not important for hydrogen; but for propane it is the leading effect, and indeed the initial energy of the bubble becomes now ~ 4000 eV if the bubble should grow in the critical time.

There are however some criticisms to be made:

(a) The coefficient of viscosity is not known for the temperature and pressure conditions around the bubble. Seitz assumed that the effects of pressure and temperature would compensate, but this is not certain.

(b) The work done against the viscosity is spent in the immediate vicinity of the surface of the bubble and transformed into heat in a region where this heat can help the bubble formation. In other words, viscosity seems to absorb much of the energy if the bubble is to be formed in the time τ, but this energy appears again as heat inside the critical volume where heat is assumed to be useful in forming the bubble.

F. CONCLUSION

In any case, we might conclude that qualitatively the theory of Seitz is successful: it seems clear that if ion clusters at the ends of δ ray trajectories recombine fast enough, there is enough energy in a sufficiently small volume to create bubbles of the critical size which will then grow and become visible. The quantitative difficulty does not lie in the explanation of why bubbles are formed but rather why so few are formed. Apart from the partial success obtained for propane (but not for hydrogen), we find that all the estimates of the energy W required to form a bubble arrive at values which are too small by at least one order of magnitude, if all or most of the δ rays of such an energy were capable of forming bubbles. Therefore, the question is what makes δ rays of sufficient energy inefficient in bubble formation. Can one obtain some information on this question by detailed experiments on the relationship between bubble density and δ ray density?

IV. Quantitative Experiments—The Relativistic Rise

A. STATEMENT OF THE PROBLEM

Let us first summarize the hypotheses and conclusions of the preceding section. Since Glaser's mechanism had to be discarded, we were forced to assume that the energy given to the liquid is first transformed into heat and then that this heat is able to produce bubbles.

According to a careful study of Tenner's (1963), the only way by which a fast charged particle can release sufficient amounts of heat inside the liquid is via ionization and subsequent recombination.

Recombination of one single pair of ions is unlikely to give enough energy to form a bubble, but δ rays can produce a greater number of ion pairs in a small volume (smaller than the volume of the critical bubble). Therefore, it is very likely that bubbles are formed at the end of δ rays.

From the range energy relations, one finds that the energy delivered inside a volume of the critical size by an electron at the end of its range is of the order of 200 eV for hydrogen and 1000 eV for heavy liquids. The last figure can be multiplied by a factor 2 or 3 if one takes into account the Coulomb scattering. If one assumes that δ rays of such an energy, or larger, are efficient in bubble formation and that the others are not, the comparison of bubble density with the formula for δ ray densities shows that the efficiency, if not 100%, should be quite large ($\sim 50\%$).

One then proceeds to see if it takes that much energy to form a bubble; and it turns out that the amount of heat required is considerably smaller, between 10 and 20 times.

There are two hypotheses for explaining the disagreement.

(a) Assume that the energy of formation W_g or W_g' calculated by thermo-dynamic considerations is a lower limit but that the dynamics of formation require in fact much more energy.

(b) Assume that a δ ray having an energy equal to or higher than the calculated energy W_g for bubble formation is indeed capable of forming a bubble, but will do so with a small efficiency and furthermore that this efficiency will not be considerably enhanced by the excess energy the δ ray is capable of delivering in the critical volume. In other words, in this case one would assume that, for instance, in heavy liquids it is not the electrons with an energy of more than 3000 eV which are 50% efficient in forming bubbles, but it is the electrons of more than 200 eV which are $\sim$ 3% efficient.

A priori, hypothesis (a) is much more likely to be correct than hypothesis (b). It is indeed very plausible that heat is very inefficiently used in forming a bubble but that if enough energy is present then the bubble is always formed. In fact, the dynamic theory of Seitz is a check on how inefficiently energy can be used, since it compares the speed of bubble growth to the diffusion and therefore to the loss of heat. As we have seen, this theory is practically successful for propane if one takes into account the viscosity of the liquid, but it is quite unsuccessful if viscosity is not important.

Nevertheless, before dropping (b), it would be good to have an independent check on what is the minimum energy of the δ rays which can form bubbles. It turns out that this can be done by studying the relativistic increase of bubble densities in heavy liquid, and the surprising result is that the result favors hypothesis (b).

B. THE NATURE OF THE RELATIVISTIC INCREASE OF IONIZATION AND δ RAYS

To understand the result, we must first recall briefly the nature of the relativistic increase of ionization. In the classical theory of ionization, one first calculates the energy communicated to a free electron by a fast charged particle passing at a distance b from the electron. The total energy loss is then computed by integrating over b between two limits. The lower limit does not interest us here. The upper limit is given by the adiabatic condition. Since electrons are not free, a perturbation can only contribute to ionization if it is applied in a time short compared to the characteristic revolution time of an electron in its orbit. For relativistic velocities, $\beta \sim 1$, the perturbation exerted on an electron at a distance b does not change with the energy of the incident particle. However, this perturbation is applied in a time which varies as $(1 - \beta^2)^{1/2}$ (Lorentz contraction) and therefore becomes shorter and shorter as the energy of the primary increases. Therefore, for increasing energy, the condition of "nonadiabaticity" applies for larger and larger b, and the ionization, after reaching a minimum, increases again. Eventually the limit for b becomes larger than interatomic distances. At this point, the electric field of the primary particle is shielded by the electrons of interposed atoms, and this prevents further increase of ionization. Some of the energy is then transferred to collective movements of the electrons which generate the Čerenkov radiation. This is the so-called density effect.

From the preceding paragraph, it is clear that the relativistic increase concerns electrons located relatively far from the trajectory of the primary, and, since the perturbation energy itself depends only on b, the average energy taken up by one electron is small. In fact, if one calculates the perturbation energy for the distant collisions, one finds that it is smaller than the binding energy of the electron. However, the theory, being a classical one, gives only the average energy given to the electrons. In terms of quantum theory, this is translated into a high probability of doing nothing to a given electron and a small probability of knocking it out of the atom. Nevertheless, this electron will most of the time have a small kinetic energy, which sometimes will be of the order of magnitude of the binding energy, but never will be much larger. If an electron receives an energy several times larger than its binding energy, it can be considered free. For such an electron, the condition of "nonadiabaticity" is practically always fulfilled, and, therefore, there is no relativistic increase for electrons of such an energy. In other words, the relativistic increase affects δ electrons with energies comparable to, or smaller than, the binding energies (for which the approximation of free electrons is bad) and does not affect δ electrons of larger energies.[4]

We can now compare the relativistic increase for elements like hydrogen and elements of relatively high Z. The energies of electrons liberated by the collisions contributing to the relativistic increase will be comparable to the ionization potential, i.e., 13 eV for hydrogen and 100 eV or more for heavier elements. Furthermore, the period of revolution for strongly bound electrons in high Z material is considerably smaller than in hydrogen, and therefore the maximum value of b is smaller. These two facts, which are connected, explain why the relativistic increase is more marked for elements of high Z, and why the density effect sets in much later (i.e. for higher energies of the primary) for these elements than it does for elements of low Z (Budini and

---

[4] There is also a relativistic increase in close collisions due to the fact that the maximum transferable energy increases with the energy of the primary. However, this effect concerns only very high energy δ rays, which appear as trajectories and not as individual bubbles and therefore are of no interest here.

Taffara, 1956). This has been established by several experiments in cloud chambers on hydrogen, helium, and krypton.

The subject of the calculation of the density effect is a very controversial one. According to certain theories, this effect should have suppressed any relativistic increase in materials like liquid propane. One fact, however, seems certain; since the relativistic increase is small in gaseous hydrogen at atmospheric pressure, no measurable increase is expected in liquid hydrogen. On the other hand, we see that, in heavy liquids, the electrons contributing to the relativistic increase have an energy which is just of the order of the calculated energy for bubble formation. If these electrons can form bubbles, a relativistic increase of bubble density will be detected. If, on the other hand, only electrons of 1000 eV or more can form bubbles, no relativistic increase will appear. The amount of increase will, of course, depend on how low the energy of a bubble-forming δ ray can be; the lower it is, the greater the relativistic increase.[5] More quantitatively, the amount of relativistic increase will depend on the relation between the energy of the δ ray and the efficiency for bubble formation.

C. The Relativistic Increase of Bubble Density

The presence of a relativistic increase of bubble densities in propane was reported first by Blinov et al. (1957) and confirmed by Argan et al. (1958). The most extensive study has been performed by Hugentobler et al. (1963) on three liquids, $CBrF_3$, SF_6, and C_3F_8, using a chamber with stabilized final pressure, a feature which assures very stable and well controlled working conditions for the chamber. They found a very sizable relativistic increase of the bubble density. Defining the relativistic increase as $(I_{(\gamma=100)} - I_{min})/I_{min}$ (I = density of bubbles, $\gamma = (1 - \beta^2)^{-1/2}$), they found it to be $(32 \pm 5)\%$ in $CBrF_3$, $(16 \pm 5)\%$ in SF_6, and $(16 \pm 5)\%$ in C_3F_8. Since the most recent theories predicted a much smaller relativistic increase of ionization because of an overestimate of the density effect, the authors performed their own calculations without taking into account this effect. This is probably justified in this case since they are interested in the density of δ rays of energy larger than 100 eV, for which the impact parameter remains relatively small and the density effect is of no great importance. They calculated the density of δ rays of energy larger than the estimated energy W_g' of bubble formation (quoted in Table I) and obtained good agreement with the experiments. Table II gives a comparison between

---

[5] This is probably not entirely correct; electrons of the smallest energy are normally produced by the most distant collisions possible, which are the first to be affected by the density effect.

experimental and theoretical values. If anything, the calculated values are too small. The uncertainties both in the measurement and in the theory make this last point insignificant. However, if it were true, it would indicate that the bubble density is proportional to the density of δ rays having an energy larger than a minimum that is lower than the estimated bubble formation energy W_g' (a fact which would indicate that the values for W_g' are overestimated).

At any rate, this experiment shows clearly that, in order to understand the relativistic increase, one has to assume that the number of bubbles is proportional to the number of δ rays integrated down to the smallest possible energy necessary to form a bubble. The average efficiency is then only

TABLE II
RELATIVISTIC INCREASE, EXPERIMENTAL AND THEORETICAL

	$(I_{100} - I_{min}/I_{min})_{exp}$ (%)	$(I_{100} - I_{min}/I_{min})_{th}$ (%)
$CBrF_3$	(32 ± 5)	22
SF_6	(16 ± 5)	17
C_3F_8	(16 ± 5)	10

somewhere between 1 and 2%,[6] and this efficiency cannot vary too much with the energy of the δ ray since otherwise the observed relativistic increase will be reduced. This proves that hypothesis (b), however unlikely it might look, is the correct one. In other words, it is hopeless to try to interpret the relatively small number of bubbles by inventing a mechanism which requires a very high energy for bubble formation. Incidentally, this demonstrates that the treatment of viscosity by Seitz must be incorrect, probably in the choice of the viscosity constant, which is likely to be much smaller for the liquid around the bubble than for the normal liquid.

D. THE DETERMINATION OF THE BUBBLE FORMATION ENERGY BY RECOIL NUCLEI

Before discussing any further the reasons for the inefficiency of δ rays for bubble formation, we must mention another experiment by Riepe and Hahn (1961). In order to check whether the estimate of the energy for bubble formation was correct, they operated a bubble chamber whose liquid

[6] These liquids have a density ≈ 1.5. The δ ray density is therefore 1.5 times larger than the one we assumed for heavy liquids in Section III.

contained traces of an α radioactive substance. The conditions of the chamber were such that the α particle could not possibly release enough energy inside the critical volume, but the recoil nucleus could. By varying the conditions of the chamber, they were able to observe the threshold for bubble formation. The value of W_g for the given temperature and pressure condition agreed very accurately with the energy of the recoil nucleus. In this case, the value of W_g was as high as 110 keV and the critical radius of the order of 800 Å. Therefore, it is not certain that this excellent verification can be extrapolated to radii 10 times smaller, i.e. to energies 1000 times smaller. In particular, the term $-4\pi r_c^2 (T\, \partial\sigma/\partial T)$ was not taken into account (it is negligible for such radii), and, therefore, the experiment does not say anything for, or against, the validity of this term.

In this experiment, the onset of sensitivity was very sharp but not absolutely steplike. The number of bubbles formed per unit time reached saturation very rapidly; and this number, when compared to the expected number of decays, showed that the efficiency of bubble formation was 100%. The experiment was completed by looking at the threshold of sensitivity for bubble formation by the internal conversion electrons of Ar_{37} (these electrons have an energy of 2.3 keV). The chamber became sensitive, but only for 1% of these electrons at conditions which corresponded to a critical radius of 95 Å for a W_g of 455 eV. The energy lost by the electron in 190 Å would be about 1500 eV, and 1000 eV in 95 Å, which is the diameter of the subcritical volume. Here we find again the same result as for δ rays; the electron is not very efficient in forming bubbles in spite of the fact that the energy given to the critical volume is more than enough.

E. Consequences of the Theory of Bubble Formation

From these different experiments, we might conclude the following. The estimates of energy for bubble formation as given in Table I are correct (if, perhaps, slightly too large). This is proved by the relativistic increase in heavy liquids in the region where this energy is roughly 200 eV, and by the recoil nucleus experiment where the energy is of the order of 100 keV. Electrons have an efficiency of only a few percent to form bubbles, more or less independently of their energy, provided it is larger than the minimum necessary.

Why δ electrons have such a small efficiency in forming bubbles is still a mystery. One could think, for instance, that recombination occurs at too small a rate to give the necessary heat in a short enough time. This hypothesis, however, is discarded by all the experts who believe that recombination occurs in a very short time. One could think that in most cases the re-combination energy is dispersed in a form other than heat (as in pure xenon) but this is unlikely in polyatomic fluids. Another hypothesis is that the heat necessary for bubble formation must be delivered into a volume much smaller than the critical or even the subcritical volume. Fluctuations in ionization density, recombination time, and heat diffusion could explain the low efficiency of δ electrons. Recoil nuclei will be much more efficient, since the energy is much more concentrated and also largely transformed directly into heat via collisions without going through ionization and recombination. But there is no reason to believe that this is indeed a correct explanation, and, furthermore, there is no way to understand why the heat released in the vicinity of the initial volume would not help substantially in the bubble formation (which would make efficiency strongly energy dependent). There is one way to make the bubble formation efficiency energy dependent and still get agreement with the data on the relativistic increase. One has to assume that this efficiency is a smooth slowly varying function of the energy which is still not zero for energies of δ rays considerably smaller than the W_g or W_g' of Table I. The (relatively) high efficiency of the few high energy δ rays whose number is not affected by the relativistic increase will be compensated for by the large number of electrons of energy smaller than W_g whose number is strongly affected by the relativistic increase, down to the point where the density effect becomes important. W_g would then have to be considered as an average energy necessary for bubble formation and not as a minimum. The only absolute minimum is of course W_m. The author believes that this may be the truth since, as we have seen in the dynamic theory of Seitz, bubbles can be formed by very small energy spikes when viscosity is neglected. He has, however, no explanation as to why the overall efficiency is so small. Indeed, it cannot be very large even for electrons of several keV (which lose all their energy in the critical volume) since in this case the bubble density would be much larger than observed.

However deep the mystery might be, it is not deep enough to make us abandon the δ ray theory of bubble formation for fast charged particles. The $1/\beta^2$ law for the bubble density of subrelativistic particles is a well established fact (Peyrou, 1960; Kenney, 1960; Ahmadzadeh and Biswas, 1961; Lea and Vittitoe, 1962; Sechi-Zorn and Zorn, 1962; Fabian et al., 1963; Willis et al., 1957; Dilworth et al., 1964); this is also the law for δ ray density. As explained at the beginning of this chapter, there is no better way of releasing clusters of energy in a liquid than by the recombination of ions at the end of the trajectory of an electron. Electrons of 2.3 keV from

Ar$_{37}$ have been found to be just as efficient in forming bubbles as δ rays seem to be.

Furthermore, we wish to point out that in all that has been said there is no reason to make a difference between hydrogen and helium on the one hand and heavy liquids on the other. The fact that hydrogen exhibits no relativistic increase is most likely due to the density effect. The fact that the bubble formation energy is different (by an order of magnitude) is due to the free choice of bubble chamber operators. Heavy liquid bubble chambers can most likely be operated under conditions which correspond to bubble formation energies as small as in hydrogen. The result will only be a very large bubble density which could no longer be measured (by conventional methods) and compared with theory. One difference must, however, be considered. The bubble formation energy in hydrogen, or rather for hydrogen bubble chamber operation, is so small that it is in order of magnitude equal to what can be gained by the recombination of one ion pair or a few ion pairs. That can barely be called δ ray formation of bubbles. However, one finds here also that the efficiency for bubble formation for such an energy release would be of the order of a few percent. The fact that one recombination contributes, or many recombinations in a cluster contribute, to bubble formation is not an essential issue for the theory. It has often been said that the fact that bubble density in hydrogen follows a $1/\beta^2$ law favors the hypothesis that the bubble density is proportional to δ ray density and not to ionization density. This argument is not valid. In the subrelativistic region, both δ ray density and ionization density, to a very good degree of approximation, follow a $1/\beta^2$ law in hydrogen. In the relativistic region, the density effect suppresses any difference. It is a mistake to contrast a δ ray theory with an ionization theory. Both theories are essentially the same. If the bubble formation energy is sufficiently small, a single ion pair can form a bubble by recombination. The real point at issue is to decide how small can be the energy necessary to form a bubble. This, as we have seen, has been solved by the observation of the relativistic rise. This effect does not make a difference, contrary to what has been assumed many times, between δ ray density and ionization density, but rather between δ rays of energy much higher than the ionization potential (no relativistic increase) and δ rays of energy comparable to the ionization potential (relativistic increase).

V. The Growth of the Macroscopic Bubble

A. Elementary Theory

The growth of a macroscopic bubble has been treated theoretically by Foster and Zuber (1954) and by Plesset and Zwick (1954). We wish to give here a very simple calculation, which, without being rigorous, will enable us to understand the role of the different parameters in the correct formula.

We will make the following hypotheses:

(1) Essentially, the growth of the bubble is governed by the fact that molecules can only evaporate at the surface of the bubble, and, therefore, is governed by the supply of heat to the surface, i.e. the heat flow from the liquid to the surface of the bubble.

(2) This heat flow is maintained solely by heat conductivity. Convection or movement of the bubble inside the liquid does not play any role. This is probably perfectly correct for the "macroscopic" bubbles which interest us here, i.e. with a radius between $1\,\mu$ and 1 mm.

We will further assume that the pressure of the expanded liquid is not zero, but rather is a positive pressure p_e which is large enough to dominate over the pressure $2\sigma/r$, for the radius of bubbles of interest. This condition is fulfilled in most bubble chambers.

The picture of the growth is the following. Evaporation cools the surface of the bubble down to a temperature T_e such that the corresponding vapor pressure is practically p_e. A gradient of temperature is thus created which maintains a certain heat flow from the liquid, still at the temperature T_i, to the bubble surface. This heat evaporates molecules and the bubble grows accordingly. We will now make an assumption which, contrary to the others, is not justified and is merely made for simplification. We will assume that the temperature gradient in the liquid is constant from the bubble surface to some spherical surface around the bubble, which is at the temperature T_i. Further away from the bubble, the temperature must, of course, be constant. In other words, we assume that all of the heat which contributed to the evaporation of all the molecules already in the gas phase at a certain time t came from a zone of thickness d around the bubble and that, in this zone, the temperature varies linearly with r between r_b and $r_b + d$ (r_b is the radius of the bubble). This hypothesis would not be very bad if d were small compared with r_b. We have a first equation:

$$\tfrac{4}{3}\pi r_b{}^3 h\rho' = 4\pi r_b{}^2\, d\,\frac{T_i - T_e}{2}c\rho\;;\qquad (18)$$

h is the latent heat of vaporization per gram, ρ' is the density of the gas at pressure p_e and temperature T_e, c is the specific heat of the liquid, and ρ is the density of the liquid. The equation expresses the fact that the heat in the cooled zone has been used for the vaporization of the vapor in the bubble. This equation gives

$$d = \frac{2}{3} \frac{r_b h \rho'}{(T_i - T_e) c \rho} . \tag{19}$$

For hydrogen, this results in d of the order of 0.1 to $0.25 r_b$, and our hypothesis is not too badly justified (a fact should not be forgotten: the ratio ρ/ρ' is larger than in the previous section since the pressure in the bubble is now p_e and not p_∞, the vapor pressure for the temperature T_i).

The equation for the increase of the bubble radius by an amount dr_b is then

$$4\pi r_b^2 \, dr_b h \rho' = \frac{\lambda(T_i - T_e)}{d} 4\pi r_b^2 \, dt , \tag{20}$$

where λ is the thermal conductivity of the liquid.

This equation expresses the fact that the amount of heat necessary to evaporate a certain mass of liquid during a time dt is equal to the heat flow during this time. Substituting d from Eq. (19) yields

$$h\rho' \, dr_b = \frac{3}{2} \frac{\lambda(T_i - T_e)^2 \rho c}{h\rho' r_b} \, dt , \tag{21}$$

which finally leads to the expression

$$r_b = 3^{1/2} \frac{\lambda^{1/2}(\rho c)^{1/2}(T_i - T_e)}{h\rho'} t^{1/2} . \tag{22}$$

The expression derived by Plesset and Zwick (1954) was

$$r_b = \frac{2(3/\pi)^{1/2}\lambda(T_i - T_e)}{h\rho' D^{1/2}} t^{1/2} , \tag{23}$$

where D is the diffusion coefficient of heat, $D = \lambda/\rho c$. Therefore, the formula reduces to

$$r_b = 2(3/\pi)^{1/2} \frac{\lambda^{1/2}(\rho c)^{1/2}(T_i - T_e)}{h\rho'} t^{1/2} , \tag{24}$$

which is the same as Eq. (22) but with a different coefficient, one that is in fact $2/\pi^{1/2}$ larger. The difference in coefficients comes entirely from the wrong assumption about the linear gradient.

B. PRACTICAL CONSEQUENCES

With this very simple calculation, we can understand clearly the roles played by the different parameters in the formula and why the law of bubble growth has the form $r = Kt^{1/2}$. The volume of the cooled zone is proportional to the volume of the bubble; therefore, the effective thickness of this zone is proportional to the radius of the bubble. The heat flow per unit time is inversely proportional to this thickness but proportional to the surface, i.e. it is proportional to the radius of the bubble. But since the heat required for an increase dr should be proportional to the surface of the bubble (the square of the radius), the rate of growth is inversely proportional to r; hence r^2 is proportional to t.

The law $r = Kt^{1/2}$ was verified in Berkeley at the beginning of the bubble chamber work. There is, however, no good agreement between the experimental coefficient K and its theoretical value. The formula of Plesset and Zwick indicates a growth of 500μ in 1 msec for a chamber operating in the conditions described in Table I, whereas the experimental values lie more in the range of 100 to 250μ. The difference is not very important for several reasons:

(a) it is quite difficult to measure the bubble diameter; and

(b) it is the opinion of the author that many times, especially in the early days of bubble chamber operations, the pressure drop $p_\infty - p_e$ was overestimated for hydrogen bubble chambers; as we shall see, the value of the constant K depends strongly on this pressure drop.[7]

Indeed, the most interesting feature in the formula is not the numerical value of the constant K, but the way it depends on the different parameters. The most important one is certainly p_e; for a larger p_e, ρ' is increased and $T_i - T_e$ is decreased, both effects reducing the rate of growth. Now we must remember that a bubble chamber operator interested in nuclear physics will try to keep the number of bubbles constant. This, for a given temperature of the liquid, determines the expansion pressure drop $p_\infty - p_e$. The lower the temperature, the greater should be $p_\infty - p_e$ and the lower should be p_e. Therefore, if for a given bubble density one wishes to have the fastest possible bubble growth, the temperature should be lowered. (One cannot of course go into a region where the needed $p_\infty - p_e$ becomes so large that bubble chamber operation is impossible.) This is true only if the operating

---

[7] This impression is confirmed by the fact that the most recent work, Fabian et al. (1963), gives the value of the rate of growth which is the closest to the theoretical value.

conditions are not too close to the critical point, because here the variation of the latent heat of vaporization might compensate for the effect.

This effect has been very well verified qualitatively. The first hydrogen bubble chambers of Berkeley operated at relatively high temperatures and required flash delays of several milliseconds. Later on, the advance in the technique of liquid expansion permitted operation at lower temperatures with much shorter flash delays. Also in the early days of bubble chambers, when "clean" bubble chambers were built, one was able to reach very large values of $p_\infty - p_e$, p_e going even into the negative region; then the bubble growth was really explosive (microseconds instead of milliseconds).

The variation of bubble growth with expansion conditions can be expressed in a very simple fashion: the less matter that is required to fill a bubble, the faster the bubble will grow. This, incidentally, explains a fact which was very striking to cloud chamber specialists in the early stages of bubble chamber study, namely the difference in the rate of growth for droplets (100 msec before visibility) and bubbles (1 msec or less). The explanation is now very clear; it takes a large number of molecules to make a visible droplet and it takes much less to make a visible bubble.

VI. Applications of the Theory to Special Chambers; Summary and Conclusions

At the beginning of Section I, the operation of a bubble chamber was described as follows: by expansion a liquid is brought into a metastable superheated state which can be maintained indefinitely unless ionizing radiation starts to form bubbles. This is the operation of what is called a clean bubble chamber, i.e. a chamber in which there is no "dirt" effect, from the walls, from dust, etc., to start vaporization. Practically all the chambers used for nuclear physics experiments are "dirty" chambers. In these chambers, there is actually boiling on the walls, at the gaskets, etc., and this boiling tends to recompress the liquid. However, the expanding action is maintained to compensate for the recompression due to boiling. The liquid is maintained at a more or less constant pressure p_e for a time long enough for bubble formation, growth, and photography. There is, therefore, no difference, as far as the theory is concerned, between clean and dirty bubble chambers. The bubble in the liquid does not know that somewhere on the outskirts there is heavy boiling going on.

A. GAS-LIQUID BUBBLE CHAMBER

The first special type of chamber we want to discuss is the gas-liquid bubble chamber. Instead of a pure liquid, one uses a solution of gas in a liquid. If the solubility of the gas is strongly pressure-dependent, a reduction of pressure will create an unstable state, and bubbles will start to form (normally on the walls). This phenomenon is more familiar to the average man (whether he drinks soda-pop or champagne) than is the boiling of superheated liquids. The gas-liquid bubble chamber was suggested by Askar'yan (1960) and realized first by Argan and Gigli (1956) and very soon after by Hahn (1956). Most of the time, CO_2 or methane is used as gas; ethyl-ether, propane, hexane and many other liquids can be used (see, for instance, Hahn and Fisher, 1957). The advantage of these chambers is that they operate normally at lower temperatures (but not lower pressure) than do ordinary boiling bubble chambers.

There should not be, of course, any essential difference as far as the theory is concerned between a gas-liquid mixed system and a pure liquid system. Here, too, the diminution of pressure creates a supersaturated state which (apart from wall and dirt effects) remains stable, since a bubble, before starting to grow, must reach a critical radius r_c defined by $p_\infty - p_e = 2\sigma/r_c$ (p_∞ is the equilibrium pressure of the gas-liquid solution at the operating temperature). Here, too, the formation of the critical bubble will require that some work ($W_m = 16\pi\sigma^3/3(p_\infty - p_e)^2$) is given to the system. Therefore, the solution will remain stable unless the energy is so small that critical bubbles can be formed by statistical fluctuations inside the solution (fizzing or foaming of the liquid). However, for larger values of W_m, the energy necessary for bubble creation can be provided by ionizing radiation. Of course, heat will not discriminate between gas and liquid molecules, and the original bubble will contain liquid vapor as well as gas. The law of growth of the bubble will follow a mechanism very similar to that described in Section V. Diffusion of gas molecules in the liquid will play a role similar to heat diffusion.

The above remarks are, perhaps, a little too simple-minded; according to the experts (Argan et al., 1957 and Hahn and Fisher, 1957), the primary effect of a gas dissolved in a liquid might be a strong reduction of the surface tension which permits bubble chamber operation at a temperature lower than that necessary for the pure liquid. This makes gas-liquid bubble chambers even more similar to ordinary bubble chambers than we have considered them to be in the preceding paragraph.

B. Liquids under Stress

The question of the fracture of liquids under stress creates, for the theory, a wider extrapolation problem than that of the gas bubble chamber. However, even there, no fundamental alteration seems to be required. Nothing in the considerations of Section I requires that the final pressure p_e should have a positive value. If p_e is negative, the radius of the critical bubble will still be given by

$$r_c = \frac{2\sigma}{p_c - p_e} = \frac{2\sigma}{p_c + |p_e|}. \tag{25}$$

One has, however, to be careful now not to approximate p_c by p_∞, since Eq. (2)

$$\frac{RT}{M} \ln \frac{p_\infty}{p_c} = \frac{p_\infty - p_e}{\rho} = \frac{p_\infty + |p_e|}{\rho}$$

remains valid and makes p_c quite different from p_∞ if $|p_e|$ is large.

However, on one point the theory for negative p_e is different from the ordinary one. As soon as the bubble reaches a radius r_c' defined by

$$\frac{2\sigma}{r_c'} = |p_e|, \tag{26}$$

the bubble can grow without any further evaporation of the liquid, and it will do so very fast. This is no more than an extrapolation of the general rule mentioned at the end of Section V. A bubble which can grow by being filled essentially by a void will do so very explosively indeed.

We have already mentioned that in the early days clean bubble chambers were expanded at moderately negative pressures. Most of the time, however, the temperature conditions were similar to normal bubble chamber conditions. The question of the radiation-induced fracture of liquid under stress has been studied by Hahn (1961). The liquid was contained in a capillary tube with open ends bent upwards at 90°, the tube being spun around a vertical axis perpendicular to its own horizontal axis. Stress is developed by the centrifugal force and can be measured easily by the rotation velocity. The experiment was done by measuring the waiting time before breaking of the liquid column at a given stress (rotation velocity), for liquids under the influence of ionizing radiation (or without ionizing radiation as a control). A graph "reciprocal value of the waiting time versus stress" is a threshold curve for the onset of radiation sensitivity. Twenty-eight liquids were studied, but the most extensive data are for freon-113 ($CCl_2F-CClF_2$) at a temperature of 20°C. The sources of radiation were traces of α radioactive substances dissolved in the liquid (bubble formation by recoil nuclei), neutrons, and γ rays.

It was found that:

(a) Above a certain stress, the waiting time for breaking when radiation was present was on the average 10 to 100 times shorter than when radiation was absent.

(b) The threshold curves were very steplike for sensitivity to α recoil nuclei or to γ rays, much less sharp for sensitivity to neutrons. No explanation of this last point was given but it may be associated with the fact that neutrons do not give a monoenergetic spectrum of recoil nuclei.

(c) The sensitivity to α recoil nuclei starts much earlier than that to γ rays ($p_e \approx -5$ atm and $p_e \approx -50$ atm respectively). The neutron (relatively) flat sensitivity curve starts at about -5 atm.

(d) The differences of sensitivity for different liquids do not depend systematically on the surface tension but depend rather on viscosity.

It is clear that, qualitatively, points (a), (b), and (c) agree very well with the predictions of the theory. Why the onset of sensitivity to γ rays is sharp is also qualitatively understood from what we have said about formation of bubbles by γ rays. In order to have sensitivity to electrons (enough energy in a small enough volume), the bubble formation energy has to be made so small that practically any Compton electron can do the work at the end of its range. (Probably it will do it with small efficiency, as in ordinary bubble chambers, but if the efficiency is relatively independent of its energy, the sensitivity onset will remain sharp.)

Before discussing the results of this experiment in a more quantitative fashion, we must first consider other experiments on radiation induced cavitation of liquids under stress.

C. ULTRASONIC BUBBLE CHAMBER

It is easy with ultrasonic vibration to put a liquid under stress (for a short period of time during each cycle). Of course, the interest in developing an ultrasonic bubble chamber is much broader than purely the extension of the theory of bubble formation. A real ultrasonic bubble chamber, which could produce tracks as sharp as an ordinary bubble chamber even for fast singly charged primaries, would probably constitute a very interesting instrument for high energy physics. The sensitive volume will, of course, be discontinuous (at pressure nodes, there will never be bubbles). But in time the chamber will be practically continuously sensitive, a feature which should be of great interest for cosmic ray physics or even for high energy physics at accelerators since the light flash could be counter triggered.

So far, however, the experiments have not produced such an instrument and their interest lies mainly in the study of radiation-induced fracture of liquids under stress. Even before the static experiment of Hahn (reported above), Liebermann (1959) and Hughes (1960) had reported that the threshold for ultrasonic cavitation could be strongly reduced if the liquid was irradiated with neutrons. γ ray irradiation had no effect. Later on, Hahn and Peacock (1963) were the first to observe instantaneous bubble formation (when the liquid was irradiated by neutrons) for a liquid in which ultrasonic standing waves were maintained. Bubble formation was observed at the points of the wave where the pressure amplitude was maximum, ± 5 atm. -5 atm is also the value reported in the static experiment for the threshold of liquid rupture induced by recoil nuclei. The liquids, however, were not the same. The freon-113 used in the static experiment was, in the ultrasonic experiment, sensitive to neutrons only for 20 msec after the ultrasound was turned on. It was freon-11 (CCl_3F) and also freon-115 and freon-12 which gave continuous neutron sensitivity in the ultrasonic chamber. The bubbles grew to visible size within a cycle and disappeared in a fraction of a cycle: a fact very important for the future of the ultrasonic bubble chamber as a nuclear physics instrument.

The point of interest for this article is that Hahn and Peacock computed the critical radius and the energy for bubble formation under their operating conditions. The critical radius is $r_c = 770$ Å. The surface energy is 9 keV (no details are given) but since σ is here about 20 dyn/cm, it is likely that the term $W_{s_1} = 4\pi r_c^2 \sigma$ is now more important than $W_{s_2} = 4\pi r_c^2 (T \, \partial\sigma/\partial T)$; the evaporation energy W_v is 13 keV and the expansion energy W_e is now negative (liquid under stress) and equal to -5 keV. The total is 17 keV whereas a recoil nucleus (from neutron collision) is expected to lose 100 keV inside the critical volume. The same sort of discrepancy was also found in the static experiment (radiation induced fracture of liquid under stress) reported above. This type of discrepancy is a result that we have not yet encountered in our considerations. Up to this point, energy releases equal to W_g or W_g' inside the critical volume were capable of forming bubbles. This was demonstrated by the relativistic increase experiments for energies of the order of 200 eV, and by the recoil nucleus experiments (under conventional bubble chamber operations) for energies of the order of 100 keV. The fact that δ rays of 200 eV were only 2% efficient is not at all the same sort of discrepancy we are encountering now. What is found in bubble formation in liquids under stress is that recoil nuclei having an energy of 100 keV do not form bubbles when the bubble formation energy, W_g', as computed in Table I is 100 keV. W_g' has to be brought down to 17 keV before bubble formation occurs.

This reinforces our opinion (which is, in fact, very intuitive and not well grounded) that there is not a very good foundation for the estimates of bubble formation energy based on purely energetic static considerations. Let us repeat once again that the dynamic approach of Seitz seems to us quite different. Here the bubble is formed as a cavity, not really empty of course, but there is no condition that the right number of molecules has to be evaporated to fill it. The condition is that the growth is fast enough (versus heat diffusion time). The estimated energies are lower than the estimates W_g' based on static considerations if viscosity is neglected. We have seen that the existence of the relativistic increase does not make the dynamic estimates completely unrealistic.

In the case of the two Hahn experiments (liquid under stress, ultrasonic chamber), the comparison between the purely energetic estimation of bubble formation energy and the dynamic estimation might be quite different from that for conventional bubble chambers. On the one hand, the term W_v is much smaller (for equivalent values of r_c) in the case of liquid under stress, because here the pressure inside the bubble, p_c, is much smaller than p_∞ and therefore there is much less matter to be evaporated to fill the bubble. Indeed, for radii of the order of 800 Å, W_v was 100 keV in the Riepe and Hahn (1961) experiment (Section IV) and is only 13 keV in the stress experiment. On the other hand, the Seitz dynamic estimates may become much larger for liquids under stress at the lower temperatures. Even if the role of viscosity was overemphasized for conventional bubble chamber operation the situation might be different at lower temperatures. The point (d) of the static Hahn experiment (the resistance of liquids to rupture seems to be related to their viscosity) could be considered as a weak confirmation of our point of view.

We come back to the subject of the ultrasonic bubble chamber, for which the static Hahn experiment shows that pressures as low as -50 atm, and not -5 atm, have to be reached in order to record tracks at minimum ionization (-50 atm is the threshold of sensitivity for irradiation by γ rays). Alternatively, one could also try to operate ultrasonically with a liquid at a temperature close to normal bubble chamber operating condition, where negative pressure is not even needed. Why this was never tried is not clear.[8] There are, of course, two difficulties:

(a) Under normal bubble chamber conditions, liquids are quite compressible (expansion ratios, by volume, are of the order of 1%) and, therefore, operation at these temperatures might require an unrealistically high power from the ultrasonic generator.

[8] *Note added in proof:* This has, in fact, been tried by Hahn and Peacock and they found sensitivity to neutrons.

(b) For reasons outlined in Section V, at such high temperatures the bubble growth might be much too slow for an ultrasonic period.

Nevertheless, it seems that it will be worthwhile to try ultrasonic bubble chambers in what could be called an intermediate region (intermediate between "cold" liquids under high tensile stress and conventionally used "hot" liquids).

D. SUMMARY AND CONCLUSIONS

The whole theory of bubble chambers can be summarized in the following way.

(1) Classical thermodynamics demonstrates that a superheated liquid cannot normally erupt into bubbles, because a critical bubble must first be formed, whose formation requires work. The critical bubble can be formed either by some supply of extra energy or, if the required work is small enough, by statistical fluctuations inside the liquid. If the extra energy is introduced in the form of heat, it has to be larger than the work of formation of the critical bubble. This is a direct consequence of the Carnot principle.

(2) The energy left in a liquid by a fast, minimum-ionizing particle is perfectly capable of generating bubbles even when the necessary work for bubble formation is much too large for the statistical fluctuation mechanism to be at all efficient. Further, the δ ray structure of ionization insures that the energy (or at least a large fraction of it) is concentrated in a very small volume.

(3) From this, two models of bubble formation can be considered: (a) the energy comes from the repulsive force due to concentration of ions of the same charge, and (b) the energy is essentially heat, coming very probably from the recombination of ions. The fact that pure xenon (which transforms ion recombination energy into light and not into heat) cannot be operated as a bubble chamber liquid, but becomes efficient if it is mixed with ethylene which transforms light into heat, strongly favors hypothesis (b).

(4) One can then make conjectures on the energy really needed to form a critical bubble and compare it to experimental results for bubble densities or sensitivity thresholds of bubble chambers. There seems to be rather good agreement between the conjectures and the energy of a particle which makes *one* bubble, provided one assumes that δ electrons have an overall very bad efficiency $\approx 2\%$ for making bubbles and that recoil nuclei have a 100% efficiency. The agreement disappears for the somehow abnormal conditions of liquids under stress. Here the energy required for a particle to make one

bubble is definitely larger: five times more than the "guessed" value of what the bubble formation energy should be.

What conclusions can one draw from this theory? They are certainly quite different depending on whether one takes the point of view of a physicist interested in the physics of fluid or that of the high energy physicist who considers a bubble chamber as a tool.

The first must consider the theory as unsatisfactory. There are too many unknowns—the bad efficiency of δ rays versus the high efficiency of recoil nuclei, the discrepancy of energy estimates for liquids under stress. It is not even certain that the heat is released via ionization and recombination. For recoil nuclei from α radioactive substances, heat is largely released directly by atoms in atomic collisions. For fast light particles, this mechanism is completely inefficient, but excitation of molecules and subsequent de-excitation could be as efficient as ionization and recombination (at least for complex molecules). There is, of course, no essential difference between ionization and excitation. One is a "bound-to-free" electron transition and the other a "bound-to-bound" transition. Therefore, the true problem is to find a real theory of the evolution of the bubble, starting from a few recombinations or de-excitation events, which produce few molecules or atoms of high energy, and going on to the state of the critical bubble filled with 1500 molecules at moderate temperatures. Classical fluid dynamics may be quite inadequate for the description of the early stages of this evolution. It is certainly difficult to decide what experiments might help to solve these problems. At least, one could consider the collection of more information on bubble formation energy. One way would be to operate a heavy liquid bubble chamber at higher temperatures than is usually done (i.e. for smaller W_g) and to try to measure the bubble density using very short flash delays and photographing the tracks in true size or even magnified (and not demagnified as usual).

From the point of view of the high energy physicist, the theory is quite satisfactory and possibly completely useless. It explains most of the facts he observes, and as far as predicting bubble chamber operating conditions, it can usually be replaced by a rule of thumb: a bubble chamber will operate correctly if the temperature of the liquid is somewhere between $\frac{1}{2}$ and $\frac{2}{3}$ of the way between the boiling point (at atmospheric pressure) and the critical point, and if the expansion reduces the pressure by a factor of 2. Anyhow, most of the interesting liquids have been tried already. The only really useful and indeed very important prediction made by the theory was the first one, which allowed Glaser to predict at what temperature bubble chamber operation should be tried. The fact that it was based on the wrong mechanism does not reduce the importance of this success, since the energetic considerations, the only ones of importance, were correct.

There remains, therefore, only one question. If there are at least two plausible mechanisms which predict that ionizing particles will produce bubbles in a superheated liquid, why was the bubble chamber not invented earlier? Indeed, after the invention of the cloud chamber, it would have seemed logical to try every possible supersaturated state to make visible the tracks of fast charged particles. Of course, there is the usual and rather philosophical answer that the bubble chamber would have been useless in those times and that, like many others, the invention came when it was needed. However, another point might have played a role. There was a theory of droplet formation on ions in a cloud chamber. This theory is probably completely correct. However, the pure extrapolation of this theory did not predict any bubble formation (by single ions) in a superheated liquid, rather it predicted correctly that single ions would help the collapse of bubbles. This might have constituted a sort of mental block. It is the merit of Glaser to have looked more deeply into the matter and to have tried. The fact that the first theory used was based upon the electrostatic mechanism illustrates, perhaps, the influence of the Thompson theory of the cloud chamber. This explanation of the nondiscovery of the bubble chamber might look very speculative but it would not be the first time that a theory, even a good one, had a bad influence on experimental physics. This should not be forgotten with regard to the theories described in this article.

ACKNOWLEDGMENTS

The author wishes to thank Professor F. Schmeissner for very interesting discussions and especially Dr. J. Schmid for his help in assembling the documentation necessary for this article.

REFERENCES

AHMADZADEH, A., and BISWAS, N. N. (1961). *Nuovo Cimento* **19**, 958.

ARGAN, P. E., and GIGLI, A. (1956). *Nuovo Cimento* **3**, 1171.

ARGAN, P. E., GIGLI, A., PICASSO, E., TOMASINI, G., and GONELLA, L. (1957). *Rept. on Padua-Venice Conf., Sept. 22.*

ARGAN, P. E., GIGLI, A., PICASSO, E., and TOMASINI, G. (1958). *Nuovo Cimento* **10**, 177.

ASKAR'YAN, C. A. (1960). *Zh. Eksperim. i Teor. Fiz.* **28**, 636.

BLINOV, G. A., KRESTNIKOV, IV. S., and LOMANOV, M. F. (1957). *Soviet Phys. JETP* **4**, 661.

BROWN, J. L., GLASER, D. A., and PERL, M. L. (1956). *Phys. Rev.* **102**, 586.

BUDINI, P., and TAFFARA, L. (1956). *Nuovo Cimento* **4**, 23.

BUGG, D. V. (1959). *Progr. Nucl. Phys.* **7**, 1.

DILWORTH, C., MORRISON, D. R. O., and MEMBRIANI, G. (1964). *Nuovo Cimento* **32**, 1432.

FABIAN, B. N., PLACE, R. L., RILEY, W. A., SIMS, W. H., and KENNEY, V. P. (1963). *Rev. Sci. Instr.* **34**, 484.

FOSTER, H. K., and ZUBER, N. (1954). *J. Appl. Phys.* **25**, 474.

GIBBS, J. W. (1878). *Am. J. Sci. & Arts* **16**, 454.

GLASER, D. A. (1954). *Nuovo Cimento,* **11**, Suppl. No. 2, 361.

HAHN, B. (1956). *Nuovo Cimento* **4**, 944.

HAHN, B. (1961). *Nuovo Cimento* **22**, 650.

HAHN, B., and FISHER, G. (1957). *Rev. Sci. Instr.* **28**, 656.

HAHN, B., and PEACOCK, R. N. (1963). *Nuovo Cimento* **28**, 334.

HUGENTOBLER, E., HAHN, B., and STEINRISSER, F. (1963). *Helv. Phys. Acta* **36**, 601.

HUGHES, A. L. (1960). *Proc. Intern. Conf. High Energy Phys., Berkeley,* p. 99. Wiley (Interscience), New York.

KENNEY, V. P. (1960). *Phys. Rev.* **119**, 432.

LEA, R. M., and VITTITOE, C. N. (1962). *Rev. Sci. Instr.* **33**, 243.

LIEBERMANN, D. (1959). *Phys. Fluids* **2**, 466.

PEYROU, C. (1960). *Proc. Intern. Conf. Instr. for High Energy Phys., Berkeley,* p. 157. Wiley (Interscience), New York.

PLESS, I. A., and PLANO, R. J. (1956). *Rev. Sci. Instr.* **27**, 935.

PLESSET, M. S., and ZWICK, S. A. (1954). *J. Appl. Phys.* **25**, 493.

RIEPE, G., and HAHN, B. (1961). *Helv. Phys. Acta* **34**, 865.

SECHI-ZORN, B., and ZORN, G. T. (1962). *Nuovo Cimento* **26**, Suppl. No. 2, 197.

SEITZ, F. (1958). *Phys. Fluids* **1**, 2.

TENNER, A. G. (1963). *Nucl. Instr. Methods* **22**, 1.

VOLMER, M. (1939). "Kinetik der Phasenbildung." Steinkopff, Darmstadt.

WILLIS, W. J., FOWLER, E. C., and RAHM, D. C. (1957). *Phys. Rev.* **108**, 1046.

CHAPTER III

Cryogenic Bubble Chambers

W. B. FOWLER

Brookhaven National Laboratory
Upton, New York

I. Introduction

The history of bubble chamber development is described in Chapter 1, Section I. In particular, the use of liquids that require low temperatures, such as liquid hydrogen, is credited to Hildebrand and Nagle (1953), who first showed that a superheated condition with radiation sensitivity could be achieved in a bubble chamber filled with hydrogen. The University of California Lawrence Radiation Laboratory's Luis W. Alvarez, foreseeing the great potential of large hydrogen bubble chambers, organized and led an extremely active and successful effort which produced useful hydrogen chambers expeditiously. Figure 1 shows the first cryogenic bubble chamber tracks, photographed in the Lawrence Radiation Laboratory, $1\frac{1}{2}$ in. diameter, liquid hydrogen bubble chamber. Other laboratories followed close behind, and by 1965 approximately 30 "cryogenic" bubble chambers were in operation, producing useful photographs for high energy physics experiments.

"Cryogenics" is defined by Webster as the science of refrigeration, especially with reference to methods for producing very low temperatures.

FIG. 1. Shown in the top photograph is the original, $1\frac{1}{2}$ in. diameter, all glass vessel used by Wood (1954) to photograph the first bubble chamber tracks in liquid hydrogen at the Lawrence Radiation Laboratory. The bright-field stereoscopic photographs of this chamber show bubbles of all sizes because of the use of a radioactive source.

In our case, we shall use "cryogenic bubble chamber" to mean any bubble chamber that operates at liquid nitrogen temperature or lower, i.e. $\leqslant 80°$K. "Cryogenic equipment" is defined in a similar way. The liquefied gases that have been used for cryogenic bubble chambers are hydrogen, deuterium, helium, and neon.

Current experimental work in high energy physics has two basic aspects, the production and the detection of particles whose characteristics are being studied. Consequently, since particles interact with single protons in hydrogen, this gas is by far the most frequently used. Deuterium is used for neutron interactions where the extra "spectator" proton usually adds only a minor complication. Helium has been used for special purposes such as K^--He capture. Neon (Prodell, 1965) has recently been suggested and shown to be effective in increasing γ-ray detection efficiency as in heavy liquid chambers or multiple heavy metal plate arrays.

Accelerator developments, since the time of the discovery of the bubble chamber, have provided increasingly powerful beams of particles for use in elementary particle research. There has been a steady increase in the energy of the beams available, and increases in available beam intensity have resulted in improved methods for separating pure beams of rare particles from beams of particles all having the same momentum.

To provide more efficient detection and more accurate measurements of particles under study, new cryogenic bubble chambers have been constructed and old ones refined or significantly improved. Present-day bubble chambers are much more effective instruments than many of those in use even a few years ago. Further developments in the future are clearly appropriate and include the design and construction of bubble chambers of volumes from 10,000 to 100,000 liters, high magnetic field chambers, and the discarding of small, outdated older chambers.

We shall limit our current interest to bubble chambers that are actively participating in high energy physics experimentation or are planned for the future. Three categories of chambers are involved: (1) bubble chambers that are in position around the multi-BeV accelerators, such as, for instance, the Brookhaven Alternating Gradient Synchrotron, and that, in general, are the active chambers which are producing results of significance to high energy physics; (2) new bubble chambers which are in the proposal stage, such as the BNL 14 foot diameter, cryogenic bubble chamber (Brookhaven, 1964, 1965), the ANL 12 foot hydrogen bubble chamber (Argonne, 1964), etc.; and (3) bubble chambers which are being discussed for effective experimental utilization of proposed new higher energy accelerator facilities such as the United States 200 BeV, the CERN 300 BeV, and the United States

600 to 1000 BeV accelerators. Cryogenic bubble chambers, grouped according to accelerator site, are listed in tabular form in the Appendix.

These chambers have been justified by the interest of physicists in the physics of strong and weak interactions. The effectiveness of large cryogenic bubble chambers for this research is described in the BNL Proposal for Construction of a Cryogenic Bubble Chamber of 14 ft Diameter (Brookhaven, 1965), from which we quote a section:

"Effectiveness of a Large Bubble Chamber

"The effectiveness of a large bubble chamber results from its ability to detect useful numbers of events in which collision and decay processes are recorded, and to provide useful measurements on the particle tracks recorded. The number of events required to be useful varies widely. It may be 1 if it is the first definite example of a new particle or reaction. It may be 10,000, or more, if detailed statistical information is required on a complicated process. There are countless examples where good statistics have led to new discoveries. For instance, the fast-decaying resonant states of particles could only have been discovered by observing large numbers of collision processes.

"A high energy proton passing through liquid hydrogen will, on the average, collide with a target proton once in each 25 feet of track length (cross section 40 millibarns or 4×10^{-26} cm^2). Processes that were considered rare ten years ago occur about once in a track length of 1000 ft. This year's rare events (with cross section of a few microbarns) occur a few times per 1,000,000 ft of track. Collisions due to neutrinos are rarer yet by a factor of about 200,000,000 (cross section 5×10^{-39} cm^2). In the Brookhaven 80 in. hydrogen bubble chamber about 10,000 photographs with 15 charged beam particles apiece are required for 1,000,000 ft of track length. To admit more particles is not useful because too many other interactions of less interest also take place, resulting in confusion of the rare events of special interest. Thus hundreds of thousands of photographs are required for a statistically significant experiment on such rare events. Study of neutrino collisions requires even more photographs, even though neutrino beam intensities can be a great deal higher because the uncharged neutrinos leave no tracks in the bubble chamber unless they interact with a nucleus. Increased chamber size is one way to make such difficult experiments more feasible.

"If the accelerator can provide a sufficiently intense beam of particles often enough, a gain in events recorded per day is possible (except for neutrino collisions) by taking more bubble chamber photographs in a given period. For instance, increasing the picture taking rate from one per 3 seconds to three per second would result in nine times as many photographs per day. This kind of factor would make experiments possible which are not now considered feasible, because they would take too long with present equipment, or, alternatively, more experiments could be run during a scheduled operating period. While higher energies open the road to new discoveries in high energy physics, high intensities and improved detectors allow us to follow the road in a time that is reasonable in relation to man's capacity for enduring drive and continuing interest, or, ultimately, to his lifetime.

FIG. 2. Aerial view of Brookhaven's Alternating-Gradient Synchrotron (AGS) and 80 in. liquid hydrogen bubble chamber complex. (1) AGS injector building. (2) Covered circular tunnel containing AGS magnet ring. (3) Main experimental area. (4) Particle beam array for 80 in. chamber. (5) 80 in. chamber building. (6) Transformers for the electric power for 80 in. chamber magnet and other major components. (7) Water cooling tower. (8) Gas storage area. (9) Safety sphere. (10) Beam direction inside AGS.

"The effectiveness of a large bubble chamber results not only from increased numbers of events recorded, but also from increased information concerning each event that *is* recorded. The basic measurements are position, angle, momentum (from curvature in the magnetic field), range, and velocity (from bubble density). Accuracy of position will be somewhat worse than in

FIG. 3. Photograph of the BNL 80 in. liquid hydrogen bubble chamber which is now operating at the 33 BeV AGS. The chamber, 80 in. long by 27 in. wide by 26 in. deep, is located in the center of the magnet structure seen in the photograph. Pictures of tracks are taken from the left side where the cameras are visible.

a smaller chamber, angular accuracy about the same, momentum accuracy improved considerably because of longer tracks and very much improved for the particles that stop in the chamber. Accuracy of velocity measurement will be improved because the longer tracks provide better statistics for bubble counting. Large chamber size will provide an increase in the number of particles that stop in the sensitive volume of the chamber. A large fraction of such stopping particles can be identified, either from the decay process, if the particle is unstable, or from measurements on its own track if it is stable. Such identification will greatly aid in the analysis of the complete event.

"A large bubble chamber will provide a very substantial increase in information concerning neutral particles emitted in the events studied. Neutrons (and other strongly-interacting particles) have a considerable probability of secondary collision with a proton before leaving the chamber. Photons (gamma rays) arising, for instance, as decay products of π^0 mesons can be detected by the electron pair into which they materialize (by electromagnetic interaction). The probability of such pair production in the hydrogen is small. Introduction of metal plates into a large chamber can provide a good probability of detecting photons."

Figure 2 shows the aerial view of a modern bubble chamber complex, the BNL (Brookhaven National Laboratory) 80 in. chamber located at the AGS (Alternating Gradient Synchrotron). Figure 3 shows the BNL 80 in. chamber which first operated in June 1963 and is typical of the 2 meter chambers listed in the Appendix. For comparison, Fig. 4 shows an artist's drawing of the proposed BNL 14 ft cryogenic bubble chamber and the existing BNL 80 in. chamber. The drawing emphasizes the increased size of the equipment which is planned for the future.

Cryogenic bubble chambers can be expected to produce large quantities of photographs in the future. Table I lists the stereo photographs taken by the BNL 20 in., BNL 30 in., and BNL 80 in. chambers from the time they were first operated through 1966. This table shows the expected improvement of reliability as the bubble chambers are operated with the accelerator complex as well as the effect of adding new chambers at any particular site.

TABLE I

STEREO PHOTOGRAPHS TAKEN BY THE BNL 20 IN., BNL 30 IN., AND BNL 80 IN. CHAMBERS
FROM THE TIME THEY WERE FIRST OPERATED THROUGH 1966

Year	1959	1960	1961	1962	1963	1964	1965	1966
Photo	124,500	454,900	531,500	1,414,100	2,792,800	4,519,600	2,167,200	4,607,000

An estimate has been made by the author of the potential photograph production of the chambers shown in the Appendix, and is presented in Fig. 5.
Actual photographs taken by the chambers will, of course, depend on a
continuing interest of physicists in the field of high energy physics as well as

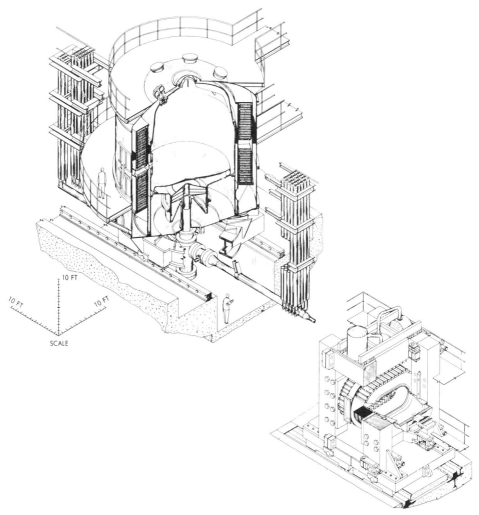

FIG. 4. Artist's drawing of the proposed 14 ft diameter cryogenic bubble chamber with a
superconducting magnet to give a 30 kG magnetic field. For comparison, at the lower right, is
shown the BNL 80 in. chamber which is now in operation at the AGS.

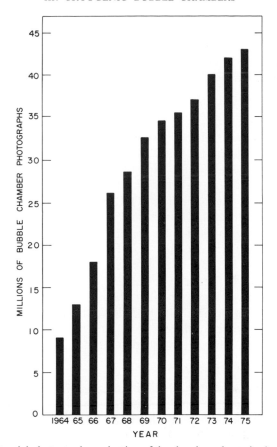

FIG. 5. Potential photograph production of the chambers shown in the Appendix.

the ability of experimenters to obtain the requisite funds. With this introduction to the present "state of the art," and to possible chambers of the future and their production capabilities, we shall now discuss the criteria for the design of cryogenic bubble chambers.

II. Criteria for Design

A. DESIRABLE PERFORMANCE

Development of performance criteria for any particular bubble chamber design is, of course, dependent on the physics research use of the chamber.

Almost all experiments require the ability to extract from bubble chamber photographs precise three-dimensional track positions relative to fixed fiducial marks. This prime criterion, as well as other important performance criteria, is presented below.

1. Uniform Bubble Sensitivity

A minimum ionizing track should have the same average number of bubbles per centimeter of track regardless of its position in the chamber[1]. The number of bubbles per centimeter of track is determined by the temperature of the liquid and the expanded pressure. For cryogenic liquids, Fabian et al. (1963) gave a change of 5 to 15 % in the bubble density for a variation of chamber temperature of 0.1°K, and they measured that variations of expanded pressure of 1 psi produce a bubble density change of approximately 10 %. For constant bubble sensitivity (say bubble density constant to 5 %), it is therefore required that the chamber temperature be constant to about 0.03°K and the expanded pressure be constant to less than $\frac{1}{2}$ psi. These are, of course, not exact rules, and variations exist for the detailed performance achieved by a particular chamber since the surface-to-volume ratio (depending on chamber size and shape) is important, as well as other factors such as bubble formation at gaskets and other bubble nucleation centers. They serve, however, as useful guides for design purposes.

2. Undistorted Bubble Positions

A track, ideally, should show no more jitter of bubble centers than is to be expected from multiple Coulomb scattering. The most important sources of distortions are the following: (a) Index of refraction variations due to temperature nonuniformities in the liquid. The position of a particular bubble can be displaced from its true position by refraction of the light rays by a region of the liquid which is at a different temperature. (b) Motion of the liquid from the time of passage of the charged particle which excited a nucleation center to the time the flash tube was triggered. The bubble must grow to sufficient size (approximately 0.3 mm, depending on chamber depth) to be photographed. Shutt (1963) has presented a quantitative analysis of bubble chamber accuracy requirements, based on work by Willis (1959), who defined an error matrix for track angles and curvatures in the following way.

[1] The average number of bubbles per centimeter varies as a function of particle velocity similar to ionization of tracks in cloud chambers or photographic emulsions. Fabian et al. (1963) found that the number of bubbles per centimeter, m, is given by the function $m = A(P_s)^n \beta^{-2}$, where, at a temperature of 27°K, $A = 7.5 \times 10^{-8}$ bubbles/cm of track, and $n = 5.4$. P_s is the superheat pressure, pounds per square inch absolute, in the chamber and is the vapor pressure minus the expanded pressure minimum. β is the ratio of particle velocity to light velocity.

"θ is the angle at the start of a track from a vertex in the plane containing its initial direction and the instantaneous radius of curvature, c is the curvature of the track in this plane, φ is the dip angle of the track helix with respect to the 'chamber plane' (parallel to the film plane). Then, the error matrix for hydrogen is, approximately,

$$
\begin{array}{c}
c \\ \\ \theta \\ \\ \varphi
\end{array}
\left|
\begin{array}{ccc}
\left(\dfrac{61.5\varepsilon^2}{L^4} + \dfrac{9.04 \times 10^{-2}}{L(p\beta)^2} \right) & \left(-\dfrac{30.8\varepsilon^2}{L^3} - \dfrac{1.13 \times 10^{-2}}{(p\beta)^2} \right) & 0 \\ \\
\left(-\dfrac{30.8\varepsilon^2}{L^3} - \dfrac{1.13 \times 10^{-2}}{(p\beta)^2} \right) & \left(\dfrac{16.6\varepsilon^2}{L^2} + \dfrac{1.13 \times 10^{-2}L}{(p\beta)^2} \right) & 0 \\ \\
0 & 0 & \left(\dfrac{35.3\varepsilon^2 \cos^2\varphi}{L^2} + \dfrac{2.26 \times 10^{-2}L}{(p\beta)^2} \right)
\end{array}
\right|
$$

Here the first, second, and third rows refer to the errors on c, θ and φ, respectively. The diagonal terms are the variances, the others the covariances for correlation terms. The square roots of the variances shall be called the 'errors' Δc, $\Delta\theta$, $\Delta\varphi$ on c, θ, and φ, respectively. We shall not consider the correlation terms. $\Delta\varphi$ is given for a stereoscopic angle of about 15° and is approximately twice as large as $\Delta\theta$, which could be considerably improved by employing a larger stereoscopic angle. In practice, the observed errors on φ are even larger, perhaps 4 times as large as those on θ."

Increasing the stereoscopic angle is difficult; however, some new large chamber designs such as the BNL 14 ft and Argonne 12 ft chambers incorporate this improvement.

"L is defined as the track length (in cm), p is the momentum (in MeV/c), β is the velocity ratio, ε is the 'measuring error,' which is adjusted to combine all uncertainties due to finite bubble image size, turbulence, optical and film distortions, and actual measuring procedure. Usually values for ε are between 35 and 70 microns."

Shutt takes $\varepsilon = 50$ microns, which is probably a good estimate for careful chamber operation.

"The first term in each matrix element is due to ε alone, the second due to multiple Coulomb scattering. The latter, therefore, depends strongly on the particular liquid used, and, as mentioned, the terms written down here refer to hydrogen. For other liquids they should be increased approximately by the factor $k = [\Sigma_i Z_i(Z_i + 1)N_i]/2N_H$, where N_H is the number of hydrogen nuclei per cm^3 in liquid hydrogen, and N_i is the number of each of the different nuclei per cm^3, of charge Z_i, present in the liquid.

"One finds that the errors $\Delta\theta$ and $\Delta\varphi$ have minima from which, for fast particles, one calculates optimum track lengths for angle measurements of

$L_{\theta opt} \approx L_{\varphi opt} = 0.42p^{2/3}$. Δc has no minimum but the term containing ε decreases with L^4 while the Coulomb term decreases much more slowly with L. Once the ε term amounts to, say, one half of the Coulomb term, further increasing L to decrease Δc, which is then proportional to $L^{-1/2}$, becomes very inefficient. One finds that this happens just about when $L = L_{opt} \approx L_{\theta opt}$. It follows that, generally, tracks longer than $L_{opt}(=0.42p^{2/3})$ are not particularly useful in a liquid hydrogen bubble chamber."

Exceptions to this statement occur when it is important to have sufficient path length to stop particles or to allow for secondary scatterings. This may be essential for particle identification or may improve efficiency of particle identification in some experiments. In general, momentum measurements based on range are more accurate than those based on curvature. Passing over these exceptions for the purpose of the discussion, Shutt found the corresponding optimum values for $\Delta\theta_{opt} \approx \Delta\varphi_{opt} \approx 0.10p^{-2/3}$ (in radians) and $\Delta c_{opt} = 0.95p^{-2/3}$ (in cm^{-1}).

"In the kinematic relations used to analyze events, θ, φ and p enter very roughly with equal weights, with exceptions for special track configurations. Therefore one can say that the relative errors on these quantities should be approximately matched. The relative errors are now defined by $\Delta\theta_{opt}/\theta$, $\Delta\varphi_{opt}/\varphi$, and $\Delta c_{opt}/c$, respectively. We shall match at an angle of about 0.5 radian which, at not too high initial energies is quite likely to occur, with track momentum still high. Since $300H/c = 10^6 p$, where H is the applied magnetic field, one obtains immediately ($\Delta c_{opt}/c = \Delta\theta_{opt}/0.5 = \Delta\varphi_{opt}/0.5 = \Delta p/p$) a value for $H = H_m$ which results in matched errors, as defined. One finds $H_m = 1.6 \times 10^4 p^{1/3}$ for hydrogen. At small angles H_m is larger than necessary for matching, at large angles H_m is smaller than necessary, but here usually the momenta p are also considerably lower so that matching remains fairly good."

Shutt's findings for hydrogen are shown in the accompanying tabulation.

	p (BeV/c) = 1	p (BeV/c) = 10
L_{opt} (cm)	42	194
$\Delta\theta_{opt}$ (degrees)	0.06	0.01
H_m (kG)	160	340
$\Delta p/p$ (percent)	0.2	0.03

Since allowances are necessary for (a) beam direction definition, (b) occurrence of production event, and (c) analysis of secondaries produced in event, the dimensions of chambers are typically 2 to 3 × L_{opt}, and present-day chambers are close to having optimum dimensions for approximately 2 BeV/c particles. Larger sized chambers are required for experiments

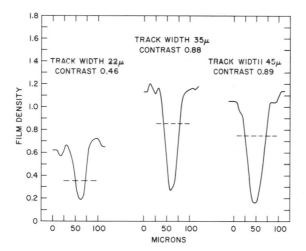

FIG. 6. Photodensitometer traces of bubble images on film from BNL 30 in. hydrogen chamber. The three traces represent different operating conditions. The center trace is typical of operation of BNL 30 in. chamber with bright-field diffuse mirror illumination photographed on Recordak Microfile AHU 70 mm film.

with weakly interacting particles such as neutrinos, and when more emphasis is given to improving neutral particle detection efficiencies, or when particle identification considerations play an important role.

Improvements in bubble chamber operation to reduce distortion of bubble positions is equivalent to reducing c. Present measurement procedures contribute approximately 20 to 30 microns to the 50 micron estimate used above. New chambers therefore must meet current standards rather than try for order of magnitude improvement in nondistortion of bubble positions.

Other effects, such as camera lens distortion, are considered capable of correction either by purchase of distortion-free lenses or by corrections that are measured and applied appropriately during analysis of the photographs.

3. Minimum Background (Good Contrast)

Visibility, as in any method that involves photographic technique, is of utmost importance. The bubble images are ideally black (or clear) circular spots, of good contrast, appearing on a clear (or black) background. Fog on windows or deposits on optical elements (dirty retrodirectors or dirty condenser lenses), for example, scatters light and decreases contrast. Ideally for dark field chambers, the bubble image is of density[2] 1.5 to 2.0 and the

[2] The degree of blackening, or photographic density, is defined as $D = \log_{10} O$, where $O = 1/T$. O is defined as the opacity and T as the transmission.

background of density 0.1 to 0.2. Window fog is less troublesome for bright
field chambers, and for this reason bright field illumination is increasingly
the choice of chamber designers. Figure 6 shows three different photodensitometer traces of tracks in the BNL 30 in. chamber. The film was 70 mm
Recordac Microfile AHU, and the chamber was using bright field illumination by a diffuse mirror. The center trace is for typical operation and shows
a track image width of 35 microns on the film and a contrast (difference
between bubble image and background densities) of 0.88. Dark field illumination might be best for neutrino experiments where the number of tracks in
any picture is so small that double exposures allow for economical use of
film without interfering with the physics experiment. (See Chapter V for
details of illumination and photography.)

4. *Magnetic Field*

A magnetic field is necessary for momentum measurements. The magnitude
of the magnetic field has usually been set by the saturation flux of iron, i.e.
approximately 20 kG. Obviously, the dominant consideration in this case
has been to keep the cost of the magnet as low as possible. Fields and
Thompson (1961) studied optimizing chamber size and magnetic field.
For hydrogen, Shutt (1963) gave a momentum error of 1.4% for a track of
nearly light velocity ($\beta \approx 1$) and a length of 25 cm in a magnetic field of
20 kG. Clearly, a larger magnetic field would allow for higher precision
momentum measurement and would help to minimize other effects such as
Coulomb scattering, turbulence, and measurement errors. Using an optimizing procedure, Shutt calculated (see Subsection 2 above) a desired magnetic
field of 160 kG to 340 kG, depending on the momentum of the particles
that are of most interest. Such high fields are discussed in Chapter I of
Volume II.

In addition to the magnitude of the field, field uniformity needs to be
specified. Nonuniformity of up to 25% can be corrected for without difficulty
by computer programming techniques in the data analysis system. However,
large variations result in lower fields in some regions of the chamber. Nonuniformities of from 1 to 15% are common.

Also necessary is a stabilized current supply for the magnet's excitation.
Electronic controllers, using saturable reactors, give current constant to
0.1% or better, which is adequate. The field needs to be measured and
calibrated to comparable accuracy.

5. *Mobility*

"Mobility" refers to the ability to locate the chamber in order to accept
desired beams from the accelerator. A bubble chamber without the ability

to be exposed to desired beams is of little use. In Chapter IV of Volume II, modern beam techniques are discussed. For the chamber designer, minimum mobility is a simplification and some very large future chambers may require almost complete disassembly in order to move them to a new location. Provisions have to be incorporated in the designs by the inclusion of beam entry ports and channels to allow for the spectrum of possible beams to be brought into the chamber, such as stopping particle beams, high energy beams, and neutral beams.

For the 2 meter chambers, it has been possible to design for a limited mobility (techniques vary, and the scope or degree of permitted motion also varies). Reliance on external beam techniques will probably reduce the mobility requirement.

B. OPERATING GOALS

For a successful bubble chamber which will produce several million pictures per year of operation, the following characteristics are required.

1. *Repetition Rate*

The chamber is best matched to the accelerator if the cycle of the chamber is at least as rapid as the accelerator's (usually from 1 to 5 sec). Recently higher intensity or rapid cycling accelerators have come into operation, and chambers have been designed to operate either at rates of several per second or in a double pulse fashion with rest periods in between, as in the Berkeley 25 in. chamber where the chamber completes two cycles separated by 90 to 100 msec and rests for about 5 sec before the next pulsing sequence occurs. Since many experiments, per pulse, require much less than the full beam of the Bevatron, with this double pulse technique more useful pictures can be obtained during a given operating period than with single pulses. In designing rapid cycling chambers, caution is required in providing sufficient cooling (Carnot cycle heating occurs with each pulse) and expansion system driving capacity. Some evidence of turbulence has been observed in the BNL 20 in. chamber at repetition rates of 1 per second; however, no quantitative evaluation is available. Studies of these fast cycling effects are being made with the BNL 80 in. chamber, the Berkeley 25 in. chamber, and the Princeton 15 in. chamber, but no results are as yet published.

2. *Reliability*

Even with the complex equipment required for a cryogenic bubble chamber, reliabilities of 60 to 90% have been achieved. As with any research equipment, very high returns result from continuous operation. This is especially true in low temperature work where cooldown and warmup times (approximately 100 hours each in the case of the BNL 80 in. chamber) have to be added to time necessary for maintenance and repair. It is the responsibility of the designer to aim for maximum reliability of each component.

3. *Controllability*

Reference is made to Subsection A above, where desired performance such as uniform bubble sensitivity is mentioned. By "controllability" we mean that after a chamber temperature has been chosen, and the temperature regulator set at this desired value, the controller will bring the chamber temperature to the set value and hold it in control. In addition, if some new value is wanted, a change of the set point will result in a new controlled temperature. Another example is the expansion system. It should be possible to set the expansion valve timing for a given expanded pressure, and the expanded pressure should remain the same for every expansion. If a new expanded pressure is necessary for proper bubble density, then a change, for instance, in expansion valve timing should result in the new desired value for the expanded pressure. Good control benefits the operators by simplifying their work, and benefits the user by assuring a reasonable length of time for the completion of the experiment with uniform picture quality.

4. *Diagnostics of Failures*

In a multisystem complex, such as a large hydrogen bubble chamber, failures of components must be expected. Frequently the failure may not exhibit itself directly, and therefore it is important to design with the aim of providing sufficient information to the operator so that he will be able to pinpoint the malfunctioning component and start its repair immediately. A simple example of this type of problem is a vacuum failure. The cause could be (a) vacuum gauge malfunction, (b) vacuum pump failure, (c) large leak into vacuum tank from outside gasket failure, or a high pressure hydrogen line leak, etc. Easy diagnosis of this failure would be possible if (1) redundant vacuum instrumentation exists, (2) isolation of pump is possible with vacuum indication of blanked-off pump, or (3) residual vacuum analyzer is connected to system giving indication of what gas is causing pressure rise, i.e. hydrogen or nitrogen. Downtime will be minimized if the chamber design includes provision for rapid diagnosis of failures.

5. *Repairability*

Components which are likely to fail have to be detachable from the system or repairable in place. It is important not to "bury" components that may have to be repaired because useful operating time may be lost while disassembly of other items proceeds in order to "uncover" the broken unit. As with modern electronic equipment, the "plug-in" type or "modular" replacement unit is highly desirable since the downtime can be minimized by using this technique. In the case of large equipment where "plug-in" is meaningless, units which can be repaired quickly should always be specified.

C. REQUIRED SYSTEM SPECIFICATIONS

In order to construct cryogenic bubble chambers which exhibit the criteria discussed in Subsections A and B, the system must meet the specifications described below.

1. Leak-Tight Vessels and Controls

Since chamber operating pressures are approximately 100 psi (6–7 atm), and refrigerators and expansion systems require even higher pressures, strong leak-tight vessels and piping are required. Extra care is necessary to prevent leaks since hydrogen is hazardous. A problem to be overcome is that, in low temperature work, pressure or vacuum elements can be perfectly tight at room temperature but upon cooling may have so-called "cold leaks." By pretesting and careful technique of manufacture and assembly of parts that are to be cold, this problem can be minimized. Control elements such as vapor pressure thermometers, bellows-operated valves, window seal bellows, etc., are also required to be completely leak-free.

2. Insulation

Cryogenic vessels need excellent insulation in order to keep heat gains within the cooling capabilities of normally available refrigerators and to keep refrigerator costs reasonable. The best method for accomplishing this insulation requirement is a multiple-layer radiation shield contained in a high vacuum (superinsulation, see Section III, B, 3, e). A traditional method used by low temperature workers to insulate liquid hydrogen temperature vessels has been to surround the vessels with a liquid nitrogen temperature radiation shield, and again, of course, the hydrogen vessel and radiation shield are surrounded by high vacuum.

3. Ability to Cool and Fill

After a chamber has been assembled and declared vacuum and pressure tight, the next requirement is the ability to cool down to cryogenic temperatures. The cooldown (and, of course, warm up) rate is usually limited by maximum allowable stress in glass elements, such as large viewing windows, due to temperature gradients. Calculations need to be performed for any particular window and a cooldown rate predicted which will not overstress the window for various expected temperature gradients. For 2 meter chambers the time required for cooling from room temperature to liquid hydrogen temperature is 50 to 100 hours. Ability to adjust the rate of cooling of various parts of the chamber so that window gradients can be reduced expedites cooldown. The BNL 80 in. chamber has a cooling loop at the top of the window ($6\frac{1}{2}$ in. thick × 30 in. high × 81 in. long) and a separately controlled loop at the bottom. By measuring the temperature at the top and bottom of the window, adjustments of flow of cold hydrogen through the loops can be used to equalize the temperatures, thereby allowing for a higher rate of cooling.

Once the chamber temperature has been lowered to 27°K where the vapor pressure of hydrogen is 70 psia, condensation filling can be started by applying hydrogen pressure > 70 psia to the chamber. This filling gas is best obtained from the refrigerator where it is already cold and highly purified so that no contaminants that might interfere with visibility will be introduced into the chamber. In some cases, preliquefied hydrogen is introduced directly through a low temperature transfer line from a liquid hydrogen dewar (often a filter is used which will not pass particles larger than a few microns in size in order to keep the liquid as free as possible of particles that scatter light). A liquid level gauge indicates when the chamber is full.

4. *Temperature Uniformity*

After a chamber has been filled with hydrogen (or deuterium, helium, or neon) and an operating temperature has been chosen, it is desirable to have static temperature uniformity to an accuracy of 0.03°K (see Subsection A). This is achievable with multiple cooling loop chambers. Some chambers do not have multiple cooling loops but depend on convection of the liquid and thermal conductivity for uniformity. As is expected, conditions under pulsing operation are different from static since heat is unevenly added to the system by the pulsing; also, pulsing stirs the liquid improving the temperature uniformity. All in all, for uniform bubble sensitivity as outlined in Subsection A, it is the condition during pulsing that counts. Stability is reached sooner after the onset of pulsing if static uniformity already exists.

5. *Expansion Pulse*

As already stated in Subsections A and B above, the expansion system must allow for an expanded pressure which is constant for every pulse and which is controlled by a piston stroke of constant amplitude for a piston-expanded bubble chamber, or by venting identical quantities of gas in a gaseous expansion bubble chamber. Uniform valve operation is the key to the success of uniform expansion pulses. The recompression part of the expansion system operation is less critical and does not directly affect chamber operation. However, fast recompression is desired in order to minimize heating effects (rapid quenching of bubble growth occurs when the initial pressure is restored to the chamber immediately after the light flash).

6. *Optics*

Clear, clean, distortion-free optical elements for the cameras to view the bubbles along each track result in "good contrast" bubble images referred to in Subsection A. Provision is necessary for allowing the flash illumination system to shine light into the chamber. (Retrodirective single-window chambers are in use as well as chambers with two large windows where "straight-through" illumination is used.) The camera must be capable of advancing the required amount of film as fast as the chamber cycles. Film platens must be flat and lenses of high resolution. (Details of optical systems and cameras are given in Chapter V.)

7. *Safety*

Hydrogen gas is highly flammable and has a very large explosive range (18 to 59% of a hydrogen–air mixture). Every precaution is necessary, therefore, to prevent hydrogen gas from escaping into a room containing a hydrogen chamber or its associated equipment where ignition and possible subsequent explosion might be catastrophic. In practice some hydrogen will probably be present occasionally around any hydrogen bubble chamber, and safety is best maintained by guaranteeing that no ignition sources are present to ignite the gas. Sealed electrical equipment, good ventilation, explosive gas detection equipment, and high-speed emergency ventilation in case of severe hydrogen spills are indicated. Experience has shown that if these precautions are taken, adequate safety is maintained at all times. The cost of safety equipment is easily justified.

8. *Construction Schedule and Cost Estimate*

To design a device that is so expensive as to discourage allocation of funds for its construction is useless, as is the similar case of a design that is so complicated that by the time construction is complete, no interest remains in using the device. As is obvious, a good design minimizes construction time and, simultaneously, cost. In some cases, the advantage of having the chamber early has justified some additional cost. It is important to have a realistic schedule so that each component can be ready when it is needed. The cost of a project is constrained by numerous regulations and controls, detailing of which is beyond the scope of this chapter.

III. Design and Some Design Solutions

A. DESIGN PROCEDURE

1. *Personnel*

Obviously, an ideal design organization consists of ingenious, well-trained and experienced personnel. Small cryogenic chambers have usually been designed by a handful of devoted, hard working physicists and engineers. Chambers of the 2-meter class have utilized large staffs of experienced physicists, engineers, draftsmen, and technicians. The BNL 80 in. chamber required approximately 250 man years of design, construction, and testing prior to initial operation. Future chambers will in all probability require little if any more effort owing to design simplifications that have been developed and to the fact that it is as easy to draw a circle that represents a vessel 1 ft in diameter as it is to draw the same circle and have it represent a vessel 10 ft in diameter. In other words, if more components or systems are not needed, then more drawings will not be required—regardless of size. Design calculations may be more elaborate for larger chambers, and manufacturing manpower and time for construction will be very different, but since large components are contracted to industrial concerns, the manufacturing personnel does not enter into our discussion except as it affects the required funds. As in accelerator construction, many builders of bubble chambers have participated in several construction projects. The construction of a chamber by a novice is not precluded, but some experience in scientific equipment construction is probably essential.

2. *Order of Work*

As mentioned briefly in Section II,C,8, a construction schedule is essential if logical, expeditious design is to proceed. The work has to be arranged so that equipment needed early in the assembly, or equipment requiring long design or manufacturing time or both receives first design priority. Some preliminary design of all components is also necessary to be sure that no insoluble problem is likely to develop. The larger the project, the more likely it is that complex interactions will develop, and it is up to coordinators to prevent major slips in schedules. When one component no longer meets the required delivery schedule, manpower should be shifted from lower priority systems into the area that has fallen behind. By this technique, the schedule can in many cases be maintained or at least the delay minimized. Scheduling aids such as the U.S. Government-developed PERT computer program are applicable to scheduling problems of bubble chamber design and construction. However, there is no substitute for an active coordinating group which keeps up to date on a day-by-day basis with the status of all components.

3. Calculations and Sizing of Components

In order to determine the required strength for various components, calculations of static and dynamic loads to which the component will be subjected are necessary. Following are some examples: (a) The coils of the BNL 80 in. chamber transfer a load of 350 tons to the vacuum tank owing to the attractive magnetic force between the coils; (b) various lines and vessels are subjected to pressure loads when the systems are being pressurized; and (c) in a piston-expanded chamber, the piston is subjected to pulsing loads when expanding and repressurizing the chamber.

Following the determination of loads, calculations have to be made to size each component. Suitable safety factors need to be applied, of course, before a final dimension is arrived at. In many cases, the ASME Boiler and Pressure Vessel Code (1959) serves as a basis for safe design of metal parts of the chamber. For example, in Section VIII, p. 9 of "Unfired Pressure Vessels," the minimum wall thickness $t(\text{min})$ in inches required for a cylindrical shell vessel is

$$t(\text{min}) = \frac{PR}{SE - 0.6P},$$

where R is the inside radius of the shell before any allowance for possible corrosion (in.); P is the design pressure (lb/in.^{2}); S is the maximum allowable stress value (lb/in.^{2}); and E is the joint efficiency (efficiency of appropriate joints in cylindrical shells). The code limits the applicability of this design formula to values of $t < R/2$ and $P < 0.385SE$. For stainless steels such as are frequently used for cryogenic vessels, $S = 18,500$ psi. For butt joints as attained by double-welding, which will obtain the same quality of deposited weld metal on the inside and outside weld surfaces, and having complete joint penetration, free from undercuts, overlaps, or abrupt ridges or valleys, and where the weld groove is completely filled so that the surface of the weld metal does not fall below the surface of the adjoining plate at any point, the value of E can be set equal to 1.0 provided the joint is fully radiographed.

Any practical vessel will have flanges, penetrations, and supports which will require more detailed investigation. For elaborate structures, procedures for stress calculations are given in more fundamental texts, such as Timoshenko's "Theory of Elastic Stability" (1936), "Theory of Plates and Shells" (1940), and "Strength of Materials" (1956), as well as various other publications. It is wise to have important calculations independently checked.

4. *Preliminary Design Drawings*

Experience has shown that for large chambers, design drawings develop in a way similar to other complex engineering projects. The usual procedure is to draw up a set of preliminary drawings that show dimensions and a possible method of fabrication. The detail does not have to be complete but the scope of the job has to be clear and assembly procedures worked out. In many cases these same drawings (issued with changes) will become the final design drawings and will then serve as the basis for construction. However, in other cases, improvements or changes in approach will dictate replacement of the preliminary drawings with entirely new ones.

5. *Feasibility of Manufacture*

When preliminary drawings are ready, discussions with manufacturers will enable verification of fabrication approach, and will allow for incorporation of suggestions based on the manufacturer's previous experience. This will result in simplifications or cost reductions. Allocation of times for construction should also be checked at this time. Sometimes different manufacturers will want to use varying techniques for fabrication because of available equipment or experience, and where there is no particular difference in the product, such freedom is recommended.

6. *Final Design Drawings and Checking*

The final drawings have to be of high quality with an absolute minimum number of errors; otherwise long periods of lost time may be required in order to rectify the mistakes. One can picture the type of trouble that would result from discovery of an incorrect dimension. Suppose that a large forging for a bubble chamber magnet had been made, inspected, machined, and shipped to the assembly site. After the arrival of the other pieces, assembly proceeds to the point of "no fit" due to the undetected mistake in dimension. Probably locally available machine tools would not be of sufficient capacity to remachine the piece. Therefore, it would be necessary to ship the forging back to the manufacturer's plant, reschedule the machining, machine the correction, and reship the forging. This type of costly (both in time and dollars) mistake can be avoided by careful checking and inspection procedures. A trained checker and an inspector (in residence during critical manufacturing operations) will facilitate a trouble-free bubble chamber assembly. Final drawings should show material, method of construction, weld joints, dimensions, tolerances, surface finishes, flatness, parallelism, perpendicularity, circularity, matching joints, etc. Those items that cannot be called out clearly on the drawings should be stated in specifications that accompany the drawings for a particular component.

7. Auxiliaries

A further step, although less critical than the generation of drawings for construction, is the addition of such items as platforms for mounting of components on the magnet structure, or for personnel who will service or operate cameras, expansion system, refrigerators, etc. The larger the chamber, the more surface area there is for mounting equipment. The BNL 80 in. chamber uses separate platforms for each different function which simplifies operation and decreases congestion. Vertical magnetic field chambers, such as the Berkeley 72 in. have single large platforms at the top level of the magnet.

8. Procurement

Multimillion dollar construction projects, such as large cryogenic bubble chambers, are subject to elaborate financial controls, and these are different for each agency supplying the funds. As an example, the BNL procurement handbook has approximately 500 pages explaining procurement procedures in detail. This handbook shows times estimated for procurements as a function of increasing costs:

	Amount of order ($)				
	1–100	101–1000	1001–2000	2001–9999	10,000+
Estimated average min-max working days	3–4	4–14	10–18	19–25	23–37

Abiding by these procedures, therefore, the designer must allow for the proper procurement times in order to have a coordinated schedule.

B. BUBBLE CHAMBER SYSTEMS

1. Magnet, Carriage, and Power Supply

a. Iron Yoke. The magnetic field for bubble chambers has in almost every case so far been accomplished by utilizing an iron yoke as in, say, cyclotron

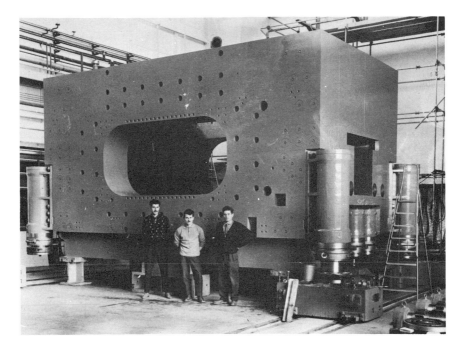

Fig. 7. The magnet steel yoke for the CERN 2 meter liquid hydrogen chamber. On the right is the opening through which the beam enters the chamber. This yoke allows for a separately excited magnet to be inserted here, which aids in steering low energy beams through appropriately thin apertures (beam windows). Note the carriage with support jacks which can be used to raise the whole magnet to the desired height in a beam of particles.

magnets. However, in order to enable one to measure tracks with components parallel to the magnetic field H, bubble chambers are quite deep in the direction of H. Also, iron cannot be present where illumination and photography have to be accomplished. The over-all result is that, for fields up to 20 kG, the iron yoke reduces the electrical power requirement by 30 to 50 % when compared with air core magnets. Another major effect of the iron is the decrease of stray fields outside the yoke structure, and since the yoke is very massive it has been used for the support of chamber components. Cost optimization needs to be performed for each design, and since relative prices of iron, copper, and power supplies have varied over the years magnet yokes have taken on different shapes and sizes. Figure 7 shows the CERN 2 meter cryogenic bubble chamber yoke as it was assembled for the first time at Geneva, Switzerland.

Several factors are of interest. In order to admit beams of particles without their having to pass through the yoke material, either a hole or slot in the yoke is required. Since low energy beam orbits have to enter at an angle of 30 to 40 degrees to the long axis of, say, a 2 meter chamber, a very wide opening is required. In the case of the CERN magnet, where the field is horizontal this width has been reduced by incorporation in the yoke of a separately excited deflecting magnet. In the case of the LRL 72 in. chamber the field is vertical, the yoke is along the long sides of the chamber, and the ends are open. Here, beam entry conditions are met by simply rotating the magnet with respect to the beam by the appropriate angle. Another important feature of the yoke design is also determined by beam entry requirements: How much coil separation is the magnet to have? If tracks are to be separated sufficiently from each other, then a distance of at least several inches between the coils in the direction of the field is needed. However, for a given magnetic field intensity, increasing the coil separation requires more iron, more copper, and more power; therefore a minimum separation is desirable and in practice separations of from a few inches to tens of inches have been used.

Assembly of heavy magnet yokes (450 tons for the BNL 80 in. chamber) has required large bridge cranes of capacities sufficient to lift and move the largest pieces. Other assembly and maintenance problems contribute to crane capacity selection but the yoke has almost always been used for specifying the capability of the crane.

b. Carriage. In order to change the elevation of the chamber or to translate or rotate it, structures which allow these motions of the magnet have been designed and are entitled here "carriage systems." The complexity of the equipment depends on the weight of the yoke, the amount of independence of the degrees of freedom, and the need, in some cases, to use the carriage for partial disassembly of the yoke for servicing other chamber components. Use of commercially available low-coefficient-of-friction slide pads for the translation of the BNL 80 in. chamber has proved to be very convenient and reliable. In the space available in this case, wheels which would stand the possible side thrust loads were not manufactured in the United States. The LRL 72 in. chamber has for its support four "feet" each of which allows, by hydraulic activation, motion of 6 in. in two directions. During the reset of the "feet" after each motion cycle the chamber rests on supports which are at a lower elevation. The load is transferred to the "feet" by self-contained hydraulic jacks and the next step follows. Rotation as well as translation in two directions is possible.

c. *Coils.* In general copper bars with a central hole for water cooling have been thought to be the most satisfactory way of obtaining the ampere-turns required for the magnetic field. Air cooling and oil cooling, both techniques which were in the past applied to accelerators and other electromagnets, have not been used for bubble chamber work. An approximate method of calculating the field H_g at the center of a rectangular set of coils in air yields:

$$H_g(\text{gauss}) = 0.4ni\frac{(b + y)(l + y)}{[(l + y)^2 + (b + y)^2 + (a + x)^2]^{1/2}}$$

$$\times \left[\frac{1}{(b + y)^2 + (a + x)^2} + \frac{1}{(l + y)^2 + (a + x)^2}\right], \tag{1}$$

where n is the total number of turns in both coils; i is the electric current (amperes); $2a$ is the distance between the faces of the coils; $2b$ is the opening in coil, smaller dimension; $2x$ is the coil cross section dimension in direction of field; $2y$ is the coil cross section dimension in direction perpendicular to field; and $2l$ is the opening in coil, larger dimension. (All lengths are in centimeters.) This calculation uses the approximation that all the current is concentrated at the center of the coil cross section so that the length of these two fictitious coils is $2l + 2y$ and their width $2b + 2x$. Experience has shown that this approximation gives reasonably good values when compared to measurements on actual coils. To correct for semicircular ends the length $(2l + 2y)$ of the coils should be determined so that it is the distance between two lines which pass through the center of mass of the curved portion of the coil.

Furthermore

$$ni(\text{ampere turns}) = \frac{1}{4(l + b + 2y)}\left(\frac{PW_{\text{Cu}}}{D\sigma}\right)^{1/2}, \tag{2}$$

where P is the total electric power (W); W_{Cu} is the total copper weight (gm); D is the copper density $= 8.9$ (gm/cm^3); σ is the copper resistivity $= 1.7 \times 10^{-6}$ Ωcm.

Also

$$W_{\text{Cu}} = 32(l + b + 2y)fxyD, \tag{3}$$

where f is the packing fraction of the coils, or that fraction of the coil cross section which is copper. A reasonable value for f is 0.6. The fraction $(1 - f)$ is for cooling water holes (about 0.25) and for insulation (0.15).

By assuming a value for the power P and copper weight W_{Cu} consistent with current relative cost information and by assuming various values of the ratio x/y, Eq. (3) can be solved for x and y. Calculation of the ampere-turns ni from Eq. (2) and the field H_g from Eq. (1) allows a table to be filled in from which a coil shape can be selected. This simple procedure has been elaborated on, and various digital computer programs exist for magnet yoke and magnet coil parameter optimization. In general, these functions are very flat near the optimum. Consequently considerable variation from the exact optimum due to other factors is permissible.

d. Water Cooling. As has been mentioned in the preceding section, the i^2R electrical power that heats the coil is usually removed by circulating water through a hole in the copper coil conductor. In order to estimate this need one can calculate the necessary pressure difference Δ by the approximate formula

$$\Delta(\text{psi}) = 7 \times 10^{-2} \left(\frac{2r_h \, dv}{\mu} \right)^{-1/4} \frac{dv^2 L}{2r_h},$$

where r_h is the hole hydraulic radius (cm), defined as cross section divided by wetted perimeter; L is the length of water path (cm); d is the density of water $= 1$; μ is the viscosity of water $= 0.8$ centipoise at $30°C$; v is the velocity of flow (cm/sec). In order to leave the inside of the coil completely free for the chamber it is best to have all water connections on the outside of the coil so that water flows inward through one set of windings (pie) and outward through an adjacent pie, all double pies being cooled in parallel.

TABLE II

COIL AND COOLING PARAMETERS CALCULATED FOR THE BNL 80 IN. CHAMBER WITH 4 MW OF
ELECTRICAL POWER (P) INPUT AND ALL COILS ELECTRICALLY IN SERIES

Copper weight, W_{Cu} (tons)	30
Ampere turns, ni ($\times 10^6$)	3.09
Current, i (amperes)	16,000
Total number of turns, n	193
Dimensions of coil cross section ($2x = 2y$)(cm)	55.8
Length of average turn, L_1 (cm)	845
Number of double pies	10
Total length, L, per conductor in each double pie (10^4 cm)	1.63
Water velocity, v (10^2 cm/sec)	3.9
Height of area containing single conductor (cm)	5.8
Width of area containing single conductor (cm)	5.6
Water pressure, Δ (psi)	118
Power necessary for water pump (hp)	34

FIG. 8. Illustration of the use of an externally installed auxiliary or "beam-pitching" magnet used in conjunction with the Bologna hydrogen bubble chamber. The external proton beams from the CERN synchrocyclotron enter from the left passing through the auxiliary "C" magnet located in the center of the photograph. The bubble chamber is on the right and the small slot in the yoke through which the beam passes is hardly visible to the right of the auxiliary magnet. Also of interest is the 20 ton bridge crane and the sealed fluorescent lighting fixtures.

A double pie is usually called a "pancake" where there is a cross-over from one pie to another at the inside. The values given in Table II were calculated for the coil for the BNL 80 in. chamber where all coils are electrically in series.

e. Auxiliaries. Various equipment will have to be connected to the magnet, and, although each item may present some individual problem, it should suffice to list only typical auxiliaries, such as (1) water pipes that carry the cooling water to and from the magnet; (2) electrical buss-bar or cables that carry the electrical power to and from the magnet; (3) platforms which allow equipment such as vacuum pumps to be mounted and connected to the chamber, etc. As mentioned in the preceding section on the magnet yoke, often an auxiliary magnet is required to satisfy beam entry conditions. Figure 8 shows an example of an externally mounted auxiliary or "beam pitching" magnet used in conjunction with the Bologna 17 cm diameter chamber when it was installed in the external proton beam of the CERN synchrocyclotron.

f. Power Supply. Sizing of the power supply results from the cost optimization, which includes yoke and coil construction costs as well as ac and dc power equipment costs. A complete cost analysis needs also to consider the cost of operation of the magnet where the dominant expense is the electric power bill. This varies widely but is usually from $\sim\frac{1}{2}$ to 1×10^{-2} dollars per kilowatt-hour. In order to estimate the operating cost, assumptions are required of number of hours per day of magnet operation and number of days per year of operation as well as the life expectancy of the chamber's utilization. From 2000 to 4000 hr/yr of operation for 5 to 10 yr would include most estimates that have been made to date. Both motor-generator sets and rectifier power supplies have been used. The motor-generator set has the advantage of a probably slower decay time of the magnetic field in the event of a power failure, which reduces eddy-current heating in the low temperature parts of the chamber. However, with stainless steel vessels with adequate support no trouble has occurred with magnet current decay times equal to the time constant of the magnet alone. The power supply needs to be regulated for a current that is constant to $\sim 0.1\%$, and this is obtained by fast response electronic control circuits acting on additional windings in the generator or supply transformer. For rectifier supplies, inversely connected diodes are used to protect the magnet from high inverse voltages due to interruption of the primary supply.

2. Vacuum Chamber and Vacuum Pumping Systems

a. General. As mentioned in Section II,C,2, cryogenic vessels need excellent insulation in order to keep heat gain at a minimum. This is accomplished by the use of a Thermos-bottle type construction; that is, a pressure vessel is provided that surrounds the chamber body. The space between the vacuum chamber and chamber body is then maintained at high vacuum by a vacuum pumping system. The vacuum chamber, therefore, must be able to withstand one atmosphere of external pressure. In addition to this requirement, the vacuum chamber serves as a safety vessel for containing hydrogen gas that might be released by leaks which might occur in lines or the chamber body proper. In deciding on the correct internal design pressure, several factors have to be considered. These are (1) volume of vacuum chamber compared to volume of liquid hydrogen; (2) venting capability; (3) internal pressure where a permanent distortion of the vacuum vessel would be allowed. Although the probability of a large quantity of gaseous or liquid hydrogen being discharged into the normally evacuated space inside the vacuum tank is very small, it is not zero, and since the vacuum chamber serves as a first line of defense against venting of large quantities of hydrogen gas into the room where the chamber is located, internal design pressures of several atmospheres have been used. Another consideration which has been applied is the simultaneous loss of vacuum due to air leaking in from outside the vacuum tank and a leak of hydrogen gas into the vacuum tank. Any source of ignition would therefore result in the vacuum tank being subjected to a hydrogen-oxygen explosion. Tests conducted by several laboratories have shown that the pressure rise inside the vacuum tank under this circumstance would be less than 200 psi, except under extremely unlikely conditions. Design calculations have been done on this basis, stressing the vacuum chamber material to 50 % of its ultimate strength. This appears to be a good, economic balance between adequate safety and vacuum chamber cost.

    b. Vacuum Pumping System. The vacuum system for a cryogenic bubble chamber must evacuate its volume rapidly (the volume, for example, in the BNL 80 in. vacuum chamber is 500 ft^3). It must also be capable of removing gas that enters the system from the normal outgasing of the various surfaces that are contained in the vacuum chamber. (The surface area in the case of the BNL 80 in. chamber is approximately 50,000 in.^{2}). Back-streaming of oil from the various pumps must be kept to a minimum in order to prevent oil films from condensing on the cold chamber windows. The pumping speed required for normal operation, when the chamber is cold, is low since the cold surfaces of the chamber body will act as a very large cryopump. However, high pumping speeds are needed to overcome hydrogen or helium leaks, which cannot be cryopumped at this temperature, owing in part to the multiplicity of lines from the chamber which pass through the evacuated space. Experience has shown that even though the system is initially tight, some leaks are almost certain to develop, especially when the system is operated for long periods. The Berkeley 72 in. chamber, for instance, has been operated for periods of longer than one year continuously without disassembly. Large pumping capacity in the 1 to 100 mm Hg range is necessary. This permits quick recovery during emergency periods and also allows for fast pumpdown, particularly during purging cycles. The outgasing rate for stainless steel at 10^{-7} mm Hg pressure is 0.014 liters/sec cm^2. Therefore, for the 80 in. chamber, the pumping speed required to keep the vacuum tank at 10^{-6} mm Hg is 450 liters/sec, whereas each of the four diffusion pumps connected to the 80 in. chamber will pump 2000 liters/sec, a total of 8000 for the group. The excess pumping capacity provides protection against leaks into the vacuum tank. These pumps have a total capacity of 12,000 liters/sec at 10^{-3} mm Hg and, therefore, have the capacity to pump 74 cm^3 per hour of liquid hydrogen leaking into the vacuum tank while maintaining a pressure of 10^{-3} mm Hg. Since the vacuum pumping system is connected to the vacuum chamber, all components must be capable of withstanding the same internal pressure as mentioned for the vacuum chamber. Most chambers utilize parallel and independent vacuum pumping systems. As protection against equipment failure, the vacuum pumping system should also be supplied with emergency power.

c. Penetrations. A large number of penetrations through the vacuum chamber are necessary. These include penetrations for the expansion system, the optical system, plumbing and electrical connections to the chamber body, beam windows, connections to vent system, and vacuum pumping system. The penetrations usually are sealed by rubber O rings and flanges.

3. Chamber Body (Low Temperature Parts)

a. General. As mentioned in Chapter 1, Section III, the most crucial development of the bubble chamber technique was the elimination of the all-glass construction and the introduction of what has been called the "dirty" chamber. This development allowed the container of the bubble chamber liquid to be made primarily of metal, with one or two glass windows, for illumination and photography, sealed to the metal structure by gaskets. These metal pressure vessels are frequently called "chamber bodies," and, in the case of the cryogenic bubble chambers, represent the low temperature parts of the chamber. The shape of chamber bodies has been both circular and oblong. The oblong shape has been used in order to obtain longer track lengths in hydrogen with minimum increase of the total hydrogen volume and magnetic field volume. The oblong shape was dictated in the 2 meter chambers by the availability of optical quality glass of the size and shape necessary. The glass window in an oblong chamber is narrower and therefore thinner than in a circular chamber of equivalent size. The 5 to $6\frac{1}{2}$ in. thick windows for the 2 meter chambers are castings of borosilicate crown glass of the largest sizes of optical quality glass ever cast. Circular cryogenic chambers of 2 meter diameter could not have been built in the 1950's or early 1960's. At operating and emergency pressures, the motion between the glass and the chamber body wall must be minimal if the seal is to remain

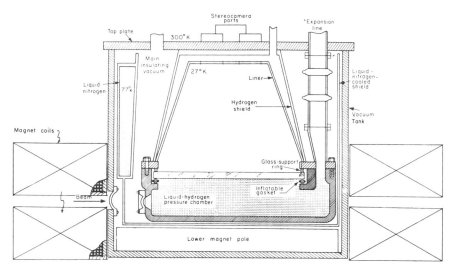

Fig. 9. Longitudinal cross section of the LRL 72 in. cryogenic bubble chamber. The $2\frac{1}{2}$ in. thick chamber casting weighs 6300 lb and has a 0.039 in. thick beam window, shown on the left. The expansion is through a pipe shown on the right, labeled "expansion line." The chamber is supported from the top plate of the vacuum chamber through which a center window allows for illumination, and three camera windows are used for stereoscopic photography. The magnet coil is shown, and the iron yoke is not indicated.

leak-tight. Therefore, oblong chamber bodies are of very heavy sections (up to 7 in. in the case of the BNL 80 in. chamber). The rapid operation of the expansion system (approximately 10 msec) imparts impact loads to the chamber body vessel. The chamber material must, therefore, have good ductility at low temperature if the integrity of the vessel is to be assured. High electrical resistance at low temperature is also desirable in order to reduce eddy-current forces which occur when the magnetic field is turned on or off or when magnet power is interrupted involuntarily. Distortions of the magnetic field can occur owing to possible changes in the permeability of the chamber material caused by low temperature cycling. This will be discussed in the next paragraph on chamber body materials. Figure 9 shows a cross-sectional view of the LRL 72 in. chamber body installed in its vacuum chamber. The chamber body, a 6300 lb casting which contains 520 liters of liquid hydrogen, is suspended from the vacuum chamber top plate through which windows allow for illumination and photography.

b. Chamber Body Materials. Stainless steel, aluminum alloys, and copper and copper alloys, have all been used for cryogenic bubble chamber bodies.

Aluminum and copper have the advantage of being always nonmagnetic, with high thermal conductivity. However, because they have lower elastic modulus and lower strength than stainless steel, the chamber walls are required to be thicker in order to sustain the pressures exerted by the chamber

TABLE III

TYPICAL CHEMICAL SPECIFICATIONS AND PROPERTIES OF STAINLESS STEELS FOR CHAMBER BODIES

| | BNL 80 in. | | LRL 72 in. | | CERN 2 meter, |
	Range	Typical	Range	Typical	Range
Analysis (%)					
Carbon	0.05 max	0.04	0.04 max	Less	0.03 max
Manganese	9.00–12.00	11	1.5 max	—	0.85–1.15
Silicon	0.50 max	—	1.5 max	Less	0.30–0.50
Phosphorus	0.03 max	—	0.03 max	—	0.015 max
Sulfur	0.03 max	—	0.03 max	—	0.015 max
Chromium	15.00–18.00	16	16–19	18	17–18
Nickel	18.00–22.00	19	13–15	14.5	14.5–15.5
Molybdenum	1.75–2.75	2.25	0.5 max	—	—
Nitrogen	—	—	—	—	0.04 max
Minimum tensile yield point (psi)					
At 20°C	25,000–28,000	—	—	32,000	—
At 20°K	—	89,000	—	—	—
Ultimate stength (psi)					
At 20°C	—	56,200	—	88,500	—
At 20°K	—	106,000	—	—	—
Martensite start temperature (°F)[a]	−2300 to −1500	—	−1100 to −700	—	−800 to −1000
Martensite deformation temperature (°F)[a]	−1700 to −900	—	−500 to −100	—	−200 to −400

[a] Temperatures below absolute zero are of course not meaningful and result from extension of the equation developed and verified for different ranges of compositions by Eichelman and Hull (1953) where compositions varied as follows: Cr, 10–18%; Ni, 6–12%; Mn, 0.6–5%; Si, 0.3–2.6%; C, 0.004–0.12%; N, 0.01–0.06%. Their formula, which was used to calculate the martensite start temperatures given in the table is

$$M_s = 75(14.6 - Cr) + 110(8.9 - Ni) + 60(1.33 - Mn) + 50(0.47 - Si) + 3000[0.068 - (C + N)].$$

The martensite deformation temperature is the martensite start temperature plus 600. It is felt that even though the equation needs to be modified for application to the alloys used in bubble chambers in order not to give values below 0°K, the correct relative stability of the alloys is probably represented by the table entries and that these alloys are stable in cryogenic bubble chamber applications.

FIG. 10. Top portion of 22,000 lb stainless steel chamber body for the BNL 80 in. chamber. This structure was made up of three major castings, and rolled stainless steel plate. The 36 in. diameter circular top of the transition section casting bolts to the cylinder that houses the expansion piston. This casting has internal ribs which were welded into place, and transforms to a rectangular section made up of rolled plate. The transition section was joined to the rectangular box by welding. The rectangular box, or neck, is joined to the main chamber body casting at the bottom, also by welding. Visible also is the refrigeration tubing attached to the top of the ribs in the transition section, which allows for cooling underneath the piston.

liquid. Larger wall thickness requires an increase in the volume of the magnetic field, which increases the cost of the magnet. Stainless steel was selected for the chamber bodies of the Berkeley 72 in., the BNL 80 in., and the CERN 2 meter chambers, as well as many of the other smaller chambers. The particular alloys selected have high magnetic stability, very good weldability, high yield strength, and high impact strength at low temperatures. Good weldability allows for freedom in design and fabrication of the chamber body. The chemical composition and properties of the stainless steels used for the three 2 meter chambers are given in Table III. These stainless steels are austenitic and therefore paramagnetic. Austenite has a face-centered cubic structure that may transform to ferrite, a stable-bodied cubic form, or to martensite, a metastable tetragonal form. Phase changes of austenite to ferrite and martensite are possible for some stainless steel chemistry. A phase change to martensite may be excited by cooling the chamber to temperatures below the transformation start temperature. The ferrite transformation is a diffusion process and is essentially completed at room temperature. Phase changes of this kind are irreversible and can lead to a partially ferromagnetic chamber body, since ferrite and martensite are ferromagnetic. The stainless steels listed in Table III have been selected for their stability against ferritic or martensitic transformation. The transformation from austenite to martensite is a shear mechanism and occurs very rapidly once the martensite start temperature is reached. It is possible to select material which has a martensite start temperature below that of normal chamber operating temperature. The martensite deformation temperature is the temperature at which austenite will transform to martensite as a result of strains that occur in operation. The magnitude of this effect is dependent on the stress pattern in the chamber body material. The BNL 80 in. chamber material has the lowest martensite deformation temperature. There is also an upper limit to the amount of nickel that can be added since the Curie point can be raised above the chamber operating temperature with high percentages of nickel. In these cases, the chamber would become magnetic when cold, and return to paramagnetic at room temperature. Martensitic transformation can also result in roughening of previously smooth seal surfaces. In severe cases, this can be as much as a few thousandths of an inch and can cause seals to leak.

The importance of having a chamber body material which has good weldability is illustrated in Fig. 10, which is a view of the BNL 80 in. chamber body. This 22,000 lb piece of stainless steel is made up of three major castings and rolled plate. Visible at the center is the round transition section which bolts to a 36 in. diameter cylinder that houses the expansion piston. The casting, which contains internal ribs, transforms from a 36 in. diameter circle at the top to a rectangular section at the bottom. This section passes between the magnet coils and joins the main chamber casting. The internal ribbing, as well as the attachment to the rectangular box, was accomplished by welding. The rectangular box neck was also attached to the chamber body casting by welding. Visible also is the heat exchange tubing that is connected to the top of the ribs. This tubing is for cooling the liquid underneath the piston.

c. Main Chamber Window. In order to minimize the total chamber volume which needs to be filled with the operating liquid, either one or two thick full-chamber-size optical windows have been used. Two windows are used when the illumination and photography are from different sides (so-called through-illumination), and one window is used when a retrodirective design is selected. Bubble positions can be distorted by nonuniformity of index of refraction in the window or by surface deviations in optical flatness. By specifying high quality optical glass, index of refraction homogeneities to 1 part in 10^5 are obtainable, and by careful polishing surface flatness can be maintained to a few optical fringes per inch. High quality must be maintained in order to minimize the number and size of bubble inclusions in the glass. It is also not unusual for large blocks of glass to contain striae. (These are local regions, usually a few millimeters in diameter and several centimeters long, with different indexes of refraction than the base glass. These striae follow an irregular curve or give a "snakelike" appearance.) Striae can be minimized by careful stirring of the molten glass prior to casting. Some window blanks may have to be rejected because of striae imperfections.

The thickness of the glass window that is needed in order to safely contain the chamber liquid is dependent on the strength of the selected glass. Glass, for all practical purposes, can be considered a purely elastic substance. It obeys Hooke's law up to the breaking point, and since it does not deform plastically it is considered a brittle material. Fractures always originate from the tensile component of the stress and nearly always start at the surface. Breaking stress is very much dependent on ambient conditions as well as the amount of aberration of the surface. The fatigue of glass, or the fact that a greater stress is required to break the glass in a few seconds than in a much longer time, is more pronounced at room temperature than at low temperature where the effect of cyclic loading is very little different from static loading when considered over the same time interval. Below room temperature, the strength of glass for a given load duration increases with decrease in temperature. According to Kropschot and Mikesell (1957) the fatigue endurance limit at 76°K appears to be greater than 9000 psi, based on tests of BSC-2 optical glass. Consequently designers have used values of 1000 to 2000 psi as the maximum safe tensile stress in untempered glass[3]. Welford (1963) has given for a long rectangular window, simply supported at the edges, a formula for the required thickness of untempered glass, which is $t = c(Wl/SL)^{1/2}$. W is the total distributed load due to the pressure in the

---

[3] Design tensile stresses of about 400 psi have been used for small windows, such as vacuum chamber windows, where an additional safety factor could be incorporated without very significant cost increases.

chamber. L is the length and l is the width of the rectangle. S is the permitted tensile stress, t is the thickness, and c is a constant between 0.75 and unity if lengths are in inches. It is wise to use a maximum safe tensile stress of 1000 psi in the above formula. Tempered glass has also been applied to bubble chambers. It permits using a reduced glass thickness which has the advantage of lower cost and faster cooldown or warmup. It is recommended that manufacturers be consulted about the reduction in thickness permitted by tempering.

During cooldown of the chamber, the window is normally stressed totally from temperature differentials that develop in the glass. These temperature differentials cause differential contractions and place the glass surface in tension. Thus, the cooling rate is determined by the permissible tension stress. After selection of the window thickness and maximum safe tensile strength, as mentioned above, the maximum permissible temperature difference in the glass, ΔT, can be calculated from $\Delta T = (1 - \mu)S/\alpha E$, where μ is Poisson's ratio, $S = $ maximum permissible stress, $\alpha = $ expansion coefficient, and $E = $ Young's modulus. Appropriate values for substitution in the above formula are found in Tables IV and V.

In order to obtain rapid cooldown rates for large glass plates, it is desirable to be able to use convective cooling on both sides of the glass window. In the case of the 80 in. chamber, it is possible to introduce approximately 5 psi of hydrogen or helium on both sides of the glass during cooldown. The gas then couples the glass to the metal heat exchange surfaces which are cooled by the refrigeration system. Using the maximum permissible temperature difference in the glass as a function of temperature, the allowable heat flux, q, can be calculated from the expression $q = 2k\,\Delta T/t$. Here k is the thermal conductivity and varies by about a factor of 2 from hydrogen temperature to room temperature. By assuming $k/\alpha = $ constant between 100°

TABLE IV

PHYSICAL PROPERTIES OF BK-7 OPTICAL GLASS

Density	2.53
Breaking strength	11,380 psi
Young's modulus at 300°K	9.8×10^6 psi
Poisson's ratio at 300°K	$\eta = 0.22$
Thermal conductivity at 273°K	0.0203 W/in./°C
Specific heat	0.17 cal/gm/°C
Refractive index	1.517
Dispersion	64.5

TABLE V

LINEAR COEFFICIENT OF EXPANSION VERSUS TEMPERATURE

Temperature (°K)	Linear coefficient of thermal expansion ($\times 10^{-6}/°K$)
20	1.8
40	2.7
60	3.4
80	4.1
120	5.1
160	5.9
200	6.6
240	7.0
280	7.4

FIG. 11. The 1500 lb optical quality glass window for the BNL 80 in. chamber is shown after completion of final polishing. This $6\frac{1}{2}$ in. thick by 81 in. × 30 in. BK-7 glass window was tempered to increase its rupture strength to approximately 11,400 psi.

and 300°K, q is found to be approximately 0.3 W/in.[2]. If along the surface of the glass there is no temperature gradient, a minimum cooldown time of about 24 hours, or an average rate of about 9°K per hour is found for windows for 2 meter chambers. In practice, the glass cooldown rate must be corrected when temperature gradients appear along the glass surface, i.e. end to end, or top to bottom, and the cooling rate must be reduced. The actual cooldown time used for large windows has been 50 to 100 hours. After the completion of a run, similar precautions are required in order to warm the window to room temperature without overstressing it. Figure 11 shows the $6\frac{1}{2}$ in. thick and 81 in. long main chamber window of the BNL 80 in. chamber.

d. Cold Seals. One of the early problems associated with very low temperature research was the difficulty of forming tight seals between metal parts at low temperature. In general, this problem was solved by using welded

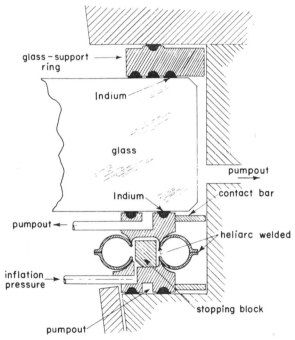

FIG. 12. Cross-sectional drawing of the inflatable gasket and related parts for the LRL 72 in. chamber. Application of helium pressure to the space between the double seal blocks flexes the circular thin wall tubes and forms the indium wire into flat strips as shown in the drawing. These strips of indium seal the glass to one gasket block and the other gasket block to the chamber. Other details shown are the pumpouts and the glass support ring at the top.

or soldered joints, say at the bottom of a dewar, and bringing any connection that might require a seal up to the top of the dewar, which was kept at room temperature. This means that only room temperature seals were required, for which ordinary rubber gaskets performed quite satisfactorily. Later on, joints were made at low temperature using metal gaskets such as lead or indium. At the beginning of the development, for cryogenic bubble chambers of small size, a tight seal was made between the chamber body and glass window by a lead gasket clamped between the glass and the metal chamber. However, as chambers became larger, the difference in thermal contraction between glass and chamber (about $\frac{3}{16}$ in. in the case of the LRL 72 in. chamber) would require the seal to slide along the surface of the glass, which would undoubtedly destroy its capability of sealing. In order to overcome this difficulty, the LRL staff devised a type of seal that could be effected at the operating temperature. Figure 12 shows a cross section drawing of the inflatable gasket and related parts for the LRL 72 in. bubble chamber. As can be seen in this figure, the seal unit is inserted between the glass and the chamber body. It consists of two gasket blocks joined by two thin split stainless steel tubes. The gasket blocks contain grooves in which indium wire is inserted. After the chamber and glass have been cooled to operating temperature, helium or hydrogen gas is inserted at high pressure through the line labeled "inflation pressure." This forces the two gasket blocks apart, pressing the indium wires against the glass surface in one case, and against the chamber body in the other. Sufficient pressure is applied in order to form the indium in the shape indicated, usually several hundred pounds per square inch. Indium is used because it is easy to form at hydrogen temperature and it does not overstress the glass surface.

Also indicated here is the technique of dual seals, with individual connections to the space between the seals called "pumpouts." When a vessel contains many seals, it is often difficult to know which seal is leaking. By using dual seals with individual pumpouts, it is possible to put helium in the chamber and check each individual pumpout with a helium leak detector for determining the integrity of the seal. On the BNL 80 in. chamber, for instance, this technique is used for all low temperature seals. This method also allows for pumping off a small amount of gas leaking by a single seal in case the seal is not absolutely tight. Frequently, this procedure has allowed for continuation of operations which might otherwise have been interrupted owing to lack of sufficiently good insulating vacuum.

For metal-to-metal seals, where there is no difference in the shrinkage between parts, compressed indium wire has been used with reliability. Performance is dependent upon maintaining (1) a 16 μin. or better surface

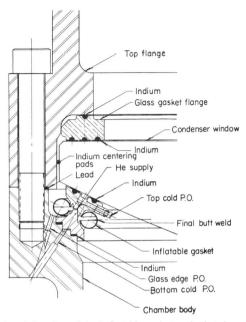

FIG. 13. Cross-sectional drawing of the inflatable gasket and related parts for the LRL 25 in. chamber. The spherical surface of the condenser window is sealed to the chamber body by the inflatable gasket. Since this assembly is part of the expansion system for the chamber, it is subject to dynamic loading conditions.

finish in the groove and surface that is to be sealed, and (2) a very rigid flange design. Since the indium undergoes cold flow when the seal is formed, any distortion of a flange, e.g. due to a pressure load, can relieve some of the sealing force and start a leak since the indium lacks resiliency. The inflatable gasket seals automatically compensate for any flange deflection or indium flow and are, therefore, very reliable. For instance, an inflatable indium seal has been used in the LRL 25 in. chamber to seal to the spherical surface of the condenser window as shown in Fig. 13.

e. Insulation. The only effective way to reduce the refrigeration requirement of a large cryogenic bubble chamber to a manageable level is to house it in a vacuum container as mentioned in Section III,B,2. It is also necessary to shield the low temperature parts of the chamber from radiant heat gain since the walls of the vacuum container are at room temperature. Originally, as seen in Fig. 9, a metallic heat shield, cooled to liquid nitrogen temperature, was incorporated in the space between the vacuum tank and the chamber

FIG. 14. Shown is part of the installation procedure for mounting the BNL 80 in. chamber in its vacuum tank; the superinsulation is visible on the rear left-hand portion of the chamber. The $\frac{1}{4}$ in. thick beam window remains to be bolted in place, sealing the rectangular opening visible in the center of the chamber structure. The assembly procedure follows by lowering the chamber onto a cart. Then the cart is moved into the rear half of the vacuum tank where bolts from above connect to the 36 in. diameter flange at the top of the chamber body for suspending the chamber. With use of dry nitrogen gas to bring the vacuum chamber to atmospheric pressure, no increase in pumpdown times due to the superinsulation has been noticed. Such an effect would occur if water vapor penetrated the space between the layers of insulation where the pumping speed is very small because of the thin gap between the layers and the limited number of unrestricted connections to the vacuum.

body. In some cases, a hydrogen temperature cold shield was also used. These shields, which were expensive and difficult to fabricate and support, were eliminated, beginning with the BNL 80 in. chamber, by the use of many layers of 2.5×10^{-4} in. thick aluminized Mylar (so-called superinsulation). The measured heat gain through this insulation is approximately 0.4 μW for a thickness of 1 cm, an area of 1 cm^2, and a temperature difference of 1°K. Two hundred layers of the aluminized Mylar should occupy approximately 2 in. of thickness. For ease of assembly and disassembly, the insulation is tailored to a stainless steel liner which conforms closely to the contours of the chamber body structure. The outer surface of the insulation is protected by 0.010 in. thick layers of Mylar. Figure 14 shows the BNL 80 in. chamber body just prior to insertion into the vacuum tank. The superinsulation on the left-hand side of the chamber body can be seen. Several shaped stainless steel plates help to hold the insulation in position and are supported against the liner by fine wires. The front part of the insulation is installed after the chamber is mounted in the vacuum tank. An overlap joint is made at the left-hand side of the open beam window and along an irregular line around the chamber in order to clear various instrumentation connections.

f. Instrumentation. Instrumentation considerations are necessary on all systems associated with a large cryogenic chamber. However, in the case of systems such as the magnet and vacuum chamber, we have considered that the techniques and equipment are sufficiently well known and that no special note is necessary. In the case of the chamber, a description of some of the more important mechanical and electrical instrumentation problems

TABLE VI

VAPOR PRESSURE AND VAPOR PRESSURE SLOPE FOR PARAHYDROGEN

Temperature (°K)	Pressure (atm)	Vapor pressure slope, dP/dT (atm/°K)
20.268	1.000	0.296
21	1.233	0.337
22	1.612	0.409
23	2.069	0.490
24	2.610	0.579
25	3.245	0.676
26	3.981	0.783
27	4.828	0.898
28	5.793	1.023
29	6.886	1.157

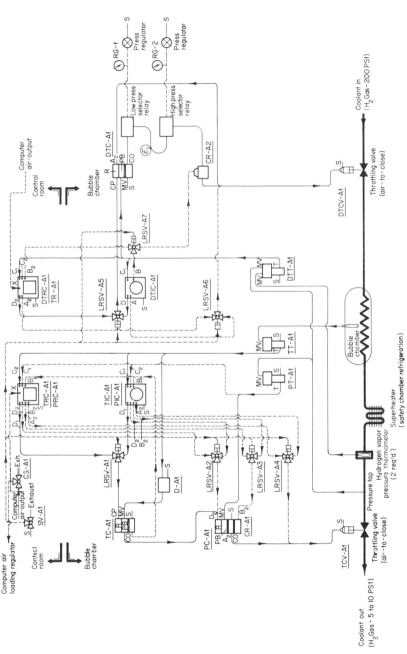

Fig. 15. Schematic drawing of BNL 80 in. chamber temperature control loop. PT, pressure transmitter; TT, temperature transmitter; TIC, temperature indicating control station; TRC, temperature recording control station; PIC, pressure indicating control station; PRC, pressure recording control station; TC, temperature controller; PC, pressure controller; LRSV, local remote switch valve; SV, selector valve; DTT, differential temperature transmitter; TR, totalizing relay; DTIC, differential temperature indicating control station; DTRC, differential temperature recording control station; DTIC, differential temperature controller; CS, computer switch; CR, cutoff relay; TCV, temperature control valve; DTCV, differential temperature control valve; RG, receiving gauge; T, transmitted; D, derivative unit; —— process flow line; CP, control point; MV, measured variable; S, supply; T, transmitted; D, derivative unit; —— process flow line; ————, primary control line; ————, secondary control line.

and solutions is justified. As mentioned in Section II,C,4, temperature uniformity over the chamber volume is perhaps the most important requirement for chamber operation. So far, the most sensitive method for measuring the temperature of the chamber liquid has been to use vapor pressure thermometers. Table VI gives the vapor pressure at ten temperatures for parahydrogen and slopes of the vapor pressure curve at these temperatures. Other cryogenic data such as the vapor pressure of helium, deuterium, neon, and nitrogen, as well as other cryogenic data concerning the properties of these gases and the properties of materials, such as specific heats, thermal expansivity, electrical resistivity have been presented by Jensen *et al.* (1966). For a chamber temperature of 25°K, a vapor pressure thermometer will read about 48 psia and the slope is about 10 psi/°K. Therefore, for the desired performance for temperature uniformity referred to in Section II, it is necessary to read the vapor bulb pressure to about $\frac{1}{3}$ psi, and this can be readily done with commercially available gauges. For instance, a 0 to 200 psi Wallace & Tiernan gauge is calibrated in 0.2 psi units and is readable to 0.1 psi accuracy. Several precautions should be observed in the design of hydrogen vapor pressure thermometers: (1) A fill system should be provided which allows for controlling the level of the liquid in the vapor pressure thermometer to approximately one-half full. (2) The tubing that connects from room temperature to the vapor bulb should be insulated and arranged so that no pockets of liquid can develop anywhere except in the bulb. (3) A catalyst, such as hydrous ferric oxide, should be placed in the bulb to ensure that liquid in the bulb has been completely converted from normal to parahydrogen. (The boiling point of parahydrogen is 20.268°K compared to 20.380°K for normal hydrogen and the vapor pressure of parahydrogen at 25°K is 3.245 atm compared to 3.176 atm for normal hydrogen.) Having incorporated vapor bulbs for sensing of chamber temperature and the temperature of the coolant in any cooling loops, it is necessary to allow for the control of the chamber temperature. This can be done by commercially available electronic or pneumatic controllers. In the case of the BNL 80 in. chamber, a pneumatic control system as shown in Fig. 15 is utilized. Hydrogen gas above the critical temperature, i.e., approximately 35°K and at 200 psi, enters the loop through valve DTCV-Al. The affluent which is partially liquid hydrogen and partially gaseous hydrogen, enters the chamber cooling loop where its effect on the chamber is sensed by a vapor bulb immersed in the chamber liquid. Upon leaving the chamber, the coolant is returned along a surface which is cooled but which is not at chamber temperature, such as the safety chamber. All liquid is removed from the flow stream and the temperature of the gas is measured by a vapor bulb. Its pressure is

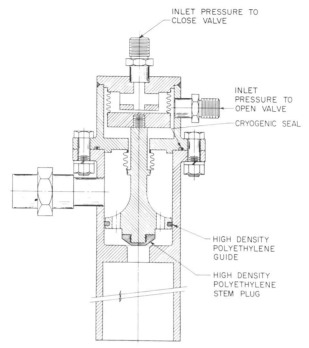

INLET PRESSURE TO
CLOSE VALVE

INLET
PRESSURE TO
OPEN VALVE

CRYOGENIC SEAL

HIGH DENSITY
POLYETHYLENE
GUIDE

HIGH DENSITY
POLYETHYLENE
STEM PLUG

Fig. 16. Cross-sectional drawing of a typical bellows-operated cold valve assembly, $\frac{1}{2}$ in. diameter. This type of valve has proved very satisfactory on the BNL 80 in. bubble chamber.

also sensed. The gas stream is then returned to the refrigerator through a throttling valve TCV-A1. A simplified explanation of the function of this control system is as follows. The chamber vapor bulb is assumed to sense a temperature higher than the desired value, as indicated by the preset control point of the temperature controller. The controller then transmits a signal to the outlet valve TCV-A1 and the valve is opened to lower the loop pressure and thereby the loop temperature. In this control system, the inlet valve regulates the amount of coolant circulated using the superheat measured across the loop as the control variable. The outlet valve controller has an improved time constant over a simple control unit by inclusion of a cascade system where the chamber temperature sets the desired loop pressure. This temperature control system has several features which are worthy of mention. Since hydrogen gas is used in the vapor bulbs and in the loop, pressure transmitters are used to isolate and limit the lines which contain hydrogen gas. This precludes the escape of hydrogen gas into the room because of any leaks which might develop in the lines to the controllers. It allows the location of these controllers in nonhydrogen areas such as the control room. Duplicate sets of controllers are provided with selector switches. One set is located on the chamber and the second set in the control room. Initial testing and debugging of the system in the BNL 80 in. chamber was carried out using the chamber controllers and later on routine operation was transferred to the control room controllers which are used during normal operations. This procedure allowed for an earlier test schedule and at the same time provided maximum convenience and safety for the operating crews.

Low and high pressure selector relays are incorporated in the inlet valve control circuit. These relays act as limits on the inlet valve so that a minimum flow is continuously maintained. This aids in keeping the lines unplugged while the other relay limits the total flow so as not to exceed the capacity of the hydrogen refrigerator.

For the temperature controller, the most sensitive control unit is selected, with a range of 0 to 20 psi, and a reference pressure system brings the normal operating point to the center of the range of this control. For instance, if the chamber operating temperature corresponds to 55 psia, the reference system is set at 45 psia and the controller registers in the center of its range at 10 psi. Sensitivity of the controller is in this case better than 0.20 psi, and adequately meets the performance criteria discussed previously. By incorporating several temperature control loops of this type, it is possible to achieve temperature uniformity over the entire chamber volume. A similar loop can be used to control the level of the liquid in the support section of the chamber where the inlet valve has the same function as in the temperature control loops and the outlet valve has cascade loop pressure.

Dynamic chamber pressure sensing is achieved by incorporation of unbonded strain gauge-type pressure transducers housed in assemblies such that the sensing diaphragm has an unobstructed view of the chamber liquid. The use of these units for control of the expanded pressure is discussed in Section III,B,5.

Another important aspect of the instrumentation associated with the chamber body concerns the low temperature valves that are used to fill, empty, and emergency dump the liquid in the chamber. Figure 16 shows a cross-sectional drawing of a typical bellows-operated cold valve assembly. This valve is closed by applying hydrogen or helium gas pressure to the inlet-pressure-to-close-valve line. The seal is made between the high density polyethylene stem plug and the high quality finished seat on the stainless steel valve housing. If hydrogen gas is used, liquid will develop in the bellows space and in the line up to the point where the critical temperature is exceeded.

Venting of the inlet-pressure-to-close-valve line allows the chamber pressure acting on the stem plug to open the valve. A more positive open position is achieved by activating the inlet-pressure-to-open-valve line. Since even a very small leak in these valves could lead to difficulty in keeping the chamber full, a second valve frequently has been incorporated in the line outside the vacuum tank. This type of valve has proved very satisfactory on the BNL 80 in. bubble chamber.

4. Refrigeration

a. General. The low temperatures required for operation of cryogenic bubble chambers are produced by refrigerators or liquefiers which contain sophisticated equipment, piping, and controls. All of the early cryogenic bubble chambers made use of already existing liquefiers which had been constructed at various low temperature laboratories. Therefore, cooling and filling of these chambers was done by obtaining the cryogen, such as liquid hydrogen, in dewars at the liquefier. After transporting the dewar and connecting it to the chamber by means of a vacuum jacketed transfer line, the cooling and fill operation would begin. Effluent gas was exhausted to the atmosphere, and, in the case of hydrogen, this was done by keeping the gas inside a vent pipe until it was well outside the building in an area where ignition of the gas was unlikely. The liquefiers that existed in the early 1950's were the result of a technology which was about half a century old. For instance, hydrogen was first liquefied by Sir James Dewar in 1898, and the first liquid helium was produced in 1908. Dewar's success was dependent on his development of the first vacuum-insulated vessel with reflecting walls, which still carries his name and which is the only technique which reduces heat transfer by radiation to a reasonable value. This has led to a parallel development of high vacuum technology and "cryogenics." Both laboratories employing low temperature for basic studies in physics and chemistry and suppliers of industrial gases have made contributions toward improving the availability of cryogenic liquids. Industrial development was aimed toward the separation of gases where large scale plants for the liquefaction of air followed by distillation gave an economic means of producing gaseous oxygen. The steel industry alone uses over 200 tons of gaseous oxygen per day. These plants were soon expanded to capture the rare gas constituents of the air, such as neon, argon, krypton, and xenon. Large quantities of pure helium gas became available by a low temperature separation process applied to helium-bearing natural gas. Major influences on the development of cryogenics included, first, its specialized use in the field of rocketry where liquid oxygen was used as an oxidant in the first practical, long-range rocket, the German V-2; second, the establishment in 1952 of the U.S. National Bureau of Standards Boulder Laboratories, at Boulder, Colorado, for the production of large quantities of liquid hydrogen for experiments and tests of an engineering nature, mainly for the U.S. Atomic Energy Commission; and third, the decision of the U.S. National Aeronautics and Space Administration to use liquid hydrogen fuel for high performance space vehicles. This decision resulted in the development of hydrogen plants with capacities of 60 tons per day. Obviously, this has had a strong effect on the economics of cryogenic bubble chamber refrigeration. For instance, the price in the United States for liquid hydrogen has changed from $5.00/liter in the early 1950's to the present value of $0.085/liter. Corresponding reductions have occurred in the cost of other cryogenic liquids.

b. Refrigerators. Beginning with the design of 2 meter chambers, closed cycle hydrogen refrigerators were designed and constructed to meet the bubble chamber refrigeration requirements. This refrigeration is required to cool, fill, and operate chambers at a temperature near 25°K. The capacity of the refrigerator is determined by an analysis of the static heat gain due to conduction (mainly along the support for the chamber), convection, and radiation. Most chambers have been supported from above (see Fig. 9), and, in the case of the BNL 80 in. chamber, the support is by means of a 36 in. diameter, $\frac{1}{4}$ in. thick, 36 in. long, Type 316L stainless steel cylinder. This cylinder has a hydrogen cooling loop at the bottom which maintains the liquid level above the lower piston rings of the expansion piston housed in the cylinder. Ten inches above this hydrogen loop is a nitrogen cooling loop, and 16 in. above the nitrogen cooling loop is a heavy flange which is at room temperature. The heat transfer rate, q, can be computed from

$$q = k_{\mathrm{eff}} A \frac{T_2 - T_1}{t},$$

where q is in watts, the effective heat conductivity k_{eff} is in watts per centimeter per degree Kelvin, A is the cross-sectional area of the conductor normal to the direction of heat flow in square centimeters, T_2 and T_1 are temperatures of the warm and cold surfaces in degrees Kelvin, and t is the conduction path in centimeters. The thermal conductivity of stainless steel varies from 1.5 W/cm°K at room temperature to 0.2 W/cm°K at 20°K. The temperature dependence is almost a straight line on a log/log plot. Approximate heat transfer calculations can use a constant thermal conductivity k_{eff} based on the appropriate temperatures. For more exact calculations, tables of thermal conductivity integrals have been prepared by Powell and Blanpied (1954). The BNL 80 in. design reduces the heat transport by conduction down its support cylinder to 8 W at hydrogen temperature and 60 W at nitrogen temperature. Other sources of heat transfer by conduction are piping and instrumentation lines and, in piston-expanded chambers, the internal structure of the piston. The heat transport due to gas convection is negligible in most cases since the cryogenic chambers are contained in vacuum tanks which are evacuated to pressures of the order of 10^{-6} mm Hg. See Section III,B,5 for details of design of the buffer volume where heat transport by gaseous conduction and convection are important contributors to the chamber's static heat gains.

The radiation contribution to static heat gains can be calculated from the equation

$$q_r = \sigma A E(T_2{}^4 - T_1{}^4)$$

where q_r, in watts, is the net radiant heat transfer through high vacuum between two surfaces at temperatures T_2 and T_1, in degrees Kelvin, σ is the Stefan-Boltzmann constant, which is equal to 5.67×10^{-12} W/cm^2°K^4, A is the area of one of the surfaces, in square centimeters, and E is a factor which depends on the emissivities, absorptivities, and geometries of the surfaces. For simplicity, one can assume that the surfaces are gray and the reflections are diffused, with the absorptivities equal to the emissivities. For the case of radiation from a surface at 300°K to a surface at cryogenic temperature, E varies from about 0.05 for stainless steel to 0.005 for copper. Expanding the equation for q_r to include n floating shields (not connected to heat sources or sinks) gives

$$q_r = \sigma A E \frac{1}{(n+1)}(T_2{}^4 - T_1{}^4).$$

Therefore, the net gradient heat transfer between surfaces can be appreciably decreased by having n large. This has been accomplished by the development of the technique called multiple-layer insulation or superinsulation, where a large number of radiation shields are incorporated in the evacuated space between the cryogenic vessel and the room temperature wall of the vacuum tank. As mentioned previously, the BNL 80 in. chamber utilizes 200 layers of aluminized Mylar contained in the 2 in. gap between the chamber body and the vacuum tank. Although the heat transfer through this superinsulation is by radiation and, to a lesser extent, by gas conduction and solid conduction, it can be characterized as an effective thermal conductivity. Heat transfer calculations can be made from the simple conductivity equation. In this case the calculated mean effective conductivity of 0.4 μW/cm °K for the 80 in. chamber insulation has been verified by experiment. Since the 80 in. chamber has a total surface area at hydrogen temperature of approximately 260,000 cm^2, the total static heat gain due to radiation is then approximately 6 W. In practice, an allowance must be added for imperfect shielding, such as at any joints between sections of insulation that may be required for assembly purposes. Consideration of all the above static heat gains, including safety factors, led to an estimated required hydrogen refrigeration capacity of 250 W for the BNL 80 in. chamber for a steady state operation at 25°K without expansions.

When a bubble chamber is expanded, bubbles are formed along the paths of charged particles that have passed through the chamber during its sensitive time, and at other places, usually at the walls of the chamber, in areas where unavoidable discontinuities occur such as at the bellows seal joint for the glass chamber window. The volume of these bubbles increases with (time)$^{3/2}$ until the recompression cycle has increased the chamber pressure sufficiently to stop further growth. As the chamber pressure builds up, the bubbles begin to collapse and usually disappear rapidly. Track bubbles of 0.3 mm size at the time of photography may grow to approximately 1 mm before quenching, and if recompression is complete in 10 msec, they will have disappeared in 50 to 100 msec. Larger bubbles occur from the wall discontinuities owing to early start of bubble growth in the expansion pulse. These bubbles can be a few centimeters in diameter before quenching and rise through the liquid at approximately 1 cm/sec until they disappear. Carnot cycle heating occurs in the liquid owing to the work done on the gas in all of the bubbles formed. Bubble growth from the walls is a significant contributor to the dynamic refrigeration load that results from pulsing the chamber. Therefore different chamber designs can vary extensively in size of refrigerator required. Of the 2 meter chambers, the LRL 72 in. chamber has an 1800 W hydrogen refrigerator, the British National 60 in. a 3000 W, the BNL 80 in. a 2600 W, and the CERN 2 meter a 4000 W hydrogen refrigerator. In the future, the ANL 12 ft chamber is scheduled for a 19 kW hydrogen refrigerator and the BNL 14 ft chamber calls for 30 kW of hydrogen refrigeration. Both of these chambers will use part of the available hydrogen refrigeration capacity for precooling of helium in the helium refrigerator for the superconducting magnet coils. As a chamber increases in size, the dynamic heat load per liter of chamber volume should decrease since the volume-to-surface ratio varies approximately as the linear dimensions. A conservative estimate of the dynamic load that can be used in sizing the refrigerator to be designed for a cryogenic bubble chamber of approximately 10,000 liters volume is 0.3 J/liter of chamber volume for a repetition rate of one pulse per second.

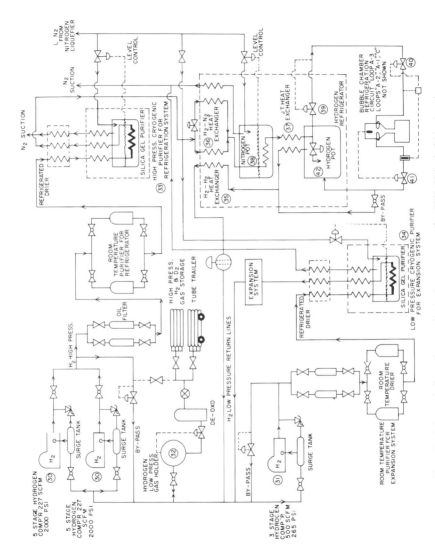

Fig. 17. Schematic flow diagram for hydrogen system for BNL 80 in. bubble chamber.

As an example of the type of hydrogen refrigerator designed to meet the refrigeration needs of the 2 meter chamber, a description of the BNL 80 in. chamber's refrigerator is given. Since one of the prime requisites for the proper operation of the chamber is the reliability of the refrigeration system, a simple Linde refrigeration cycle was chosen. Figure 17 shows a schematic flow diagram of the hydrogen system for the BNL 80 in. chamber. The schematic of the hydrogen refrigerator is contained inside a dotted box on the right side of the schematic. In the Linde cycle, cooling is obtained by an isenthalpic Joule–Thomson expansion. A temperature drop can only be achieved if the initial temperature of the high pressure gas that is expanded through an orifice (called a J-T valve) is below the inversion temperature at the pressure of the gas stream. For hydrogen, the maximum inversion temperature is 195°K. Since liquid nitrogen is required at other places in the bubble chamber, liquid nitrogen was chosen as the precoolant for the hydrogen, as has been standard since the very first hydrogen liquefiers. A description of how the gas is delivered to the refrigerator is given in the next section (on gas handling). For an understanding of the refrigerator, it suffices to know that approximately 500 ft^3 at standard conditions per minute (scfm) of 2000 psia purified hydrogen gas enters the refrigerator at room temperature through the dual flow path of the hydrogen-hydrogen counterflow heat exchanger (35) and the hydrogen-nitrogen counterflow heat exchanger (36). A balancing valve determines the optimum flow divisions for various load conditions. The hydrogen flow proceeds further by entering the liquid nitrogen pot (38) where the temperature of the gas stream is lowered to about 80°K, the boiling point of liquid nitrogen. The evaporated nitrogen gas is directed through the hydrogen-nitrogen heat exchanger for cooling of the incoming hydrogen stream as just mentioned. As the level of the liquid nitrogen in the liquid nitrogen pot decreases, a level sensor opens a level control valve, allowing the liquid nitrogen to be replenished. The main hydrogen stream then enters the counter-flow Joule–Thompson heat exchanger (37) where the temperature of the gas is further lowered. In this refrigerator, two possibilities exist for directing the hydrogen flow stream at the exit of the J-T heat exchanger. Normally, the flow stream proceeds through the valve (39) where the pressure of the hydrogen gas is reduced to about 200 psi, but the temperature is still above critical for hydrogen, guaranteeing that downstream of valve (39) only hydrogen gas is present. This cold hydrogen gas is directed into a vacuum-jacketed manifold where the gas is distributed into the four refrigeration loops, A-1, A-2, A-3, or C; or into the chamber. Loop A-3 is shown. This is the cooling loop which is located directly under the expansion piston. Valves (40) and (41) play the same role as valves DTCV-Al and TCV-Al in Fig. 15, which were discussed in detail in Section III,B,3,f. The pressure of the cold hydrogen on the outlet side of valve (40) is sufficiently low to produce liquid hydrogen. Therefore, two-phase flow consisting of liquid hydrogen and hydrogen gas at saturation temperature occurs through the cooling circuit. The outlet valve (41) acts as a back-pressure regulating valve that controls the pressure and consequently the temperature of the refrigerant. Each of the cooling loops' flow is collected in a vacuum-jacketed manifold and is returned to the refrigerator by a vacuum-jacketed transfer line where the gas enters the hydrogen pot (42). The cold gas is used in the J-T heat exchanger and the hydrogen-hydrogen heat exchanger to cool the incoming gas stream and therefore the return gas leaves the refrigerator at about room temperature and at about 1 psig. The alternate mode for operation of this refrigerator is as a liquefier. In this case, valve (39) is closed and the cold hydrogen is exhausted into the hydrogen pot (42) through a J-T valve. Liquid then accumulates in the hydrogen pot and the expanded gas is returned through the J-T heat exchanger and the hydrogen-hydrogen heat exchanger for cooling of the incoming gas stream as before. A bypass valve is included after valve (41) to allow for bypassing part of the flow stream past the J-T heat exchanger. This is used for cooldown and warmup of the refrigerator and chamber. The capacity of this refrigerator is 2600 W at 25°K.

c. Gas Handling. In order to supply the high pressure (2000 psi) purified hydrogen gas to the hydrogen refrigerator, many pieces of commercially available equipment have to be obtained and connected together. An example of the type of equipment needed can be seen by referring to the schematic flow diagram for the hydrogen system for the BNL 80 in. bubble chamber (Fig. 17). Hydrogen enters the system by delivery from commercial sources of high pressure tube trailers of approximately 40,000 scf capacity. After connection to the system, the pressure is reduced and the gas is passed through a Deoxo unit which removes oxygen by catalytic conversion to water. The gas pressure is reduced to about 1 psi and the gas enters a 2000 scf low pressure gas holder (32). The pressure in this gas holder is controlled by a weighted diaphragm to 20 in. of water above 1 atm. This variable volume gas holder is directly connected to all of the return lines in the system and to the suction of the compressors. Since these lines are kept at a positive pressure, any leak in this part of the system results in gas escaping, and therefore prevents the entry of air into the system. The hydrogen gas pressure is raised to 2000 psi by two five-stage, tandem, in-line compressors (30). These compressors are oil-lubricated and have water inner coolers between

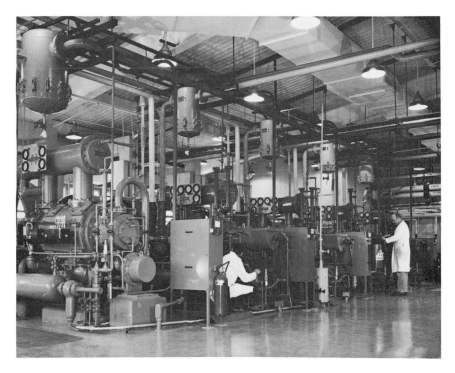

FIG. 18. View of the compressors installed at the BNL 80 in. bubble chamber. Beginning at the left is the expansion system compressor followed by two high pressure hydrogen compressors, followed by two high pressure nitrogen compressors. This equipment is typical of that required for a 2 meter cryogenic bubble chamber.

stages and a water after-cooler to remove the heat generated by the compressing process. Each compressor has a capacity of 220 scfm when operating at a discharge pressure of 2000 psi. The output pressure of the compressors is sensed by a controller which opens a bypass valve between the output pressure line and the compressor suction in case no flow is called for by the rest of the system. Following the compressors, an oil and water removal system, operating at room temperature, is provided. The oil filter removes hydrocarbons to 10 parts per million total impurity. From the output of the oil filter, the gas flow enters a room temperature purifier. This purifier removes water so that the residual gas has a dew point of $-100°F$ at 2000 psi, or better. The oil and water removal systems are of dual tower design so that one tower may be in operation while the other is being reactivated. Figure 18 is a photograph showing the compressors that are installed in the compressor room at the BNL 80 in. bubble chamber. From the left, the first

compressor is the expansion system compressor to be described later. The
next two compressors are the high pressure hydrogen compressors just
referred to, and the last compressors are the high pressure nitrogen compressors for a nitrogen liquefier. Some of the interconnecting piping is also
visible. After leaving the room temperature purifier, the hydrogen gas is
piped to the chamber where it enters a cryogenic purifier for further purification. This high pressure cryogenic purifier (33) consists of a refrigerated
drier and a silica gel coil immersed in liquid nitrogen. The purification of
the hydrogen gas before it enters the refrigerator-liquefier is a highly important process if the refrigerator is to function properly for long periods
of time. Purification in this sense means the removal and disposition of
unwanted contaminants. Failure to remove these contaminants in the
purifiers will result in their accumulation in the refrigerator or cooling loops
of the chamber, or in the chamber itself when the refrigerator is being used
to fill the chamber. These contaminants can cause the refrigerator to cease
to operate by plugging lines or valves, or, in the case of accumulation in the
chamber, can cause deposits on windows or other optical elements which
prevent adequate contrast for photography. A discussion of the detailed
operation of the cryogenic purifiers can be found in texts devoted to cryogenic
engineering (Scott 1959), or in an excellent article of Daunt (1956), which not
only gives a detailed historical account of the production of low temperatures
down to hydrogen temperatures, but also contains a thorough discussion of
the theory of operation of this equipment.

5. Expansion System

a. General. An expansion system is required to produce a momentary
increase in the volume of the liquid in the chamber and thereby to reduce
its pressure in order to make the liquid sensitive to the formation of bubble
tracks by charged particles. Thus, the chamber liquid is initially in a sub-
cooled state and is superheated by a sudden, temporary pressure reduction
which causes the liquid to be at a pressure lower than its vapor pressure at
the existing temperature. It is during this time of minimum pressure that the
particles are admitted to the chamber and that the bubble tracks are formed
and photographed. As the expansion cycle is completed, the chamber is
brought back to equilibrium pressure and the bubbles are quenched as the
pressure rises. At the completion of this expansion-recompression cycle,
which typically lasts from 0.010 to 0.030 sec, the chamber is at equilibrium
conditions again and ready for another pulse.

The increase in the volume of the liquid in the chamber to produce a
pressure drop sufficient to cause the liquid to be sensitive is about 0.5 to 0.75%

for hydrogen. For helium chambers this increase is approximately 0.75%
and for neon and neon-hydrogen mixtures a volume increase of approximately 1% is required. The repetition rate for the expansion system must be
matched to the beam output capability of the particular accelerator at which
the chamber is to be used as already mentioned in regard to refrigerator
sizing. Various possibilities exist for accomplishing this volume change.
These include gas expansion, piston expansion, or bellows or diaphragm
expansion. The first two cases require a liquid gas interface as will be described later, whereas the bellows expansion is applied to changing the position of one wall of the chamber so that the chamber liquid finds itself
momentarily contained in a vessel of larger volume. A more detailed description of each of these three types of expansion systems follows.

  b. Gas Expansion. An example of a schematic for a gas expansion system
is shown in Fig. 19. The operation of this system is as follows. Liquid hydrogen is added to the chamber until the level has risen a few inches into the
expansion duct pipe. The temperature of this stainless steel pipe increases

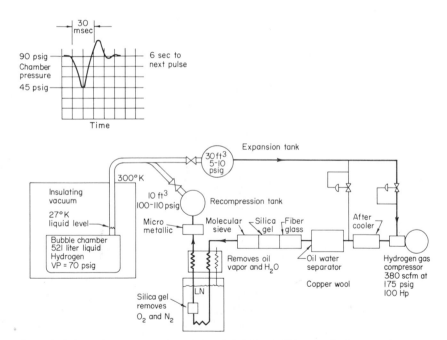

FIG. 19. Schematic representation of the LRL 72 in. bubble chamber's expansion system.
In the upper left-hand corner is a graph of the chamber pressure during an expansion pulse.

up to room temperature, where it penetrates the vacuum chamber. The gas is stratified in the expansion pipe. Both valves connected to the expansion line are closed. The expansion begins by operating the fast, large aperture expansion valve which allows gas to flow into the 30 ft^3 expansion tank held at 5 psig. The liquid level rises in the expansion pipe and as it enters warmer regions, some gas is evolved. The line length and cross section were selected to minimize the heat load due to this effect. As can be seen from the insert in Fig. 19, the pressure drops from 90 psig to 45 psig in about 15 msec (later changes have reduced this time to approximately 10 msec). The expansion valve is closed and the fast large aperture recompression valve connects the 10 ft^3 recompression tank at 110 psig, to the expansion line. Pure hydrogen gas enters the expansion line forcing the liquid back to its original level. The heat loss is kept at a low level by bringing the minimum amount of cold gas into the room temperature part of the expansion line. The quicker the liquid is forced back into the cold region, the less chance it has to evaporate in the expansion line. This is aided by as fast a recompression as is possible. Since the recompression gas comes in direct contact with the chamber liquid, it must be very clean. Therefore, the hydrogen gas is purified by the purification system as indicated in the schematic. Any residual contaminants will accumulate in the chamber where their accumulation may force chamber warmup for their removal. The Berkeley Group reports that only a small amount of mixing occurs in the expansion line and that the upper portions of the line remain at room temperature and the expansion and recompression valves operate near ambient temperature. Disadvantages of this system include the higher required expansion ratio (up to 1.8%), greater heat load for equivalent chamber volume and expansion repetition rate, and the injection of some liquid at temperatures sufficiently above the chamber operating temperature that optical distortions are observed. A significant advantage of this system is the location of equipment which may need servicing at positions outside the vacuum tank where shutting manual valves enables maintenance operations to be independent of the chamber.

An interesting feature of this expansion system is the use of Grove-type boot valves for the fast acting, large aperture expansion and recompression valves. A cross-sectional drawing of a Grove-type boot valve is shown in Fig. 20. Two identical 6 in. size valves of this type are used to expand and recompress the LRL 72 in. bubble chamber. These valves are similar in design to the Grove Company "flex-flow" Model 80 valve which uses a rubber boot over a slotted aluminum core as shown in the figure. The valve appears in the open position with the rubber boot forced against the valve housing by the chamber pressure. The heavy arrows indicate the flow path of the gas through the valve. To close the valve, the rubber boot is forced in against the core by injecting gas through the actuating gas inlets. LRL reports that the valve opens in 6 to 10 msec with hydrogen gas. When cold gas flows through the valve, the life of the rubber boot is reduced. Therefore coils which allow for warming the valve have been added in order to increase the boot life, which is reported as 150,000 cycles for the expansion valve and 2 million cycles for the recompression valve. About 25 gm of gas pass through the expansion valve per normal pulse.

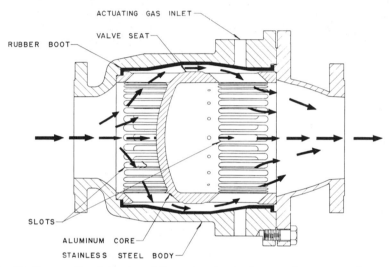

FIG. 20. Cross-sectional drawing of Grove-type boot valve used for gas expansion and recompression of the LRL 72 in. chamber. The valve is shown in the open position. The heavy arrows indicate the flow path of the gas through the valve. The rubber boot is forced in against the core by injecting gas through the actuating gas inlet in order to close the valve.

Since the expansion line connects directly to the chamber liquid, the integrity of this line must be maintained at all times. A leak or rupture could result in dumping the entire chamber contents into the room that houses the chamber. A design pressure of 20 atm and protection against vibration are desirable for this part of the system.

   c. *Piston Expansion.* The expansion of a chamber by means of a piston is accomplished by having the surface of a piston, which is housed in a cylindrical portion of the chamber vessel, in contact with the chamber liquid. The piston is moved outward, effecting the approximately 1 % volume change required to drop the chamber pressure to that required for track sensitivity.

Two types of piston have been used: the first, called the driven piston, usually has a long, smaller diameter portion connected to the part of the piston in contact with the chamber liquid. This cylindrical rod contains a thermal gradient and, when sufficiently warm, is brought through a sliding seal at

FIG. 21. Thirty-six inch diameter piston for the BNL 80 in. cryogenic bubble chamber. Inconel sheet metal 0.003 in. thick has been corrugated and brazed together with eleven 36 in. diameter face sheets to form a cellular structure. Also brazed to the assembly are the rings at top and bottom carrying high density polyethylene seal-and-wear rings. A rod at the top of the 250 lb piston leads to a pneumatic control for positioning it between expansions.

room temperature. It is then connected to a drive unit. The liquid is sealed at the cold end by low temperature piston rings, such as high density poly-ethylene. A liquid-gas interface forms along the cylinder wall where the temperature of the wall is such that the adjacent liquid's vapor pressure reaches equilibrium with the operating pressure of the chamber. A geometry similar to hydrogen liquefiers is easiest to understand, where the piston is located at the top of the chamber and the piston rod extends upward, finally penetrating the vacuum vessel. It is possible to invert the piston cylinder geometry so that the piston is at the bottom of the chamber, and the piston moves downward rather than upward (Brookhaven National Laboratory, 1965). The gas volume between the liquid-gas interface and the warm seal on the shaft is usually called the buffer volume. The driven piston adapts itself readily to a hydraulic drive unit.

The free piston is a modification of the gas expansion system and has a light-weight piston with one end in contact with the liquid hydrogen, and the other end at room temperature. A temperature gradient exists from one end of the piston to the other as well as along the cylinder wall that houses the piston. The piston is driven by the compressed liquid hydrogen contained in the chamber. The piston prevents warm gas from mixing with cold gas, thereby making the system more efficient than a gas expansion. As an example, to expand the BNL 80 in. bubble chamber, a 36 in. diameter free piston, shown in Fig. 21, is moved approximately 1 in. by the pressure of the chamber liquid on its 1000 in.[2] surface. This system operates as follows. The expansion begins by venting warm gas above the piston to a low pressure reservoir. This allows the pressure on the bottom face of the piston to push it upward, increasing the volume available to the chamber liquid. The cycle is completed by using high pressure gas from a reservoir to act on the top face of the piston to move the piston back to its original position, thus restoring the chamber volume and pressure to their original value. The gas moves from the volume above the piston to the low pressure reservoir, through a compressor and purifier, back to the recompression reservoir, and thence to the volume above the piston. The 250 lb piston is of special light-weight construction and is also designed to minimize the heat flow from the cold bottom to the warm top. Low mass is required for the piston in order to keep the expansion-recompression cycle consistent with isentropic expansion where the expansion ratio and heat load due to the expansion pulse are minimal. This system utilizes the same type valves as shown in Fig. 20; however, major modifications were made in the valve design. The expansion valve has a 14 in.[2] equivalent flow area, and opens and closes in 1 msec after the rubber diaphragm begins to move. Venting and filling of the

activating gas inlet volume takes about 20 msec. The recompression valve
has a 4 in.² equivalent flow area. Each of these valves is open during an
expansion pulse for about 6 msec. Computer simulation studies for the
design of this system were conducted by Goodzeit (1966). The results of
these studies were used in the design of the system.

The drive unit for the BNL 80 in. chamber expansion system consists of
a three-stage hydrogen compressor of 500 scfm capacity at 265 psi. This
system is included as part of the schematic shown in Fig. 17 and consists of
the compressor (31), a dual tower, room temperature purifier, and a low

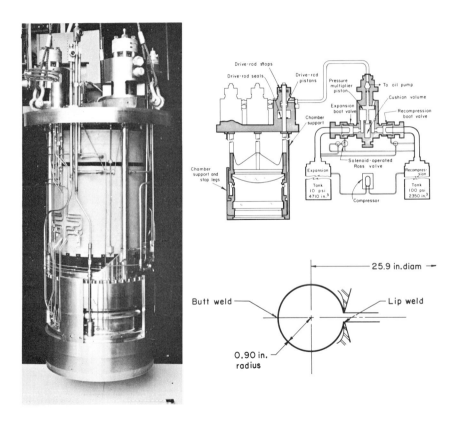

FIG. 22. Composite of LRL 25 in. chamber's bellows-expanded chamber parts. In the lower
right are shown the detail dimensions of the stainless steel bellows. The locations of the bellows
and the drive system are shown schematically in the upper right-hand drawing. A photograph
of the entire chamber assembly, just prior to assembling it in its vacuum tank, is shown on the
left.

pressure cryogenic purifier (34). The expansion system compressor is shown in Fig. 18 as already mentioned.

d. Bellows or Diaphragm Expansion. The successful design and fabrication of an omega-type stainless steel bellows which has exhibited a very long life time during testing and operation has demonstrated the feasibility of bellows-expanded chambers. Figure 22 shows a composite of the LRL 25 in. bellows-expanded chamber parts. A cross-sectional drawing of the critically important bellows is shown in the lower right. The 0.0179 in. thick 0.9 in. radius, 25.9 in. diameter omega bellows was formed with three precision welds as shown in the drawing. The location of this bellows can be seen in the cross-sectional view of the chamber and the hydraulic drive system. The photography is from below through a flat window, and illumination is from above through a spherical condenser lens. The detail of the seal that seals this window to the chamber is shown in Fig. 13. It is this part of the chamber that is moved by the hydraulic drive unit, and the omega bellows is the flexible element that allows this motion. A bellows that is not properly designed could overstress the stainless steel, thereby resulting in work-hardening and finally cracking of the material, which would then allow the chamber contents to leak into the vacuum tank. On the left is a photograph of the chamber assembly just prior to insertion into the vacuum tank. The photograph is illustrative of cryogenic plumbing techniques. Advantages of this type of expansion system include elimination of the possibility of dirt in the chamber as the result of piston ring wear and elimination of the need to add gas to the chamber continuously, which also reduces the accumulation of dirt in the chamber.

The SLAC 40 in. chamber and the ANL 12 foot chamber are planned to have metal bellows similar to that used in the LRL 25 in. chamber. The BNL 14 foot chamber design contains a 14 foot diameter flexibly mounted fiber glass reinforced baffle or diaphragm which is coupled to the expansion piston by liquid hydrogen. As in the metal bellows case, the intent here is to provide a uniform liquid motion during the expansion cycle, and also to isolate possible expansion system turbulence from the photographed volume of the chamber.

6. *Illumination and Cameras*

General. Chapter 5 of this volume contains a discussion of the illumination and photography of bubble chambers by Welford. Although written from a general viewpoint, i.e. not just for cryogenic bubble chambers but for other bubble chambers as well, it contains the information needed for the design as well as descriptions of various design solutions for the optical systems of cryogenic chambers.

In addition to Chapter 5 and the material in this chapter concerning the main chamber window (Section III,B,3,c) a few points are probably worthy

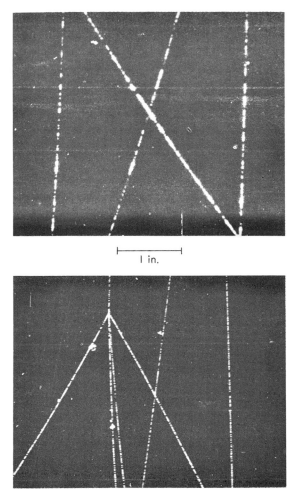

FIG. 23. Shown in the top photograph are tracks in the BNL 80 in. bubble chamber taken on microfile film at $f/11$ with a demagnification of 100, and blown up to size indicated in this figure by 1 in. scale. The bottom photograph is presented for comparison, and is a normal BNL 80 in. bubble chamber photograph, taken on Dacomatic film at $f/27$ with demagnification 15, and shown at the same size as top figure.

of emphasis. Among various critical systems associated with the cryogenic chamber, the optics system is one of the most critical. Since the utility of the chamber is based on its ability to produce photographs of bubble chamber tracks for physics research, great care is needed in the design of the mounting hardware of optical elements, especially for those pieces that are at cryogenic temperatures where large shrinkage effects occur and the properties of the materials can change appreciably. Also, as can be seen from Table I, the large scale use of bubble chambers has required a parallel development of facilities to process the film that is being produced. Most major laboratories have set up automatic equipment which is capable of processing several million feet of film per year.

As discussed by Welford, one of the most important design problems associated with bubble chambers is the selection of film size. Especially in the case of future chambers, it is desirable to use as large a demagnification as possible in order to minimize film costs. Some experimental work has been carried out at Brookhaven, a result of which is shown in Fig. 23. Figure 29 also shows a comparison of picture quality in various cryogenic chambers. In the future, the use of bright-field illumination, the availability of improved emulsions, and the need to reduce film costs will undoubtedly lead to demagnifications of about 100 being common practice.

7. Instrumentation and Control

a. General. The purpose of an instrumentation and control system for cryogenic bubble chambers is to provide reliable means for operating the chamber with good efficiency and safety. In order to produce the maximum number of useful pictures accompanied by appropriate related data, a central control room is believed to be required. This means that data channels for communication, monitor, and control use have to be provided between the control room and the equipment that makes up the chamber. Flexibility can be achieved by terminating all the wiring at a central switch point such as in a telephone system's central office. This facilitates trouble-shooting and rearrangement of equipment or circuits. The wire data channels are paralleled by pneumatic tubing for pneumatic controls and indicators. All elements critical to the chamber operation must have their status displayed continuously. The ability to make adjustments on system controls or to keep the chamber operating properly, along with the need for a point remote from the chamber where operators can deal in safety with possible emergency conditions, always justifies the central control room concept. Figure 24 shows a portion of the BNL 80 in. control room, which is typical of 2 meter chamber, central control facilities.

b. Timing Equipment. A cryogenic bubble chamber has to be precisely synchronized to the timing of the beam from the accelerator where the chamber is in use. Most accelerators have a basic master oscillator, and the chamber can obtain these pulses for synchronization. In order to carry out the several timing operations, the master oscillator pulses are multiplexed. The usual procedure is to use scaler circuitry to move the entire bubble chamber timing system with respect to the accelerator by any amount of time which is predetermined by setting up a series of switches. If the accelerator beam timing is incorrect for best bubble chamber operation, then the operator is able to establish the proper synchronization by dialing the correct time on the predetermined timer. Perfect synchronization of the beam and the chamber minimum pressure is accomplished by this method. The maximum accuracy required is 0.0001 sec.

FIG. 24. Photograph of part of the BNL 80 in. bubble chamber control room. From this central control point, monitoring and control of all operations in both routine and emergency situations are carried out.

c. Test and Calibration Equipment. Many of the systems associated with the bubble chamber have a limited operational range. Some parameters have to be known to great accuracy, such as the magnetic field, whereas others interact only indirectly with the data that are being accumulated. To some extent every voltage, current, temperature, pressure, flow, and displacement indication contributes to the over-all operation, and each needs to be routinely tested to verify that it is operational and in calibration. For this purpose a large variety of instruments, from dead weight testers for gauges to nuclear magnetic resonance probes, is required.

d. Monitor, Communications, and Control Equipment. Closed circuit television systems have been used to keep the control room operators aware of conditions at the chamber or other areas. The alarm-annunciator system is perhaps one of the most important in the instrumentation area. The intent is to give an audible indication whenever a parameter drifts from its normal operating value by a significant amount. For instance, the development of a new leak in a hydrogen line could show up as a high flow rate in that system. The sequence of the occurrence of alarms can at times be important in diagnosing the failure. For this purpose, the BNL 80 in. chamber system prints a chronological record of alarm sequence. Other important pieces of instrumentation equipment are the continuously operating fast-response hydrogen gas detectors. These should be strategically placed in order to sense, as quickly as possible, the leakage of any hydrogen gas. Frequently these detectors can automatically actuate emergency ventilation. The availability of interphone, intercom, and public address communications equipment has been shown to facilitate the maintenance, testing, and operation of various large bubble chambers. Control equipment should be located and displayed so as to facilitate its use. Equipment that is related should be in the same area. Graphic display panels are very useful since they facilitate understanding of the relationship of the control equipment to the system that it is controlling.

C. SAFETY CONSIDERATIONS

Safety is a vital factor in arriving at a correct design for a large cryogenic bubble chamber or for the building which is to house the chamber. The most severe hazards exist when large quantities of hydrogen are in use. It is wise to isolate areas wherever possible in order to decouple possible interactions between hazardous components. Equipment such as storage tanks should be removed to distances which reduce the possibility of interaction during an emergency. Reinforced concrete fire walls designed to resist a minimum pressure of 1 psi can be used to separate a compressor room using hydrogen from the chamber proper and to isolate the control room from both of these areas. Isolation of the control room ensures that a safe area remains under emergency conditions and that the operating personnel will be able to assess the emergency and take corrective action such as dumping the liquid from the chamber or shutting down the compressors. All areas where flammable gas or volatile liquids are present should be classified as Class 1, Group B, Division II of the National Electrical Code. Attention should be given to the location of emergency exits and doors to allow for more than one means of exit for the operating personnel. Areas where hydrogen gas might be accidentally present should be provided with emergency forced ventilation systems changing the air completely once per minute in order to eliminate any hydrogen-air mixtures as quickly as possible from these areas. This equipment should be operated automatically by continuously operating hydrogen gas detectors placed near the equipment. Electrical power failure is protected against by using pneumatic controls with high pressure instrument air storage, and by providing emergency power from a gasoline or diesel driven emergency generator. The emergency electrical power can be used to power equipment crucial to safely holding the chamber in standby until the power failure is over.

In the equipment that is to be at cryogenic temperatures, maximum care must be exercised in the design to ensure the integrity of the vessels for both static and dynamic loading. Where possible, all the welded joints should be radiographed. The vessels should be tested at $1\frac{1}{2}$ times the design pressures at room temperature. The vacuum chamber, used to house the cryogenic vessels that contain liquid hydrogen, should be designed for a pressure of 200 psi and is best constructed of stainless steel. A vent system should be provided which allows either liquid hydrogen or gaseous hydrogen to be vented rapidly in case of some severe equipment malfunction. The vent line should also be connected to the vacuum vessels by check valves in case liquid hydrogen leaks into the vacuum tank.

With proper attention to the above items, it should be possible to prevent hydrogen gas from escaping into rooms that house the hydrogen equipment. In the unlikely event that at some time there is a hydrogen and air mixture, the elimination of ignition sources and incorporation of the emergency ventilation should result in no ignition occurrence. Figure 25 shows some of the consequences possible if large scale hydrogen leakage is followed by an explosion. Forty liters of liquid hydrogen were spilled into a concrete block house typical of those used for background radiation shielding of small hydrogen chambers. The upper left-hand photo shows the block house

Fig. 25. A series of photographs showing the results of a test spill of 40 liters of liquid hydrogen followed by an explosion in a concrete block house typical of those used for background radiation shielding of small hydrogen chambers. The upper left photograph shows the block house before the test. The upper right photograph, taken from a motion picture frame, shows the block house immediately following the explosion. The two lower photographs show the block house after the explosion.

before the test. The upper right-hand photo is taken from a motion picture frame and shows the block house immediately following the explosion. The two lower photographs show the block house after the explosion, demonstrating shifting of the blocks.

IV. Operations and Some Performance Data

A. GENERAL

Operating procedures for cryogenic bubble chambers have developed over the years since the early chambers were first built and operated. At the present time a high degree of sophistication is required for the operation of 2 meter chambers if the aim of achieving high efficiency for the production of photographs with good utility for high energy physics research at reasonable cost and with maximum safety is to be achieved. As mentioned in Section II, assumptions made during the design phase of each individual chamber will to a large extent control the chamber's operation and performance. In many cases, inadequacies in initial operations have led to modifications in some systems for improving performance, as with other research equipment such as high energy accelerators.

When a chamber is vacuum-tight and ready for cooldown, all systems which will be cold should be evacuated and purged with the gases to be used. Evacuation and purge procedures are of great importance and complete records should be kept of these operations. Purified gas should be used for purging. The cooldown rate for the chamber may be limited by the main chamber window, as mentioned in Section III,B,3,c, or by the refrigeration system's capacity. When the chamber has reached operating temperature, it may be filled with liquid by condensing at a pressure above the corresponding vapor pressure. In order to save time, several chambers have the capability of transferring liquid from a storage vessel or from a separate part of the refrigerator to fill the chamber. After the chamber is full of liquid, the most important aspects of the operation are temperature uniformity, expanded pressure minimum, and bubble image size and contrast on the film. There are, of course, interactions between all of these. However, we shall discuss them independently in the above order, using the BNL 80 in. bubble chamber as an example.

B. TEMPERATURE UNIFORMITY

Temperature control loops on the BNL 80 in. chamber are in accordance with the schematic drawing shown in Fig. 15, and described in

Section III,B,3,f. The BNL 80 in. chamber contains three control loops: the A-3 loop located directly under the expansion piston, the A-2 loop at the top of the chamber's photographed volume, and the A-1 loop at the bottom. Figure 26 shows the chart records of the control of the chamber temperature by these three loops, the top chart being the A-3 loop, the middle chart the A-2 loop, and the bottom chart the A-1 loop. A period of 11 hours during 1965 is typical of the control achieved at that time. Each chart is a graph of two parameters. The first is a vapor bulb pressure reading on an expanded

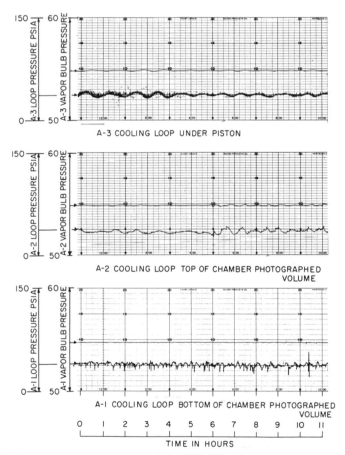

A-3 COOLING LOOP UNDER PISTON

A-2 COOLING LOOP TOP OF CHAMBER PHOTOGRAPHED VOLUME

A-I COOLING LOOP BOTTOM OF CHAMBER PHOTOGRAPHED VOLUME

TIME IN HOURS

FIG. 26. Chart records of the control of the BNL 80 in. chamber temperature. The charts show the chamber temperature as sensed by vapor bulbs located at the positions indicated in the captions. This is typical of the control achievable in 1965.

scale, the bulb being located in the chamber near the loop. It is thought to be representative of the temperature of the chamber liquid in the vicinity of the loop. As indicated, each vapor bulb reading is graphed on a 50 to 60 psia scale. As seen, the maximum variation in any of the three vapor bulb pressure readings is $\pm\frac{1}{2}$ of a division, where a division is $\frac{1}{4}$ psi, or 0.025°K. The set point for each loop was 54.75 psia. Graphed also is the loop pressure of each of the three loops on a 0 to 150 psia scale. Normal loop pressure variations of $\pm 1\frac{1}{2}$ to 2 divisions or ± 6 to 8 psi correspond to the most uniform temperature control. Examination of this chart shows loop A-1 exhibiting the best performance over this sample period. Interactions between the loops and the expansion system control prevent adjustment of all three loops to give this quality of performance. Optical turbulence due to the amount of temperature nonuniformity displayed here is thought to be undetectable.

C. EXPANSION SYSTEM PERFORMANCE

The BNL 80 in. chamber is expanded by means of a 36 in. diameter piston. This piston moves approximately 0.6 in. and the chamber pressure drops from about 75 psia to 20 psia. The piston motion is the result of the opening and closing of the large aperture expansion valve, and the operation of the large aperture recompression valve. These valves are described in Section III,B,5,c. Figure 27 shows oscilloscope photographs taken at two different sweep speeds. The top photograph shows four traces taken at a sweep speed of 10 msec/grid division. In order, the top sweep is the piston stroke, the second is the chamber pressure, the third is the expansion valve actuating pressure, and the bottom sweep is the recompression valve actuating pressure. The lower two traces indicate the dynamic pressure in the case surrounding the rubber boot as shown in Fig. 20. In particular, looking at the expansion valve actuating pressure, at about 5 msec after the initiation of the oscilloscope sweep, the case pressure begins to drop as shown in the figure. This drop in the pressure is due to the electrical actuation of a solenoid valve that vents this space to return pressure. At about 10 msec after the initiation of the pressure drop, a flat portion, approximately 2 msec in duration, appears on the expansion valve actuating pressure curve. A similar flat portion is noted on the recompression valve actuating pressure curve about 5 msec after the start of its pressure drop. These pressure responses are interpreted as the transit time of the rubber boot from its initial position against the core of the valve to its fully opened position. Electrical solenoid valves are also used to restore both the expansion and recompression valves to their normally closed positions. Variations in the times and duration of the electrical impulses to the solenoid valves allow for the control of the expansion pulse. The lower portion of Fig. 27 shows the chamber pressure, the beam time, and the arc light flash time. The beam from the accelerator is adjusted to arrive at the time of minimum chamber pressure, and the arc light flash, in this case, is shown as 0.8 msec after beam time. Figure 28 shows the results of a test to evaluate the control performance of the BNL 80 in. chamber with and without the use of closed loop computer control. A time

EXPANSION SYSTEM PULSE

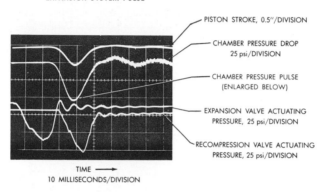

PISTON STROKE, 0.5"/DIVISION

CHAMBER PRESSURE DROP
25 psi/DIVISION

CHAMBER PRESSURE PULSE
(ENLARGED BELOW)

EXPANSION VALVE ACTUATING
PRESSURE, 25 psi/DIVISION

RECOMPRESSION VALVE ACTUATING
PRESSURE, 25 psi/DIVISION

TIME ⟶
10 MILLISECONDS/DIVISION

ENLARGED PORTION OF CHAMBER PRESSURE PULSE

TIME ⟶
1 MILLISECOND/DIVISION

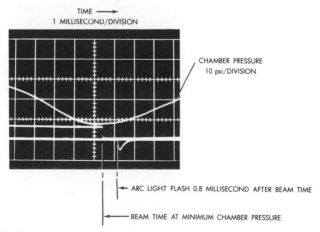

CHAMBER PRESSURE
10 psi/DIVISION

ARC LIGHT FLASH 0.8 MILLISECOND AFTER BEAM TIME

BEAM TIME AT MINIMUM CHAMBER PRESSURE

FIG. 27. Oscilloscope photographs of the expansion system pulse showing the time functions of the piston motion, chamber pressure, and actuating valves. The lower figure shows the chamber pressure near its minimum and the beam timing and light delay on an expanded time scale.

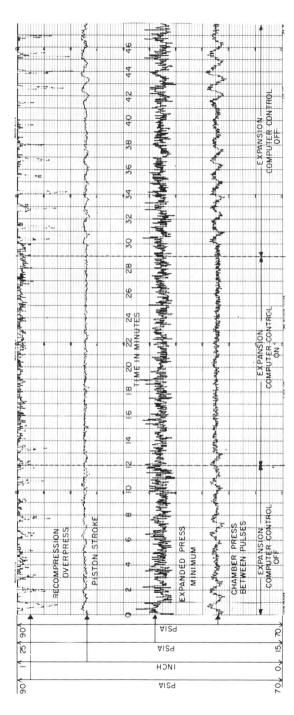

FIG. 28. Result of computer control of BNL 80 in. bubble chamber's expansion system as indicated by time graphs of the chamber pressure minimum. Shown also are the chamber overpressure during recompression, the piston stroke, and the static chamber pressure between pulses.

graph of four parameters is plotted. The horizontal scale is one minute per division for a total of 48 minutes. From 0 to 12 minutes the expansion system operated with identical timing pulses being supplied to all valves. From 12 to 29 minutes the valve timing was adjusted by means of the closed loop computer control program, and from 29 to 48 minutes, the expansion system was operated by identical timing pulses. The top trace is the recompression overpressure, on a 70 to 90 psia scale. The next graph is the piston stroke on a 0–1 in. scale. The next graph is of the expanded pressure minimum on a 15 to 25 psia scale. The bottom graph is of the chamber pressure between pulses on a 70 to 90 psia scale. Immediately obvious is the improvement in the stability of the chamber pressure, the piston stroke, and the recompression overpressure by the use of the computer control. A small improvement in the expanded pressure minimum is also seen. The maximum variation in the expanded pressure minimum during the computer control "on" period is $\pm\frac{1}{2}$ psi. However, most of the pulses show a much smaller variation. Very uniform chamber operation is achieved with this level of performance. One of the major advantages of this type of elaborate system is the achievement of uniform operation without the need for continuous attention and action by the operators. The computer is restricted to making small adjustments in the timing pulses and, therefore, unusual values of the input data that might result from some component starting to fail cannot lead to severe control action. This protects the system from escalation of troubles which without this safeguard might occur. In addition to the uniformity of operation just described[4], reliability of the components is of prime importance since chambers should be expected to operate for several million pulses per year, as seen in Table I.

D. Bubble Images and Contrast on the Film

The final measure of the successful operation of a cryogenic bubble chamber is seen by examination of the photographs actually produced. The optical system is largely responsible for the quality of the photographs as measured by the bubble image size and contrast. A survey of typical performance by seven liquid hydrogen chambers is shown in Fig. 29 and a photograph from the Northwestern helium chamber in Fig. 30. In each of the illustrations shown in Fig. 29, a print of the entire chamber is shown on

---

[4] Operating conditions for deuterium differ from those for hydrogen in the following way for the BNL 80 in. chamber. The chamber temperature is higher as indicated by a vapor bulb (filled with deuterium) reading of 76 psia. The recompression overpressure is increased to 95 psia, and the expanded pressure minimum for equivalent track sensitivity is 27.5 psia.

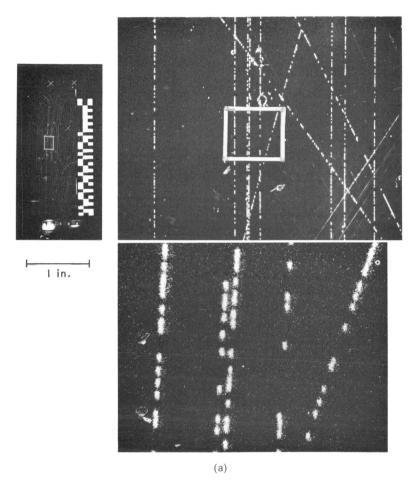

1 in.

(a)

FIG. 29. Photographs taken during normal operation of various cryogenic bubble chambers. On the left of each set is a contact print (1 in. scale is also shown) of the image on the film. A white (or black) box indicates the region which has been enlarged and is shown in the upper right print. Again, a box indicates the area enlarged and shown in the lower right print. (a) BNL 20 in. chamber.

the left. A 1 in. scale under this print provides a means of cross comparing the photographs. Besides showing the various fiducial marks and some light source reflections, and in some cases the data box information, a typical region has been outlined for a higher magnification reproduction which is shown in the upper right-hand print. Individual bubble images begin to

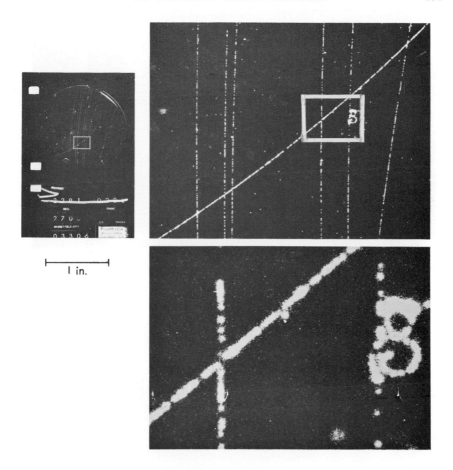

FIG. 29b. LRL 25 in. chamber.

appear and some indication of the uniformity of bubble sensitivity can be deduced. Again, a typical region has been outlined for a higher magnification reproduction as shown in the lower right-hand print. Here, very great detail is seen concerning the individual bubble images. The center photodensitometer trace of Fig. 6 can be compared directly with Fig. 29c where the individual bubble images are 35 μ on the film. It is interesting to note that the chambers of this wide a variety are all operated so as to give the same bubble image size to within a factor of 2. Some slight jitter in the position of the bubbles is apparent in the LRL 72 in. chamber and can be attributed to the index of refraction nonuniformities induced by the gas expansion

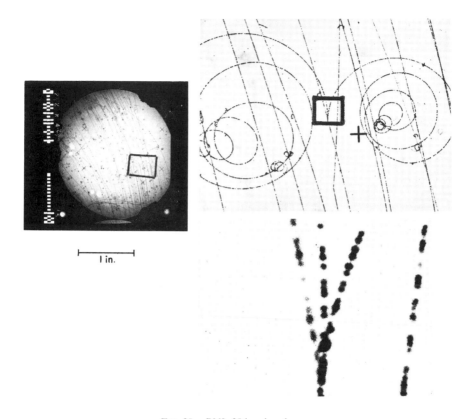

FIG. 29c. BNL 30 in. chamber.

system. The photograph from the 20 in. long by 10 in. high Northwestern helium chamber is typical of helium bubble chamber operation. The dark-field photography used here requires light to be scattered by about 2 degrees. With helium, it is necessary to use scattered light which is very close to the incident direction because the index of refraction of the liquid is only 1.025. The chamber normally operates at 3.2°K and uses 300 liters/day of liquid helium when operating with a $\frac{3}{4}$% expansion ratio and a 2 sec repetition rate. About one half of this helium use is due to the static heat load.

A recent measurement has been made by the University of Notre Dame Bubble Chamber Group using engineering data from the BNL 80 in. chamber (Biswas *et al.*, 1966). The results of these measurements are shown in Fig. 31. The abscissa is labeled P_F (psia) and is the expanded pressure

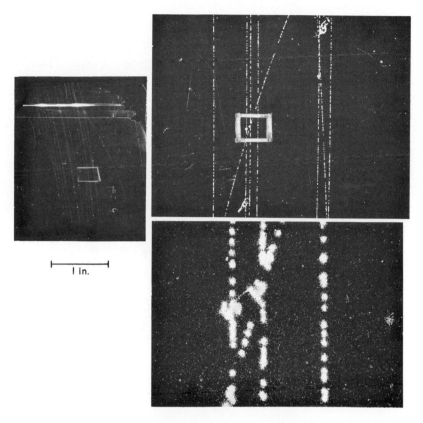

Fig. 29d. ANL/Wisconsin 30 in. chamber.

minimum. The ordinate is the bubble density in bubbles per centimeter in the chamber. Curves are presented for four chamber temperatures: $T = 25.05°K$, $25.47°K$, $25.91°K$, and $26.71°K$. Over this restricted region the chamber sensitivity C is an approximately linear function of the expanded pressure, namely $C = AP_E + B(T)$, where the slope $A = -2.6 \pm 0.8$ bubbles/cm-psia, and the intercept $B(T) = (48.2T - 1170)$ bubbles/cm. Such performance curves for minimum ionizing particles can be expected to vary from chamber to chamber and are even known to differ for the same chamber depending on the amount of dirt or contaminants that may be in the chamber at a particular time, and perhaps also on temperature distribution. However, they serve as a useful guide for adjusting from one operating point to another.

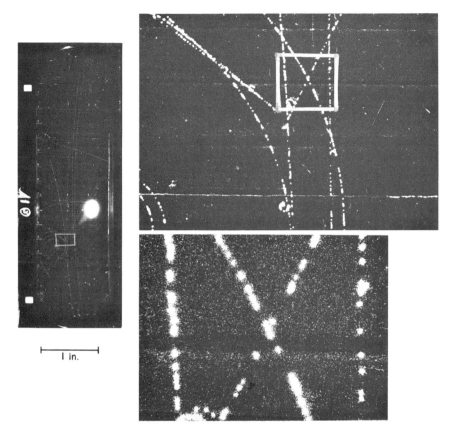

I in.

FIG. 29e. LRL 72 in. chamber.

E. SPECIAL BUBBLE CHAMBER ARRANGEMENTS

Of the various possible improvements to the cryogenic bubble chamber technique, the most frequently exploited today by a special arrangement is the inclusion of metal plates in the chamber to improve the detection of photons mainly resulting from π^0 decay. The radiation length for liquid hydrogen at its normal operating pressure and temperature, where the density is $0.06 \, \text{gm/cm}^3$, is 1145 cm, much longer than any chamber now available. An example of the use of a 2.5 mm thick lead plate in a liquid hydrogen bubble chamber is shown in Fig. 32. Here the 50 cm Saclay chamber was operating in a 1.59 BeV/c π^+ beam. A two-prong interaction in hydrogen

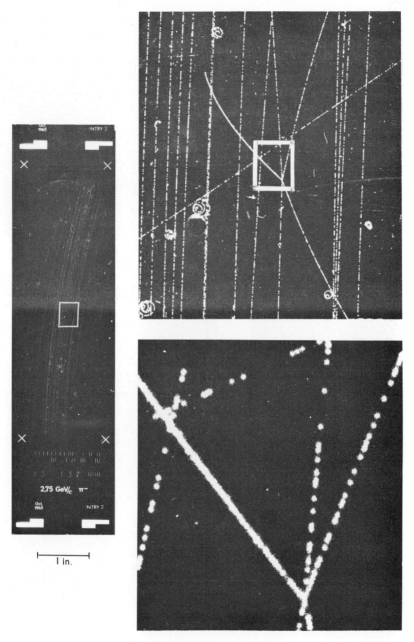

FIG. 29f. CERN 2 meter chamber.

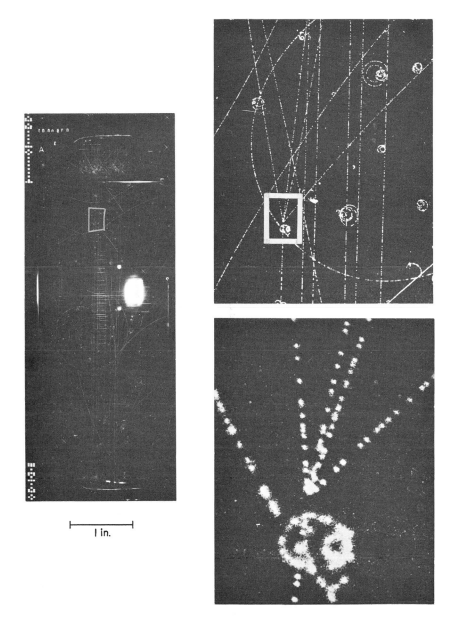

1 in.

Fig. 29g. BNL 80 in. chamber.

produced a π^0 meson which decayed and sent γ rays forward where they converted into electron-positron pairs whose tracks are visible below the plate. Consideration has been given to incorporation of plate arrays in large chambers. These could consist of several plates with a thickness of a fraction of a radiation length each. This then would give a high probability for materialization of a γ ray into an electron pair. Sufficient track length between the plates would make possible momentum measurements on the electrons and positrons converted. Therefore one could deduce the photon's energy as well as its direction. Photons from high energy collisions are concentrated in a forward direction; however, some may emerge at fairly wide angles to the incident beam; therefore high efficiency arrays will have to be quite wide and high in order to cover a large solid angle. For future neutrino experiments, plates of several radiation lengths will be useful in distinguishing between electrons and μ mesons.

Another possible special chamber arrangement is the dual chamber. Here, either a small hydrogen bubble chamber could be incorporated in a larger heavy liquid chamber or a small heavy liquid chamber could be incorporated in a large hydrogen chamber. The MIT Group (Chrétien *et al.*,

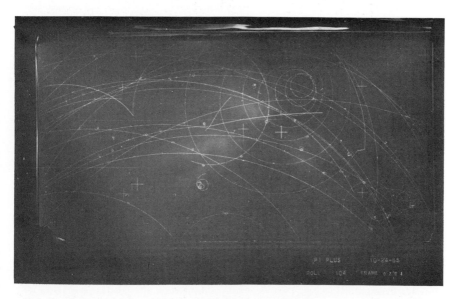

FIG. 30. Photograph of tracks in the Northwestern helium chamber operating in a π^+ beam from the Chicago Cyclotron.

1963) reported the use of a small hydrogen target inside of a heavy liquid chamber, but, so far, even though this combined-chamber technique has frequently been discussed, serious operation of this type of combined system has not been reported (see also Chapter 4).

A development that shows great promise, particularly with the giant chambers of the future, is the operation of cryogenic bubble chambers with hydrogen-neon mixtures. The first tests of this new technique used the BNL 20 in. chamber (Prodell, 1965). In this and subsequent work it has been found possible to obtain track sensitivity with fractions of neon varying from 6 to 94 at. %, and with 100 % neon fillings. Experiments utilizing various

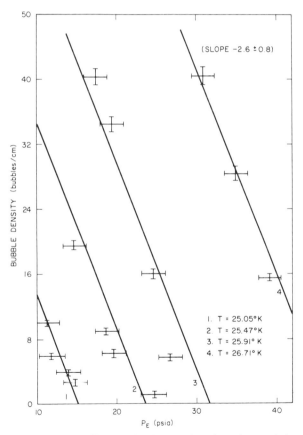

FIG. 31. Experimental values of bubble density as a function of expanded pressure for different temperatures. Data from BNL 80 in. chamber were analyzed by the Notre Dame Bubble Chamber Group.

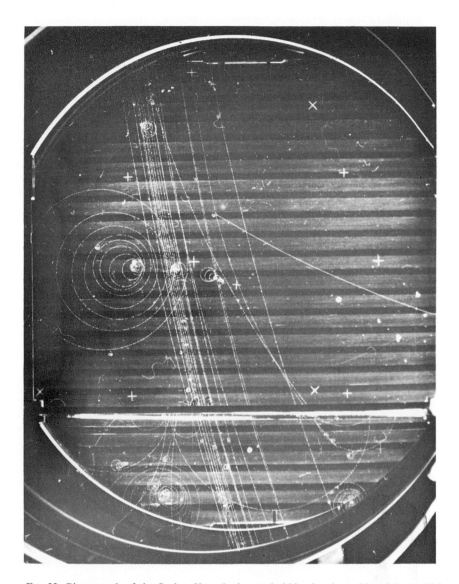

Fig. 32. Photograph of the Saclay 50 cm hydrogen bubble chamber with a 2.5 mm thick lead plate which in this case converts the γ-rays resulting from a π^0 meson decay in the two-prong interaction of a 1.59 BeV/c π^+ beam particle. Electron-positron pairs appear below the plate. The direction of the π^0 can be inferred and this aids in analysis of the event.

percentages of neon are now in progress or planned. Therefore, the utility of this new technique for high energy physics experiments should be known shortly. About one order of magnitude reduction in radiation length is obtained by adding approximately 20 % neon. For a large cryogenic chamber filled with a 20 % neon-hydrogen mixture, if a potential flight path of 2 meters for the γ rays from π^0 mesons made in a primary interaction is available, the probability of converting both γ rays in the chamber is about 60 %. The neon possibility also may be used in investigations of the feasibility of a combination of chambers operating at uniform temperature and pressure. For instance, a pure hydrogen chamber might be at the upstream end of such a chamber for the production event and a hydrogen-neon mixture downstream. Experiments are underway to investigate whether this possibility is practical.

REFERENCES

ARGONNE NATL. LAB. (1964). Proposal for the construction of a 12 ft hydrogen bubble chamber. Argonne Natl. Lab., Argonne, Illinois.

ASME Boiler and Pressure Vessel Code (1959), Section VII, p. 9. The American Soc. of Mech. Engrs., New York, N.Y.

BISWAS, N. N., CASON, N. M., DERADO, I., KENNEY, V. P., POIRIER, J. A., SHEPHARD, W. D., and CLINTON, E. M., Sr. (1966). Proc. Intern. Conf. Instrumentation High Energy Phys., Stanford, September 1966.

BROOKHAVEN NATL. LAB. (1964). Proposal for construction of a 14 ft diameter liquid hydrogen bubble chamber for use at the Brookhaven alternating gradient synchrotron. BNL No. 8266. Brookhaven Natl. Lab., Upton, New York.

BROOKHAVEN NATL. LAB. (1965). Proposal for construction of a cryogenic bubble chamber of 14 ft diameter for use at the Brookhaven alternating gradient synchrotron. BNL No. 8266(R); 14 ft cryogenic bubble chamber proj., Pre-Title I Rept. BNL No. 9695. Brookhaven Natl. Lab., Upton, New York.

CHRÉTIEN, M., FIRTH, D. R., YAMAMOTO, R. K., PLESS, I. A., and ROSENSON, L. (1963). Nucl. Instr. Methods 20, 120.

DAUNT, J. G. (1956). The production of low temperatures down to hydrogen temperature. In "Handbuch der Physik" (S. Flügge, ed.), Vol. 14, p. 1. Springer, Berlin.

EICHELMAN, G. H., and HULL, F. C. (1953). Proc. 34th Internl. Metal Congr. and Expo., Philadelphia, 1952. American Soc. Metals, Cleveland, Ohio.

FABIAN, B. N., PLACE, R. L., RILEY, W. A., SIMS, W. H., and KENNEY, V. P. (1963). Rev. Sci. Instr. 34, 484.

FIELDS, T. H., and THOMPSON, R. W. (1961). Bull. Am. Phys. Soc. 6, 241.

GOODZEIT, C. L. (1967). Simulation techniques applied to the design of the 80 in. liquid hydrogen bubble chamber expansion system. Proc. Sci. Computing Symp., New York, 1966, pp. 181–192. IBM Corp., White Plains, New York.

HILDEBRAND, R. H., and NAGLE, D. E. (1953). Phys. Rev. 92, 517.

JENSEN, J. E., STEWART, R. B., TUTTLE, W. A. (1966). "Selected Cryogenic Data Notebook," BNL No. 10200. Brookhaven Natl. Lab., Upton, New York.

KROPSCHOT, R. H., and MIKESELL, R. P. (1957). *J. Appl. Phys.* **28**, 610.

POWELL, R, L., and BLANPIED, W. A. (1954). *Natl. Bur. Std.* (U.S.), *Circ.* 556.

PRODELL, A. G. (1965). *Rev. Sci. Instr.* **36**, 1174.

SCOTT, R. B. (1959). "Cryogenic Engineering," p. 90. Van Nostrand, Princeton, New Jersey.

SHUTT, R. P. (1963). *Nucl. Instr. Methods* **20**, 71.

TIMOSHENKO, S. (1936). "Theory of Elastic Stability." McGraw-Hill, New York.

TIMOSHENKO, S. (1940). "Theory of Plates and Shells." McGraw-Hill, New York.

TIMOSHENKO, S. (1956). "Strength of Materials," Vol. II. Van Nostrand, Princeton, New Jersey.

WELFORD, W. T. (1963). *Appl. Opt.* **2**, 1037.

WILLIS, W. J. (1959). Error matrix. Internal Report, BNL No. 7932. Brookhaven Natl. Lab., Upton, New York.

WOOD, J. G. (1954). *Phys. Rev.* **94**, 731.

APPENDIX

CRYOGENIC BUBBLE CHAMBERS

Operating site	Builder	Dimensions	Year of completion	Status (1965)	Useful volume (liters)	Comments	References[a]
Proton accelerators							
200 BeV accelerator	—	—	1973	Included in 200 BeV proposal	2000	To be in operation when accelerator first operates	89
	—	20 ft φ	1974	Separate proposal in preparation	100,000	Proposed large volume chamber for 200 BeV accelerator	89
33 BeV BNL, AGS, and 3 BeV Cosmotron, Upton, N.Y.	BNL	6 × 3 × 2 in.	1956	Retired	—	—	2, 90
	BNL	14 in. φ, 8 in. deep	1959	Semiretired	—	BNL 14 in.	35, 46, 81
	BNL	6 × 2½ × 2 in.	—	Retired	—	Model for BNL 20 in.	—
	BNL	20 × 9 × 10 in.	1959	Rebuilt as BNL 31 in.	28	BNL 20 in.	72, 73, 92, 109
	BNL	31 × 13 × 10 in.	1966	Active	51	BNL 31 in. (rebuilt BNL 20 in.)	—
	Columbia	30 in. φ, 13 in. deep	1962	Active	160	BNL 30 in.	118
	BNL	80 × 27 × 26 in.	1963	Active	900	BNL 80 in.	16, 17, 20, 21, 22, 40, 47, 48, 49, 64, 65, 66, 67, 68, 81, 82, 83, 87, 88, 97, 98, 99, 109, 110, 114, 117, 118, 123, 124, 125
28 BeV CERN	BNL	14 ft, 12 ft deep	1971	In design	46,000	Proposed BNL 14 ft.	38, 39, 103
	CERN	10 cm	—	Retired	—	—	—

Accelerator	Institution	Size	Year	Status		Name	References
PS, Geneva, Switzerland	CERN	32 cm ϕ, 15 cm deep	1959	Retired	9.5	CERN 32 cm	107
	Saclay	81 × 30 × 30 cm	1959	Active	70	CERN 81 cm	6, 19, 59, 61, 62, 71, 106, 118
	CERN	200 × 60 × 50 cm	1964	Active	—	CERN 200 cm	1, 14, 15, 60, 107, 115, 118, 120
	CERN	3.5 m ϕ × 2 m	1971	Construction approved 1967	20,000	Proposed CERN large volume chamber	—
12 BeV ANL ZGS, Lamont, Illinois	Illinois	15 in. ϕ	1963	Semiretired	—		—
	Wisconsin	30 in. ϕ, 15 in. deep	1964	Active	200	ANL 30 in.	—
	ANL	10 in. ϕ, 14 in. deep	1964	Active	—	High magnetic field chamber	—
	ANL	12 ft ϕ	1969	In design	20,000	Proposed ANL 12 ft	18
10 BeV Synchrophasotron, Dubna, USSR	Dubna	25 cm ϕ, 10 cm deep	1959	—	8	—	30, 31, 32
		40 cm ϕ	—	—	55	Small camera windows only	—
		95 × 35 × 30 cm	1964	Active	—	—	28
		200 cm length	1965	Final construction	—	—	—
7 BeV Synchrophasotron, Moscow, USSR	Institute of Theoretical & Experimental Physics	10 cm ϕ, 10.5 cm deep	1957	Retired	1	—	85, 86, 102
		25 cm ϕ	1958	Retired	—	—	4, 85, 86
		55 × 35 × 35 cm	1963	Active	—	ITEF 55 cm	84, 101, 121
		50 cm ϕ, 20 cm deep	1964	Active	—	—	—
		205 × 60 × 45 cm	1965	Final construction	—	—	—

Proton accelerators (cont.)

Operating site	Builder	Dimensions	Year of completion	Status (1965)	Useful volume (liters)	Comments	References[a]
7 BeV NIM-ROD, Rutherford High Energy Lab., Harwell, England	British National Project	150 × 50 × 45 cm	1963	Active	—	British national chamber 150 cm	37, 41, 42, 54, 112, 118
	Saclay	82 × 50 × 50 cm	1963	Active	180	Saclay 82 cm. This is rebuilt 50 cm	118
	Oxford	80 × 40 × 42 cm	1966	Final construction	120	Helium	116
6 BeV Bevatron, LRL, Berkeley, California	LRL	$1\frac{1}{2}$ in. ϕ, $\frac{1}{2}$ in. deep	1954	Retired	—	First liquid hydrogen chamber to show tracks	9, 122
		$2\frac{1}{4}$ in. ϕ, $1\frac{1}{2}$ in. deep	1954	Retired	—	First metal hydrogen chamber	8, 9, 63, 104, 105
		4 in. ϕ, 2 in. deep	1955	Retired	—	LRL 4 in.	3, 8, 9, 104, 105
		10 in. ϕ, $6\frac{1}{2}$ in. deep	1956	Retired	8	LRL 10 in.	8, 9, 33, 36, 43, 69, 105
		15 in. ϕ	1957	Retired	40	LRL 15 in. replaced 10 in.	10, 36, 69
		72 × 20 × 15 in.	1959	Active	300	LRL 72 in.	9, 11, 12, 36, 69, 70, 77, 78, 79, 93, 118, 119
		25 in. ϕ, 12 in. deep	1964	Active	85	LRL 25 in. replaced 15 in.	13, 24, 25, 78
3 BeV Princeton-Penn Accelerator, Princeton, N.J.	Princeton	15 in. ϕ, 10 in. deep	1964	Active	30	Rapid cycling chamber	34, 94

2.5 BeV Saturne, Saclay, France	20 cm ϕ, 10 cm deep	1958	Retired	3	—	95, 96, 108, 113
Saclay	35 cm ϕ	1959	Retired	21	—	96, 108
	50 cm ϕ	1960	Rebuilt as Saclay 82 cm	70	Saclay 50 cm	91, 108
	160 cm ϕ, 450 cm long	1969	In design	7000	Will move to Serpukhov 1969	—
Miscellaneous Birmingham	9 in. ϕ, 4 in. deep	1959	Retired	3.8	Pulsed field hydrogen, deuterium chamber	45, 51, 52
Bologna	17 cm ϕ, 12 cm deep	1959	—	—	Being moved to 1 GeV Frascati Electro-synchrotron	26, 27
Chicago	—	1953	Retired	0.003	First liquid hydrogen chamber to show ionization sensitivity	63
	1 × 1 × 4 in.	1956	Retired	0.087	—	100
	23 cm. ϕ, 15 cm deep	1960	—	—	—	23
Columbia	12 in. ϕ, 6 in. deep	1957	—	—	—	53
Duke	3.8 cm ϕ, 10 cm long	1955	Retired	—	First liquid helium chamber	55, 74
	1½ in. ϕ, 4 in. long	1956	Retired	—	—	56, 57, 75, 76
	8 × 5 × 4 in.	1957	Retired	—	Duke 8 in. helium	29, 58
Imperial College, London	40 cm ϕ, 15 cm deep	1960	—	—	—	—
Leyden	30 cm ϕ, 20 cm deep	1961	Retired	14	—	111

Operating site	Builder	Dimensions	Year of completion	Status (1965)	Useful volume (liters)	Comments	References[a]
	Liverpool	10 in. ϕ, 4 in. deep	1959	—	—	—	7
	Northwestern University	20 in. ϕ	1965	Final construction	—	Largest helium chamber	—
	Oxford	12 cm ϕ, 9 cm deep	1961	Retired	1	Hydrogen and deuterium	80
	Rome	20 × 20 × 10 cm	1961	—	4	Helium	50
Electron accelerators							
45 BeV SLAC II	Stanford	—	1973	—	20,000	Proposed large volume chamber for SLAC II	—
20 BeV SLAC I	Stanford	40 in. ϕ	1967	Final design	300	—	44
6 BeV CEA, Cambridge Electron	M.I.T.	40 in. ϕ	1965	Final testing	500	—	—
6 BeV DESY, Hamburg, Germany	Saclay	82 × 40 × 40 cm	1964	Active	125	DESY 82 cm	—

[a] References to the Appendix are listed on p. 151.

REFERENCES TO APPENDIX

1. A. H. ACHERMANN. The turn-table for the 2 m liquid hydrogen bubble chamber. CERN, European Organ Nucl. Res. CERN 63-6 (1963).
2. R. K. ADAIR and L. B. LEIPUNER. Piston-operated liquid hydrogen bubble chamber. *Bull. Am. Phys. Soc.* **2**, No. 7 (1957).
3. H. E. ADELSON, H. A. BOSTICK, B. J. MOYER, and C. N. WADDELL. Use of the 4 in. liquid hydrogen bubble chamber as a fast neutron spectrometer. *Rev. Sci. Instr.* **31**, 1–10 (1960).
4. M. S. AINUTDINOV, S. M. ZOMBKOVSKII, S. YA. NIKITIN, and YA. M. SELEKTOR. Liquid hydrogen bubble chamber with a diameter of 25 cm. *Instr. Exptl. Tech. (USSR) (English Transl.)* p. 31–35 (1961) [*Pribory i Tekhn. Eksperim.* , 35–39 (1961)].
5. YU. A. ALEKSANDROV and YU. I. NECHAEV. A pulsed radiation source. *Instr. Exptl Tech. (USSR) (English Trans.)* p. 391 (1962) [*Pribory i Tekhn. Eksperim.*, 168–169 (1962)].
6. C. ALLARD and R. FLORENT. The liquid hydrogen bubble chamber CBH-81: The electromagnet and electronic circuits. *L'Onde Elec.* **41**, No. 417, 1020–1024 (1961).
7. M. H. ALSTON, D. C. CUNDY, W. H. EVANS, R. W. NEWPORT, and P. R. WILLIAMS. A 10 in. diameter liquid hydrogen bubble chamber. *Phil. Mag.* **5**, 146–153 (1960).
8. L. W. ALVAREZ. Operation of liquid hydrogen bubble chamber. *Proc. Ann. Rochester Conf. High Energy Nucl. Phys., 1955*, **5**, p. 181–182. Wiley (Interscience), New York, 1955.
9. L. W. ALVAREZ. Liquid hydrogen bubble chambers. *CERN Symp. High Energy Accelerators Pion Phys. Geneva, 1956, Proc.* (A. Citron, *et al.* eds.), **2**, pp. 13–15. CERN European Organ. Nucl. Res., Geneva, 1956.
10. L. W. ALVAREZ. High energy physics with hydrogen bubble chambers. *Proc. U.N. Intern. Conf. Peaceful Uses At. Energy, 2nd, Geneva, 1958*, **30**, p. 164–165. United Nations, New York, 1958.
11. L. W. ALVAREZ. Experience with a large hydrogen bubble chamber. *Proc. Intern. Conf. Instrumentation High Energy Phys., Berkeley, 1960*, p. 145–149. Wiley (Interscience), New York, 1961.
12. L. W. ALVAREZ. Liquid hydrogen bubble chambers, in "Experimental Cryophysics" (F. E. Hoare, L. C. Jackson, and N. Kurti, eds.) pp. 258–274. Butterworths, London, 1961.
13. L. W. ALVAREZ *et al.* LRL 25 in. bubble chamber. Lawrence Rad. Lab., UCRL 11521. Univ. of California, Berkeley, California, 1964.
14. P. AMIOT. The selections of stainless steels for use in liquid hydrogen bubble chambers. *Nucl. Instr. Methods* **4**, 118–119 (1959).
15. P. AMIOT, G. NULLENS, and R. SPONDLIN. Some of the expansion mechanisms considered for liquid hydrogen bubble chambers. CERN, European Organ. Nucl. Res. CERN 59–20 (1959).
16. J. G. ANDROULAKIS. Some considerations on the configuration and stability of the hydrogen temperature control loops of the 80 in. bubble chamber. BNL 7497. Brookhaven Natl. Lab., Upton, New York. 1963.
17. J. G. ANDROULAKIS *et al.*, Brookhaven National Laboratory 80 in. hydrogen bubble chamber status and plans. *Nucl. Instr. Methods* **20**, 100–119 (1963).
18. ARGONNE NATL. LAB. Proposal for the construction of a 12 ft hydrogen bubble chamber (1964).
19. J. BADIER. The liquid hydrogen bubble chamber CBH-81: The optical system. *L'Onde Elec.* **41**, No. 417, 1025–1028 (1961).

20. J. A. BAMBERGER. Cooldown refrigeration requirements for 80 in. bubble chamber. BNL 7496. Brookhaven Natl. Lab., Upton, New York, 1960.

21. J. A. BAMBERGER, D. P. BROWN, and J. E. JENSEN. General description of the 80 in. bubble chamber refrigeration system. BNL 7492. Brookhaven Natl. Lab., Upton, New York, 1962.

22. J. A. BAMBERGER, D. P. BROWN, and J. E. JENSEN. Hydrogen refrigerator design capacity for 80 in. chamber. BNL 7487. Brookhaven Natl. Lab., Upton, New York, 1962.

23. A. BARNA. Temperature regulator for a 9 liter liquid hydrogen bubble chamber. *Nucl. Instr. Methods* **26**, 109–116 (1964).

24. F. BARRERA et al. The 25 in. liquid hydrogen bubble chamber. Lawrence Rad. Lab., UCRL 11384. Univ. of California, Berkeley, California, 1964.

25. F. BARRERA et al. The 25 in. liquid hydrogen bubble chamber expansion system. Lawrence Rad. Lab., UCRL 11558. Univ. of California, Berkeley, California, 1964.

26. P. BASSI, R. CANO, S. FOCARDI, A. MICHELINI, and F. SAPORETTI. Distortion of tracks in bubble chamber. *Proc. U.N. Intern. Conf. Peaceful Uses At. Energy, 2nd, Geneva, 1958.* **30**, p. 177–178. United Nations, New York, 1958.

27. P. BASSI, R. CANO, S. FOCARDI, G. G. A. MICHELINI, and F. SAPORETTI. Three liters liquid hydrogen bubble chamber. *Nuovo Cimento Suppl. No. 2*, **16**, 184–191 (1960).

28. A. V. BELONOGOV et al. A liquid hydrogen bubble chamber of volume $950 \times 350 \times 300$ mm^3. *Nucl. Instr. Methods* **20**, 114 115 (1963).

29. M. M. BLOCK, W. M. FAIRBANK, E. M. HARTH, T. KIKUCHI, C. MELTZER, and J. LEITNER. A liquid helium bubble chamber. *Proc. Intern. Conf. High Energy Accelerators Instrumentation, CERN, 1959* (L. Kowarski, ed.), p. 461–465. European Organ. Nucl. Res., Geneva, 1959.

30. T. D. BLOKHINTSEVA et al. Eight liter hydrogen–deuterium bubble chamber in magnetic field. JINR P 848. Joint Inst. Nucl. Res., Lab. Nucl. Problems, USSR. 1961. [Transl. available as UCRL Trans. 810. Univ. of California, Berkeley, California, 1961.]

31. T. D. BLOKHINTSEVA et al. An 8 liter hydrogen deuterium bubble chamber in a magnetic field. *Instr. Exptl. Tech. (USSR) (English Transl.)* 917–926 (1963) [*Pribory i Tekhn. Eksperim.* No. 5, 51–59 (1962)].

32. T. D. BLOKHINTSEVA et al. An 8 liter hydrogen deuterium bubble chamber in a magnetic field. *Cryogenics* **4**, 17–25 (1964).

33. R. L. BLUMBERG, J. D. GOW, and A. J. SCHWEMIN. The development and operation of the 10 in. liquid hydrogen bubble chamber. *Proc. Cryog. Eng. Conf., 2nd, Boulder, 1956*, p. 318–324. U.S. Natl. Bur. Std., Boulder, 1957.

34. H. A. BLUMENFELD, T. BOWEN, R. L. McILLWAIN, M. SCHEIBNER, L. SEIDLITZ, and C. R. SUN. Design of a 30 liter rapid-cycling hydrogen bubble chamber with counter-controlled photography. *Proc. Intern. Conf. Instrumentation High Energy Phys., Berkeley, 1960*, p. 103–105. Wiley (Interscience), New York, 1961.

35. E. M. BOLZE et al. Liquid hydrogen bubble chamber expanded by a piston in the liquid. *Rev. Sci. Instr.* **29**, 297–299 (1958).

36. H. BRADNER and D. A. GLASER. Methods of particle detection for high energy physics experiments. *Proc. U.N. Intern. Conf. Peaceful Uses At. Energy, Geneva, 1958*, **14**, p. 412–422. United Nations, New York, 1958.

37. The British National hydrogen bubble chamber. *Instr. Pract.* **17**, 380–381 (1963).

38. BROOKHAVEN NATL. LAB. Proposal for construction of a 14 ft diameter liquid hydrogen bubble chamber for use at the Brookhaven Alternating Gradient Synchrotron. BNL 8266. Brookhaven Natl. Lab., Upton, New York, 1964. [Revised 1965. BNL 8266 (R).]

39. BROOKHAVEN NATL. LAB. 14 ft cryogenic bubble chamber project: final pre-title I report. BNL 9695. Brookhaven Natl. Lab., Upton, New York, December 1, 1965.

40. D. BROWN. Evaluation of multi-layer insulation. BNL 7494. Brookhaven Natl. Lab., Upton, New York, 1963.

41. C. C. BUTLER. Particle hunting with the big British bubble chamber. *New Scientist* **23**, 147–148 (1964).

42. C. C. BUTLER. Britain's National hydrogen bubble chamber. *New Scientist* **7**, 22–25 (1960).

43. D. B. CHELTON, D. B. MANN, and R. A. BYRNS. A large liquid hydrogen bubble chamber. *Proc. Cryog. Eng. Conf., 2nd, Boulder, 1956*, pp. 325–329. U.S. Natl. Bur. Std., Boulder, 1957.

44. W. CHINOWSKY. Some considerations of bubble chamber experiments with M. In some aspects of the prospective experimental use of the Stanford two-mile accelerator. SLAC 5, p. 79–89. Stanford Linear Accelerator Center, Stanford Univ., Stanford, California, 1962.

45. D. C. COLLEY, J. B. KINSON, and L. RIDDIFORD. 9 in. liquid hydrogen bubble chamber in a pulsed magnetic field. *Nucl. Instr. Methods* **4**, 26–29 (1959).

46. H. COURANT, J. E. JENSEN, R. I. LOUTTIT, and J. R. SANFORD. Performance of a piston-expanded bubble chamber. *Rev. Sci. Instr.* **30**, 280–281 (1959).

47. B. B. CULWICK. 80 in. bubble chamber magnet coils. BNL 7481. Brookhaven Natl. Lab., Upton, New York, 1959.

48. B. B. CULWICK. Magnet coils detailed conductor design. BNL 7491. Brookhaven Natl. Lab., Upton, New York, 1960.

49. B. B. CULWICK. Some parameters of the 80 in. chamber magnet coils. BNL 7488. Brookhaven Natl. Lab., Upton, New York, 1960.

50. E. DI CAPUA, U. DORE, G. C. GIALANELLA, P. GUIDONI, I. LAAKSO, and G. C. MONETI. A four liter liquid helium bubble chamber. *Nucl. Instr. Methods* **15**, 273–281 (1962).

51. W. P. DODD, G. A. DORAN, J. B. KINSON, L. RIDDIFORD, and B. TALLINI. Operation of a 9 in. bubble chamber with deuterium. *Nucl. Instr. Methods* **13**, 127–130 (1961).

52. G. A. DORAN, J. G. HILL, J. B. KINSON, and L. RIDDIFORD. 9 in. hydrogen bubble chamber in a pulsed magnetic field. *Proc. Intern. Conf. High Energy Accelerators Instrumentation, CERN, 1959*, (L. Kowarski, ed.), p. 460–460a. European Organ. Nucl. Res., Geneva, 1959.

53. F. EISLER *et al.* Bubble chamber study of unstable particle production in $\pi^- $-$p$ collisions at 910, 960, 1200 and 1300 MeV. *Nuovo Cimento* **10**, 468–469 (1958).

54. Emerging order in high energy physics. *New Scientist* **17**, 443–444 (1963).

55. W. M. FAIRBANK, E. M. HARTH, M. E. BLEVINS, and G. G. SLAUGHTER. Report on a liquid helium bubble chamber (abstract). *Bull. Am. Phys. Soc.* **30**, 25–26 (1955); also in *Phys. Rev.* **100**, 971–972 (1955).

56. W. M. FAIRBANK, M. E. BLEVINS, M. M. BLOCK, M. J. BUCKINGHAM, E. M. HARTH, and G. G. SLAUGHTER. Observations below the lambda point using a liquid-helium bubble chamber (abstract) *Bull. Am. Phys. Soc.* **1**, 218 (1956).

57. W. M. FAIRBANK *et al.* Liquid helium bubble chamber. *Proc. Cryog. Eng. Conf., 2nd, Boulder. 1956*, p. 330–335. U.S. Natl. Bur. Std., Boulder, 1957.

58. W. M. FAIRBANK, J. LEITNER, M. M. BLOCK, and E. M. HARTH. A liquid helium bubble chamber. *Bull. Inst. Intern. Froid, Annexe* **1**, 45–54 (1958).

59. R. FLORENT, B. GREGORY, and R. MAILLET. The liquid hydrogen bubble chamber CBH-81: Generalities. *L'Onde Elec.* **41**, No. 417, 1001–1006 (1961).

60. F. FRUNGEL, H. KOHLER, and H. P. REINHARD. The illumination of the CERN 2 meter hydrogen bubble chamber. *Appl. Opt.* **2**, 1017–1024 (1963).

61. A. GARCON. The liquid hydrogen bubble chamber CBH-81: Chamber and its expansion. *L'Onde Elec.* **41**, No. 417, 1007–1015 (1961).

62. A. GARCON and R. BLONDET. The liquid hydrogen bubble chamber CBH-81: Thermal regulation. *L'Onde Elec.* **41**, No. 417, 1016–1019 (1961).

63. D. A. GLASER. The bubble chamber, *Sci. Am.* **192**, 46–50 (1955).

64. C. GOODZEIT. Selecting reservoir sizes for 80 in. bubble chamber expansion system. BNL 7482. Brookhaven Natl. Lab., Upton, New York, 1960.

65. C. GOODZEIT. Expansion system status report. BNL 7486. Brookhaven Natl. Lab., Upton, New York, 1962.

66. C. L. GOODZEIT. 80 in. bubble chamber expansion system. Summary of piston motion studies, October–November 1962. BNL 7490. Brookhaven Natl. Lab., Upton, New York, 1962.

67. C. L. GOODZEIT. 80 in. bubble chamber expansion system. Preliminary operating procedures. BNL 7493. Brookhaven Natl. Lab., Upton, New York, 1963.

68. C. GOULD. Bubble chamber vacuum system. BNL 7478. Brookhaven Natl. Lab., Upton, New York, 1961.

69. J. D. GOW. Development and operation of liquid hydrogen bubble chambers. *Proc. U.N. Intern. Conf. Peaceful Uses At. Energy, 2nd, Geneva, 1958*, **30**, p. 166–173. United Nations, New York, 1958.

70. J. D. GOW and A. H. ROSENFELD. Berkeley 72 in. hydrogen bubble chamber. *Proc. Intern. Conf. High Energy Accelerators Instrumentation, CERN, 1959* (L. Kowarski, ed.) p. 435–439. European Organ. Nucl. Res., Geneva, 1959.

71. B. GREGORY. The liquid hydrogen bubble chamber CBH-81: The CERN experiments. *L'Onde Elec.* **41**, No. 417, 1034–1041 (1961).

72. E. L. HART. Film format and fiducial marks of the 20 in. chamber. BNL 7896. Brookhaven Natl. Lab., Upton, New York, 1962.

73. E. L. HART. Revised optical constants for the BNL 20 in. chamber. BNL 7896. Brookhaven Natl. Lab., Upton, New York, 1962.

74. E. M. HARTH, W. M. FAIRBANK, M. E. BLEVINS, and G. G. SLAUGHTER. A liquid-helium bubble chamber (*Conf. Phys. Basses Temp., Paris, 1955*), *Bull. Inst. Intern. Froid, Annexe* **3**, 371–374 (1955).

75. E. M. HARTH, M. E. BLEVINS, M. M. BLOCK, M. J. BUCKINGHAM, W. M. FAIRBANK, and G. G. SLAUGHTER. Operating characteristics of the helium bubble chamber (abstract) *Bull. Am. Phys. Soc.* **1**, 177 (1956).

76. E. M. HARTH, M. M. BLOCK, W. M. FAIRBANK, M. J. BUCKINGHAM, G. G. SLAUGHTER, and M. E. BLEVINS. Liquid helium bubble chambers. *CERN Symp. High Energy Accelerators Pion Phys., Geneva, 1956, Proc.* (A. Citron, *et al.*, eds.), **2**, pp. 22–24. CERN European Organ. Nucl. Res., Geneva, 1956.

77. H. P. HERNANDEZ. Cryogenic experience with the 72 in. bubble chamber. *Advan. Cryog. Eng.* **5**, 38–48 (1960).

78. H. P. HERNANDEZ and B. W. BIRMINGHAM. Liquid hydrogen bubble chambers. *In* "Technology and Uses of Liquid Hydrogen" (R. B. Scott, W. H. Denton, and C. M. Nicholls, eds.), pp. 228–284. Pergamon Press, Oxford, 1964.

79. H. C. HITCHCOCK and R. D. WATT. Reduction of optical distortion in gas-expansion bubble chambers. *Proc. Intern. Conf. Instrumentation High Energy Phys., Berkeley, 1960*, pp. 121–122. Wiley (Interscience), New York, 1961.

80. H. W. K. HOPKINS, M. DAVISON, L. LYONS, J. M. BREARE, D. ROAF, and D. F. SHAW. A 12 cm liquid deuterium bubble chamber. *Nucl. Instr. Methods* **12**, 323–328 (1961).

81. J. E. JENSEN. Performance of a piston expanded bubble chamber. *Advan. Cryog. Eng.* **3**, 418–425 (1960).

82. J. E. JENSEN. The Brookhaven National Laboratory 80 in. liquid hydrogen bubble chamber. BNL 8309. Brookhaven Natl. Lab., Upton, New York, 1964.

83. D. A. KASSNER. Design consideration for 80 in. bubble chamber. BNL 7495. Brookhaven Natl. Lab., Upton, New York, 1960.

84. G. K. KILGER, V. Z. KOLGANOV, A. V. LEBEDEV, V. T. SMOLYANKIN, and A. P. SOKOLOV. Problems in designing liquid-hydrogen bubble chambers (a survey). *Instr. Exptl. Tech.* (*USSR*) (*Engl. Transl.*) No. 3, 495–512 (1964) [*Pribory i Tekhn. Eksperim.* No. 3, 5–25].

85. V. Z. KOLGANOV, A. V. LEBEDEV, S. YA. NIKITIN, and V. T. SMOLIANKIN. Liquid hydrogen bubble chamber. *Instr. Exptl. Tech.* (*USSR*) (*Engl. Transl.*) No. 1, 30–34 (1958) [*Pribory i Tekhn. Eksperim.* No. 1, 30–34 (1958)].

86. V. Z. KOLGANOV, A. V. LEBEDEV, S. YA. NIKITIN, V. T. SMOLIANKIN, and A. P. SOKOLOV. Liquid deuterium bubble chamber. *Instr. Exptl. Tech.* (*USSR*) (*Engl. Transl.*) No. 4, 487–488 (1958) [*Pribory i Tekhn. Eksperim.* No. 4, 30 (1958)].

87. H. L. KRAYBILL. Illumination of 80 in. chamber. BNL 7806. Brookhaven Natl. Lab., Upton, New York, 1960.

88. H. L. KRAYBILL. Retrodirectors (for) 80 in. chamber. BNL 7806. Brookhaven Natl. Lab., Upton, New York, 1960.

89. LAWRENCE RAD. LAB., 200 BeV Study. UCRL No. 16,000, 2 vols. Univ. of California, Berkeley, California, 1965.

90. L. B. LEIPUNER and R. K. ADAIR. Production of strange particles by $\pi^-\text{-}p$ interactions near threshold. *Phys. Rev.* **109**, 1358–1363 (1958).

91. Liquid hydrogen and deuterium bubble chambers of the Laboratory of High Energy Particle Physics, Saclay. *L'Onde Elec.* **42**, 403–425 (1962).

92. R. I. LOUTTIT. Performance of the Brookhaven National Laboratory 20 in. hydrogen bubble chamber. *Proc. Intern. Conf. Instrumentation High Energy Phys., Berkeley, 1960*, pp. 117–120. Wiley (Interscience), New York, 1961.

93. L. R. LUCAS and H. P. HERNANDEZ. Inflatable gasket for the 72 in. bubble chamber. *Rev. Sci. Instr.* **30**, 941–942 (1959).

94. R. L. MCILLWAIN. Temperature regulation of the 15 in. hydrogen bubble chamber. PPAD 465D. Princeton-Penn. Accelerator, Princeton Univ., Princeton, New Jersey, 1962.

95. J. MEYER. Three-liter hydrogen bubble chamber. *L'Onde Elec.* **39**, 615–617 (1959).

96. J. MEYER, P. PRUGNE, and P. ROUBEAU. Temperature setting and thermal regulation system for liquid hydrogen bubble chamber. *Proc. Intern. Congr. Refrig., 10th, Copenhagen, 1959* **1**, pp. 203–206. Comite du Congres Intern. du Froid, Paris, 1960.

97. D. M. MILLER. 6 kV capacitor charging supply. BNL 6442. Brookhaven Natl. Lab., Upton, New York, 1962.

98. S. G. MO. Structural analysis of magnet return iron (80 in. bubble chamber). BNL 7484. Brookhaven Natl. Lab., Upton, New York, 1960.

99. S. C. MO. Stresses in magnet coil (preliminary) 80 in. bubble chamber. BNL 7485. Brookhaven Natl. Lab., Upton, New York, 1963.

100. D. E. NAGLE, R. H. HILDEBRAND, and R. J. PLANO. Hydrogen bubble chamber used for low-energy meson scattering. *CERN Symp. High Energy Accelerators Pion Phys., Geneva, 1956, Proc.* (A. Citron et al., eds.), **2**, pp. 16–21. CERN European Organ. Nucl. Res., Geneva, 1956; also in *Rev. Sci. Instr.* **27**, 203–207 (1956).

101. S. YA. NIKITIN. The hydrogen bubble chamber of the Institute of Theoretical and Experimental Physics, Moscow. *Nucl. Instr. Methods* **20**, 95–99 (1963).

102. S. YA. NIKITIN, V. Z. KOLGANOV, A. B. LEBEDEV, V. T. SMOLIANKIN, A. P. SOKOLOV, and L. G. LANDSBERG. Investigation of the production of π^- mesons in n, p collisions by means of a liquid hydrogen bubble chamber. *Proc. Intern. Conf./Mesons and Recently Discovered Particles, 43rd Congr. Naz. Fiz. Padova-Venezia, 1957*, pp. 79–86. Ciclografia Borghero, Padova (1958).

103. R. B. PALMER. A large hydrogen bubble chamber. Talk given to High Energy Discussion Group, February 1964.

104. D. PARMENTIER, Jr., and A. J. SCHWEMIN. Liquid hydrogen bubble chambers. *Rev. Sci. Instr.* **26**, 954–958 (1955).

105. D. PARMENTIER, Jr., and A. J. SCHWEMIN. Liquid hydrogen bubble chambers. *Rep. Conf. Recent Develop. Cloud-Chamber Assoc. Tech. Univ. Coll. London, 1955* (N. Norris and M. J. B. Duff, eds.), pp. 122–128. University College, London, London, 1956.

106. F. PENET. The liquid hydrogen bubble chamber CBH-81: Protection and safety. *L'Onde Elec.* **41**, No. 417, 1029–1033 (1961).

107. C. PEYROU. Some features of CERN hydrogen bubble chambers. *Proc. Intern. Conf. High Energy Accelerators Instrumentation, CERN, 1959* (L. Kowarski, ed.), p. 454–459. European Organ. Nucl. Res., Geneva, 1959.

108. P. PRUGNE. Construction program for hydrogen bubble chambers at the High Energy Particle Division of the Nuclear Research Center, Saclay. *L'Onde Elec.* **39**, 623–626 (1959).

109. D. C. RAHM. Discussion on Brookhaven 20 in. and 80 in. hydrogen chambers. *Proc. Intern. Conf. High Energy Accelerators Instrumentation, CERN, 1959* (L. Kowarski, ed.), pp. 440–442. European Organ. Nucl. Res., Geneva, 1959.

110. R. R. RAU. 80 in. chamber—low energy beams. BNL 7480. Brookhaven Natl. Lab., Upton, New York, 1959.

111. J. REUSS, D. Z. TOET, and B. VAN EIJNSBERGEN. Description of a 30 cm hydrogen bubble chamber. *Appl. Sci. Res. Sect. B* **9**, 309–358 (1962).

112. L. RIDDIFORD *et al.* Some features of the British national hydrogen bubble chamber. *Proc. Intern. Conf. High Energy Accelerators Instrumentation, CERN, 1959* (L. Kowarski, ed.), pp. 445–454. European Organ. Nucl. Res., Geneva, 1959.

113. A. ROGOZINSKI and J. VILAIN. Programme de construction des chambres a bulles a Saclay. *CERN Symp. High Energy Accelerators Pion Phys., Geneva, 1956, Proc.* (A. Citron *et al.*, eds.) **2**, pp. 31–32. CERN European Organ. Nucl. Res., Geneva, 1956.

114. S. ROSIN. Illumination of 80 in. bubble chamber. *Appl. Opt.* **2**, 1003–1012 (1963).

115. F. SCHMEISSNER and J. HAENNY. Refrigeration plant for the 2 metre hydrogen bubble chamber of the European Organization for Nuclear Research (CERN). *Sulzer Tech. Rev. (Switz.)* **43**, 12–16 (1961).

116. D. F. SHAW. Hydrogen and helium bubble chambers. *Cryogenics* **4**, 193–203 (1964).

117. R. P. SHUTT. Considerations on the magnet for the 80 in. hydrogen bubble chamber. BNL 7479. Brookhaven Natl. Lab., Upton, New York, 1959.

118. R. P. SHUTT. Recent advances in the bubble chamber technique. *Nucl. Instr. Methods* **20**, 71–94 (1963).

119. H. SLATIS. On bubble chambers. *Nucl. Instr. Methods* **5**, 1–25 (1959).

120. C. TREPP. The liquid hydrogen refrigerating plant of the CERN 2 metre bubble chamber. *Sulzer Tech. Rev. (Switz.)* **45**, 111–120 (1963).

121. P. I. VATSET, V. I. VOLOSHCHUK, L. YA. KOLESNIKOV, V. O. (A.) Nikitin, and S. G. Tonapetyan. A liquid hydrogen bubble chamber. *Ukr. Fiz. Zh.* **6**, 175–180 (1961).

122. J. G. Wood. Bubble tracks in a hydrogen filled Glaser chamber. *Phys. Rev.* **94**, 731 (1954).
123. D. H. Wright. General operation and construction features of the undercarriage system for the 80 in. bubble chamber. BNL 7498. Brookhaven Natl. Lab., Upton, New York, 1960.
124. S. Yamamoto. Final coathanger design. BNL 7489. Brookhaven Natl. Lab., Upton, New York, 1961 [Revised 1963].
123. S. S. Yamamoto and W. P. Sims. The trigger circuit for the 80 in. bubble chamber light source. *Appl. Opt.* **2**, 997–998 (1963).

Chapter IV

Heavy Liquid Bubble Chambers

A. Lagarrigue[1] and A. Rousset

École Polytechnique, Paris, France

I. General Characteristics of Heavy Liquid Bubble Chambers

A. Introduction

The first bubble chamber ever to work might have been called a heavy liquid chamber. It consisted of a polished glass tube, 3 cm^3 in volume, filled

[1] *Present address:* Laboratoire de l'Accélératour Lineaire, Faculté des Sciences, Orsay, France.

with ether at a temperature of 130°C and a pressure of 20 atm, the vapor pressure of ether at that temperature. It was noticed that quickly expanding to atmospheric pressure would cause the liquid to boil suddenly after a delay of around 30 sec; this corresponded to the average time interval between the passage of two cosmic rays in the chamber. If a radioactive source were brought close to the chamber during the expansion, the effect could be produced without delay, which shows its dependence on ionizing radiation (Glaser, 1952).

The first picture of a trajectory (in fact, an alignment of several bubbles) was made with a similar setup. A flash lamp was fired with a delay of a few microseconds after the passage of a cosmic ray through the counters surrounding the chamber.

The "father" of the heavy liquid bubble chamber (HLBC) is the propane chamber. Most of these chambers still use propane either in pure form or in a mixture with heavier liquids in order to obtain an optimum radiation length. The idea to use propane stems from its high concentration of hydrogen, which permits the study of reactions on free protons. For several years, the only bubble chambers with a useful volume greater than 1 liter were propane chambers. The technique of hydrogen chambers had not evolved to the point of allowing larger chambers to be built.

In propane, as in all heavy liquids, it is practically impossible to distinguish between reactions on hydrogen and reactions on carbon or heavier nuclei without a magnetic field. Only in the case of some intermediate energy reactions, such as the production of Λ^0 and K^0 pairs by 1 BeV mesons, is this relatively easy.

The ease of detection of photons was rapidly recognized as an important property of the HLBC. It was thus possible to prove the existence of the Σ^0 hyperon by its disintegration mode

$$\Sigma^0 \rightarrow \Lambda^0 + \gamma$$
$$\rightarrow e^+ + e^-.$$

The detection of π^0 mesons by materialization of their two disintegration photons became of utmost importance in 1957 when tests of the selection rule of strange particle decay, $\Delta I = \frac{1}{2}$, necessitated the measurement of the decay rates of Λ^0 hyperons and K_1^0 mesons in the modes $\Lambda^0 \rightarrow n + \pi^0$ and $K_1^0 \rightarrow \pi^0 + \pi^0$. Bubble chambers were at that time of modest size (around 10 liters) and it was impossible to measure these rates because of the relatively high radiation length of propane (118 cm). Two solutions were tried with success.

The first was the xenon chamber (Brown *et al.*, 1956). Because of its high atomic number, xenon has a very short radiation length of 3.9 cm. Thus, even with a small chamber, it is possible to obtain a high probability of photon materialization. Unfortunately, xenon is very expensive. Also, a very high magnetic field would have been necessary to obtain proper precision in the measurement of momentum by magnetic curvature. Because it was impossible to achieve such high fields by classical methods at a reasonable cost, the chamber was used without any field.

The second solution was invented and developed by the group of I. Pless at M.I.T. and later used by the École Polytechnique group in Paris. It consisted in the use of a mixture of propane and methyl iodide, CH_3I. This mixture has the double advantage of being rich in hydrogen and having a short radiation length because of the iodine ($Z = 53$). Here again the necessity of a high magnetic field was a problem. Nevertheless the collaborating team of Brandeis, Brown, Harvard, and Padova Universities, and M.I.T. (Chrétien *et al.*, 1962) achieved great success in its experiment: the discovery of the disintegration of the η^0 meson into $\gamma + \gamma$, with its important theoretical consequences.

Chambers as long as 1 meter had to be constructed in order to combine good photon detection with precise curvature measurements. It would seem that these two properties are incompatible since the error due to multiple Coulomb scattering increases with decreasing radiation length. But the precision in curvature measurements increases with the length of the track, and with a longer chamber a small radiation length is no longer necessary. Let us explain this point. Neglecting distortions and measurement errors, we get the following formula for the relative precision in the measurement of the momentum (see Section III,A):

$$\frac{\Delta p}{p} = \frac{K}{\beta B (X_0 l)^{1/2}}, \tag{1}$$

where K is a constant equal to 57.0, β is the velocity of the particle in units of light velocity c, B the magnetic field intensity in kilogauss, X_0 the radiation length in centimeters, l the length in centimeters along which it is possible to measure the track. As long as l is not greater than the interaction mean free path, the ratio X_0/l should be a constant for a given photon detection probability. Thus, for a given precision in the measurement of the momentum, the product Bl is a constant. As long as it is not possible to obtain at reasonable cost magnetic fields greater than 20 kG, the heavy liquid bubble chamber has to be as large as possible in order to obtain a high value of l. It can be added that a large size has many other advantages.

The first big chamber was built by Powell at Berkeley in 1957. At that time, one of its main advantages was its being larger than any other existing chamber. Since hydrogen chamber techniques were still restricted to smaller sizes, the presence of hydrogen played a very important role in this propane chamber.

The first substantially larger heavy liquid bubble chamber was built at the École Polytechnique in Paris (Bloch et al., 1959; Rousset, 1960). It consisted of a rectangular chamber, 1 meter long, with a volume of 300 liters. It was used for the first time at the Saclay 3 BeV accelerator in 1960 and was later taken to CERN. The chamber has a magnetic field of 21.5 kG; it was filled with a mixture of propane and freon-13B (CF_3Br) to achieve a radiation length of 20 cm, for good photon detection, and an error in momentum measurements of only 10 to 15%.

In the following year, at CERN, a cylindrical chamber with a volume of 500 liters was put into operation, with a field of 26.7 kG.

The evolution of the HLBC will probably progress in two directions. There will be an increase in size by a factor of 10 or more for experiments such as the detection of neutrino reactions. Then the magnetic field will increase by a factor of 2 or 3 with the advent of superconducting coils. The resulting gain in precision will be considerable.

B. ADVANTAGES OF HEAVY LIQUID BUBBLE CHAMBERS

One of the principal advantages of the HLBC is the high density of the liquid. As a consequence, there are many useful reactions per photograph, i.e. per cycle of accelerator time. This is particularly evident in neutrino detection experiments. If freon-13B (CF_3Br) with a density of 1.5 is used, there is a factor of 12.5 with respect to a deuterium chamber of similar size (density 0.12).

A high density is also advantageous for other experiments. For example, let us compare reactions of 2 BeV K^- mesons in a 1 meter chamber filled with freon-13B and the same reactions in a hydrogen chamber of similar size. In the freon chamber, 4 to 5 reactions per picture are acceptable in a fiducial volume of 80 cm length, which means 7 to 8 particles entering the chamber at a time. In a hydrogen chamber, 15 K^- mesons per picture produce only 3 events per 2 pictures, a factor of 3 in favor of the freon chamber.

Another consequence of the higher density is the increased stopping power of the liquid. Many particles stop in the liquid, and unstable particles can be identified by their disintegration products. For positively charged stopped particles, the problem is simple. All but electrons and protons have disintegration products. The latter two can easily be identified by their distinctive curvature patterns. K^+ mesons are easily separated from π^+ and μ^+ mesons, but recognizing the π^+ meson as such is possible only if the intermediate μ^+ is visible by its decay. This is almost always the case in propane and is true in 50% of the cases in freon-13B. An example of a photograph showing K^+ mesons stopping in freon is shown in Fig. 1.

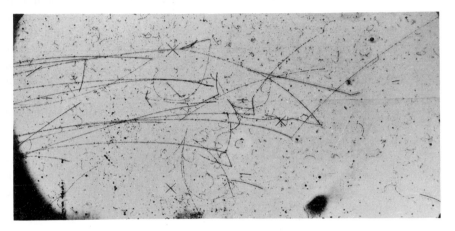

FIG. 1. Stopping K^+'s in freon C_3F_8 (Berkeley Bubble Chamber).

Negative stopped particles are more complicated to recognize. The strongly interacting particles (K^- and π^-) are always captured by a nucleus and do not disintegrate, but they can be recognized by their reaction patterns: star for π^- mesons, Λ^0 or Σ emission for K^- mesons. The μ meson interaction is weak, and therefore μ mesons have a 50% chance of disintegrating before a reaction with a proton in a nucleus may occur. The emitted electron is then an excellent characteristic of the μ.

The heavy liquid bubble chamber also allows easy identification of electrons during the scanning of the film, whatever their energy. The problem will be studied in detail in Section III,A. Slow electrons lose energy rapidly and so have a distinctive spiral trajectory. Electrons with energies of a few hundred MeV usually leave the picture before spiraling is apparent. Fortunately, the photons emitted by radiation generally materialize in a distance short enough to identify the primary electron.

High energy electrons lose so much energy by radiation that a distinctive shower is produced, and, often, very long δ rays eliminate the possibility of a μ meson or heavier particle.

The immediate identification of electrons allows selection at the scanning table of rare events without the need to resort to measurements. An example is the beta decay mode of hyperons and K mesons; such events occur at a rate of one in a thousand normal decay modes.

Another advantage is the high probability of materialization of photons. In general, the potential length of tracks is several times the radiation length (the potential length is defined as the maximum visible length of a track in the chamber, assuming no reactions or disintegrations occur); assume, for example, it is 50 cm with a radiation length X_0 of 20 cm. Under these conditions, the probability of detecting a photon is 80%, taking into account the track length necessary to measure the electron pair. Of course, the main application of this property is the identification and measurement of π^0 mesons. In theory, measuring the energy and direction of the electrons allows a complete reconstruction of the π^0, giving its direction and momentum. The study of photons themselves can be interesting, as will be shown in Section IV,B, in investigations of the disintegration of the η^0 into two photons. Let us also mention the radiative disintegration of K^0 mesons: $K^0 \rightarrow \pi^+ + \pi^- + \gamma$.

Finally, the heavy liquid bubble chamber is quite easy to build at a cost which is modest in comparison with a similar hydrogen chamber. It is not particularly difficult to operate, and the risk of interrupting an experiment because of a breakdown is low indeed.

C. Disadvantages of Heavy Liquid Bubble Chambers

Unfortunately, heavy liquid bubble chambers have serious drawbacks and can compete with hydrogen chambers in restricted areas only.

The main disadvantage is the fact that the liquid contains heavy nuclei. Even in propane, the majority of reactions occur with complex nuclei. Although at the energies encountered the reactions occur with single nucleons, one does not know whether they are protons or neutrons, and, in addition, the nucleons are not at rest since they are parts of complex nuclei. This introduces four unknowns into the kinematic formulation of a reaction. It is therefore difficult to perform a kinematic fit of the production.

More annoying still is the problem of secondary reactions within the nucleus in which the primary reaction occurred. The energies and directions of the secondary particles are changed. Even the nature of the particle may change when more than simple scattering occurs. Nucleons or π mesons may undergo a charge exchange. Resonance-type particles, such as the ρ or the ω, may even disintegrate within the nucleus. In this case, the number of secondaries increases, and usually a secondary reaction occurs. The result is a higher background noise and a flatter peak in the mass spectrum of the resonance. For example, in reactions of 18 BeV π mesons with carbon nuclei, 4 or 5 charged particles are produced. The probability that no secondary particles react in the nucleus is about 40%.

Another disadvantage is the relatively low precision of curvature measurements. Let us consider formula (1) in Section I,A for the relative error on the momentum p. This formula neglects distortion and measurement errors, which is almost always justified if X_0 is of the order of 20 cm and if the momentum is not too high. On the average, l cannot be greater than the mean free path, taking into account large angle Coulomb scattering. Since the term $(X_0 l)^{1/2}$ is equal to about 20 cm, the highest precision obtainable for relativistic particles is about 10%.

Finally, in a hydrogen bubble chamber, when a track is seen to change its direction at a point, one usually can be sure an unstable particle has disintegrated at that point. In a heavy liquid chamber, such a change of track direction is more frequently due to simple nuclear or Coulomb scattering. It is, therefore, impossible to identify a disintegration in flight directly unless the track ionization changes appreciably. This is a serious disadvantage in the study of jets because it prevents any serious study of $\Sigma^{\pm}$ hyperons.

D. The Various Solutions

The early propane chambers which had a volume of about 10 liters are no longer in use. Relatively easy to build, they were useful in taking the place of hydrogen chambers while the technology of the latter was being developed. The main reason for building small chambers now is that they may contain liquids heavier than propane.

There are two main categories of heavy liquid chambers: small chambers having a volume of about 20 liters and filled with a short radiation length liquid such as xenon or methyl iodide, and larger chambers with volumes of hundreds of liters and a radiation length between 10 and 100 cm. In the latter case, a strong magnetic field plays an important role.

The following is a brief description of the main chambers in use or being built.

1. Short Radiation Length Chambers

There are two xenon chambers in use, one at Berkeley (Brown *et al.*, 1956), the other in Russia at Dubna. The size of the two chambers is approximately 20 liters. Equation (1) shows that, to be useful, a magnetic field would have to have a strength of at least 50 kG.

The M.I.T.–Harvard chamber is used with propane-methyl iodide mixtures of a slightly longer radiation length, justifying a magnetic field, although the curvature measurement precision is still quite low. This chamber has a volume of 50 liters and a magnetic field of 18 kG.

2. Large Bubble Chambers

At present, seven large chambers are in operation: the new Berkeley chamber, an enlarged version of the previous one; the École Polytechnique chamber in operation at Scalay after 4 years of operation at CERN; the new CERN chamber, also an enlarged version of the first; the Columbia University chamber in operation at Brookhaven; the University of Michigan chamber in operation at Argonne; the University College chamber of the British accelerator "Nimrod"; and the 2-meter Dubna chamber.

These chambers have magnetic fields between 15 and 45 kG and volumes of several hundred liters. Table I lists the various characteristics of the large chambers. The liquids used range from pure propane to freon-13B (CF_3Br), giving radiation lengths between 11 and 110 cm and densities from 0.45 to 1.5.

TABLE I

EXISTING IMPORTANT HLBC IN OPERATION

Name of builder	Year of operation	Accelerator	Volume (liters)	Shape	Dimensions (cm)	Magnetic field (kG)
UCLRL, Berkeley	1958 1963 (new)	Berkeley Bevatron	130	oblong	80 × 55 × 30	15
École Polytechnique, Paris	1960	Saclay and CERN PS	300	rectangular	100 × 50 × 50	22
CERN, Geneva	1961 1965 (new)	CERN PS	500	cylinder	115 diam.	26.7
Columbia Univ., New York	1962	Brookhaven AGS	150	cylinder	75 diam.	17
Univ. of Michigan, Ann Arbor	1964	Argonne	500	cylinder	100 diam.	45
Univ. College, London	1964	Harwell Nimrod	375	oblong	150 × 50 × 50	14
Dubna, USSR	1965	Dubna	550	rectangular	210 × 65 × 40	15

TABLE II

PRINCIPAL CHARACTERISTICS OF LIQUIDS USED

Liquids	Density ρ (gm/cm^3)	Radiation length X_0 (cm)	Proportion of reactions on hydrogen	Mean interaction length (cm) assuming $\sigma_{(mb)} = 45\ A^{2/3}$	Operating temperature T (°C)	Vapor pressure P (atm)	Laboratories that have used these liquids
Propane C$_3$H$_8$	0.43	110	34%	154	58	19	Many laboratories
Xenon Xe	2.3	3.9	0	80	−19	26	Ann Arbor, Berkeley, Dubna
Freon CF$_2$Cl$_2$	1.12	21.5	0	97	70	18	CERN
Freon CF$_3$Br	1.50	11	0	82	30	18	École Polytech., CERN
Freon C$_2$F$_5$Cl	1.20	25	0	83	40	14	École Polytech.
C$_3$H$_8$ + CF$_3$Br 86% 14%	0.56	52	29%	137	49	18.5	École Polytech.
C$_3$H$_8$ + CF$_3$Br 50% 50%	0.91	22	17%	107	37	18	École Polytech., Berkeley
C$_2$F$_5$Cl + CF$_3$Br 50% 50%	1.35	17	0	82.5	36	16	École Polytech.
C$_3$H$_8$ + CH$_3$I + C$_2$H$_6$ 33% 33% 33%	1.05	11.4	23%	107	28	31	M.I.T., Harvard

The different combinations of these liquids which have been employed, and their use in the different pressure and temperature ranges required, present no particular difficulties. The disadvantage of these mixtures is that they contain little hydrogen and still retain the safety risk associated with propane. When the radiation length is more important than the presence of hydrogen, other types of freon can be used. Freon (C_2F_5Cl) has a radiation length of 25 cm. Furthermore, it has a density of 1.2 as compared to 0.8 for a propane-freon-13B mixture with the same radiation length.

Another mixture that can be used for a greater hydrogen content and small radiation length contains propane, methyl iodide, and ethane.

Table II lists the properties of the most important liquids and mixtures used. Many other types of liquids have been used in trials in smaller chambers. The quantity "proportion of reactions on hydrogen" was calculated for strongly interacting particles, using a cross section proportional to $A^{2/3}$. For mixtures, the proportions indicated are by volume.

II. Construction of Large Heavy Liquid Bubble Chambers

A. THE ESSENTIAL PROBLEMS OF CONSTRUCTION

The two principal parameters of a heavy liquid chamber are the dimensions of the useful volume and the strength of the magnetic field. As we have seen, one of the great advantages of these chambers is that they combine accuracy of curvature measurement with a good photon sensitivity. For example, in a 1 meter chamber with a field of 20 kG and a radiation length of 20 cm, the precision of the curvature measurements is of the order of 10% and the photon detection efficiency 75%.

A strong magnetic field and a large useful volume inevitably lead to heavy equipment (of the order of 100 tons). Yet this equipment must be easily movable, since interesting physics can be done in most of the beams around an accelerator. A strong magnetic field, a large volume, and mobility are the qualities desired by the physicist, but these desires rapidly run into technical and financial limitations.

In this section, we shall study the general construction problems, and, in the following sections, the various solutions that have been found, with a description of several existing chambers. It is impossible to describe all the existing chambers, so we will be forced to restrict ourselves to the more representative ones.

1. *The Magnetic Field Problem*

The precision of curvature measurements increases linearly with the magnetic field. Also, the length of a measurable segment of track is limited by nuclear and Coulomb scattering. The only way to increase the measuring accuracy is, therefore, to maximize the magnetic field, and this is a fundamental problem in the construction of a heavy liquid bubble chamber.

When classical techniques are used, the saturation of iron and economic considerations limit the strength of the magnetic field to about 20 kG. Because the volume of a large chamber is of the order of a cubic meter, the power necessary to apply a magnetic field to this volume will be in the megawatt region. Therefore one tries to meet the two following requirements.

(a) The field coils must be as close as possible to the sensitive liquid. This leads to the problem of containing the high pressure in the chamber without wasting an important part of the pole gap region.

(b) Certain parts of the chamber itself should be able to form a part of the magnetic circuit.

Since increasing the intensity of the magnetic field is the only way to increase the accuracy, the construction of chambers with a 45 kG field is being developed. It is hoped that the magnetic field problem eventually may be solved through the use of superconducting coils.

2. *The Pressure Problem*

Under operating conditions, the vapor pressures of propane and the freons in current use are about 18 atm. Therefore, the recompression pressure must be about 20 atm and the expansion pressure about 12 atm.

A cylindrical chamber would be relatively light since this shape has a high strength to weight ratio. On the other hand, a rectangular chamber needs very thick walls since the ultimate rupture strength is not the only consideration. Deformations of the window bearings and the sealed joints must be small. To avoid the need to increase the electric power for the magnetic field, it is necessary that the walls either be a part of the pole piece or be outside the gap. The main problem of high pressure is the window stress. In all the big chambers, a counterpressure is applied to the outside of the window to decrease the pressure difference. The size of the windows approaches the technical limits of fabrication of a homogeneous slab of glass. There are still very many unknowns in the calculation of the mechanical resistance of very thick glass slabs. Consequently, before being used, the windows are run through many pressure tests.

In the case of the floating window, the glass can be much thinner, since it "floats" on a volume of nearly incompressible liquid. The window is sealed by a flexible membrane around its perimeter.

3. *The Illumination Problem*

The problem of illuminating the bubbles can be solved in the same way as in hydrogen chambers. The apparatus would then be quite similar.

Another solution is also possible. Because of the higher refractive index of the heavy liquids, the light scattered by a bubble is not as strongly concentrated in a narrow cone about the incident direction as in hydrogen. Sufficient light is scattered at a 90° angle to permit taking pictures. The technique has many advantages:

(a) It is simpler and does not require a delicate optical system; the chamber is illuminated with a light beam roughly parallel to the window. The light coming directly from the flash lamps without a condensing lens is sufficiently uniform.

(b) There are no problems of parasitic reflections from the many windows, as encountered in hydrogen chambers.

(c) Construction of the solid rear pole piece is much easier since there are no rear windows.

4. *The Temperature Problem*

Contrary to hydrogen, the heavy liquids in use operate at very nearly normal temperatures: 60°C for propane, between 30°C and 70°C for most of the freons, $-20°C$ for xenon. The only problem is the uniformity of the temperature throughout the liquid, for two essential reasons:

(a) to obtain uniform bubble density in all parts of the chamber for particles of the same velocity, and

(b) to avoid optical distortions which would introduce measurement errors.

The temperature must be uniform to $\frac{1}{10}°C$. Such conditions are reached even in the largest chambers: it is only necessary to cool the metal at the top of the chamber, where bubbles can reliquefy.

5. *The Safety Problem*

The dangers presented by heavy liquid bubble chambers are due to

(a) the high pressures involved and enormous potential energy of the great quantities of superheated liquid under pressure, and

(b) the presence of inflammable and explosive liquids such as propane and hydrogen (when it is used as a target medium).

The fire hazard disappears when freon is used either pure or in a mixture.

Standard industrial techniques such as the use of safety valves can be applied to the high pressure reservoirs and tubing, but the large windows in a propane chamber present an uncommon problem. Several solutions have been tried; these will be described when each particular case is examined.

The presence of explosive gases requires the following precautions.

(a) Nitrogen or helium must be used, instead of compressed air, in the control lines and the expansion system.

(b) The safety valves must discharge into a duct system to draw the dangerous gases away from buildings and equipment. This system can also be used to evacuate waste gases during emptying or flushing of the apparatus.

(c) Double gaskets must seal in the propane.

(d) The chamber must be placed in a well ventilated enclosure with a non-porous floor, propane being heavier than air.

(e) Only sparkproof electrical apparatus must be allowed within the enclosure.

6. *The Mobility Problem*

Heavy liquid chambers do not usually have priority over other experiments in a beam. It is, therefore, essential for them to be easily moved and set up. This means no dismantling, and rapid electric and plumbing connections.

An easy way to move a hundred tons of equipment is to use

(a) jacks for vertical movements,
(b) rails for horizontal displacements, and
(c) ball bearing platforms for rotations.

Plumbing connections are simplified through use of flexible couplings and O-ring seals.

Under these conditions, moving a chamber and setting it up again should not require more than two or three days.

Conclusion: The technical problem of building a HLBC can be solved in different ways. Two important choices face the builder. Will the window mounting be solid or floating, and the lighting longitudinal or lateral? The combinations of these possibilities lead to four different types of chambers, which will be encountered in the following studies of the main bubble chambers now in use or under construction.

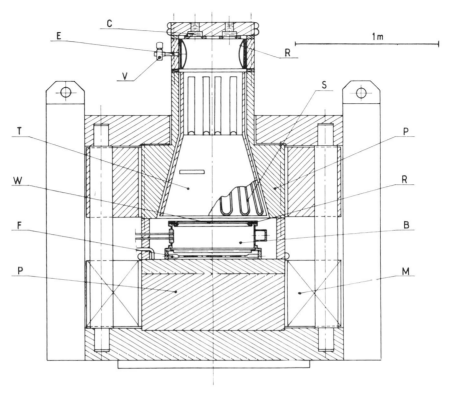

FIG. 2. The Berkeley bubble chamber. B, chamber body; C, camera porthole; E, expansion system; F, flashtube; M, magnet coil; P, pole piece; R, rubber membrane; S, heating system; T, safety tank; W, main window; V, Barksdale valve.

B. THE BERKELEY HEAVY LIQUID BUBBLE CHAMBER

1. *General Characteristics of the Chamber*

The Berkeley chamber was the first of the big chambers. It started performing experiments in 1958 (Powell *et al.*, 1958). Its most significant characteristic is the use of a "floating" window system (Fig. 2). The propane enclosure is a thin-walled oval chamber immersed in a high pressure tank filled with mineral oil. The expansion and recompression cycles are applied to the oil. The thin front window is mobile, being sealed to the chamber by a flexible rubber membrane around its periphery. Pictures are taken through the oil by cameras mounted behind small portholes in the high pressure tank.

The chamber has been modified recently to make it deeper and to improve the optical system. The original chamber will be described in detail with indications of the subsequent modifications (Powell *et al.*, 1963a,b).

2. *The Magnet*

The steel walls of the pressure tank act as the hollow top pole of the magnet. The bottom pole piece is solid. The magnetic field, therefore, has a vertical gradient, being maximum at the bottom. The variation remains less than 5% of the value at the center of the chamber. The average magnetic field was 13 kG with a field current of 1100 A. A recent modification of the magnet increased this value to 15 kG.

3. *The Chamber and the Expansion System*

The sensitive liquid is contained in a stainless steel tank 80 cm long, 55 cm wide, and 16 cm deep. (Fig. 3.) The whole lighting system is immersed in the oil under the lower window, which is stationary.

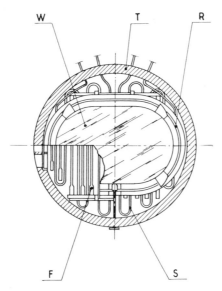

FIG. 3. The Berkeley bubble chamber (top view). F, flashtube; R, rubber; S, heating system; T, safety tank; W, main window.

The upper window acts as a diaphragm to transmit the pressure variations of the oil to the propane. The vertical displacements of the window are guided by two sliding ball bearings, and a "rectipot" connected to the top glass gives an indication of its position (Fig. 2).

The expansion cycle is obtained through a cylindrical rubber membrane at the top of the pressure tank near the camera portholes. The back of the membrane is connected to high and low pressure reservoirs through eight Barksdale valves. The expansion cycle takes 45 msec, and the top window moves a total of 0.5 cm.

During an experiment on K_2^0 regeneration, iron plates of varying thickness were placed in the front part of the chamber; this did not impair its operation.

4. *Lighting and Photography*

In the first version of the chamber, 13 flashtubes beneath the chamber supplied the illumination through a "venetian blind" collimator (Fig. 2). Only 7 of the 13 tubes were flashed at one time; the remaining 6 were kept as spares since to change a tube required complete dismantling of the chamber. A total energy of around 50 J was required to flash the tubes. Two cameras were used to provide stereo views of the chamber with a demagnification of 7. To eliminate the important chromatic aberrations introduced by the thick layer of oil, the lenses were covered with red Wratten filters (G-25). A different illumination system is used in the second chamber (Powell *et al.*, 1963a, b) (Fig. 4). A special beaded reflective sheet (known

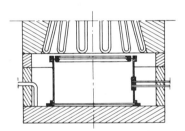

FIG. 4. The Berkeley bubble chamber (new chamber).

under the trade name "Scotchlite") replaced the "venetian blind" collimator. The reflective sheet consists of a uniform layer of extremely fine glass beads (2μ in diam.) giving a high reflectivity within a 3° angle. The quality of the sheet is such that there is only a small decrease ($\lesssim 20\%$) in the reflectivity at incident angles up to 45°.

The illumination is supplied by two circular 20 J flashtubes surrounding each camera lens. This modification resulted in a substantial increase in the quality of the photographs. Furthermore, it allowed an increase in the depth of the propane chamber from 16 to 30 cm, overcame the previous difficulty in changing the flashtubes, and removed the flashtubes from the high magnetic field region.

5. *Temperature Control*

Two independent systems of hot water tubes are used to heat the oil, one for the space above, the other for the space below the chamber (Fig. 2). The water in the lower tubing is 5°C warmer than above so as to maintain a uniform sensitivity throughout the propane. In the beginning, this temperature difference created convection currents in the oil which blurred the pictures, due to variations of the index of refraction of the oil. More efficient heating accomplished by more vigorous stirring of the oil bath eliminated this problem.

6. *Safety Features*

An additional safety feature was added to the chamber through the choice of the oil. Tests showed that, if the propane enclosure should rupture, the propane would mix with the oil, resulting in a drop in the vapor pressure of the propane from 18 to 10 atm.

C. THE ÉCOLE POLYTECHNIQUE HEAVY LIQUID BUBBLE CHAMBER

1. *General Characteristics*

The characteristics of the chamber (Bloch *et al.*, 1959; Rousset, 1960; Bloch *et al.*, 1961) are summed up in the following four sentences:

(a) The dimensions of the useful volume of the chamber are $100 \times 50 \times 50$ cm.

(b) The tracks are photographed through a large window and a safety tank containing air or nitrogen under pressure; this results in good optical conditions for photography.

(c) Side illumination of the tracks is used.

(d) Mechanical rigidity of the chamber is maintained by the pole pieces of the magnet.

The main quality of the chamber is its size, which is sufficient to take full advantage of the properties of heavy liquids. This was made possible through efficient use of the available volume in the magnetic field, the latter being limited by budgetary and power considerations.

2. *The Magnet*

The magnet (Fig. 5) is composed of 2 copper coils weighing 10.5 tons and 4 pieces of soft steel weighing 45 tons to close the magnetic circuit. The

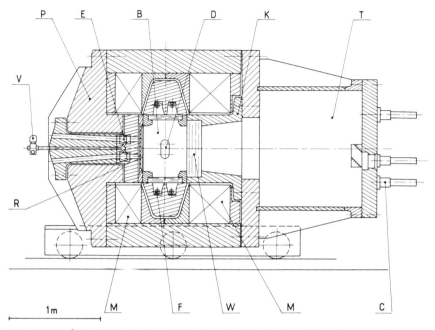

FIG. 5. The École Polytechnique bubble chamber. B, chamber body; C, camera; D, beam window; E, expansion system; F, flashtube; K, frame of the main window; M, magnet coil; P, pole piece; R, rubber membrane; T, safety tank; V, Barksdale valve; W, main window.

hole in the magnet has a rectangular shape, 127 × 74 cm, and the two coils are separated by 50 cm. These figures should be compared with the dimensions of the useful volume of the sensitive liquid: 100 × 50 × 50 cm. With a 4.5 MW power source, the field is 22.5 kG; with 2 MW, it is 17.5 kG.

The front pole piece has a large hole to receive the front window. The rear pole piece is almost solid, with a number of small holes for the expansion and recompression valves. The coil around the front pole piece is bigger than the rear one to avoid nonuniformities in the field; it consists of 11 double "pancake" coils whereas the rear coil consists of 7. The field in the liquid is uniform to within 5% of its value at the center.

3. The Chamber

The chamber body (Fig. 6) is open on four sides to accommodate the main window, the expansion membrane, and the two flash windows. Consequently, it is quite weak and could not alone resist the high pressure; its rigidity is maintained by the massive pieces that surround it: the front and rear poles and the two side beams that contain the flashtubes. The pole

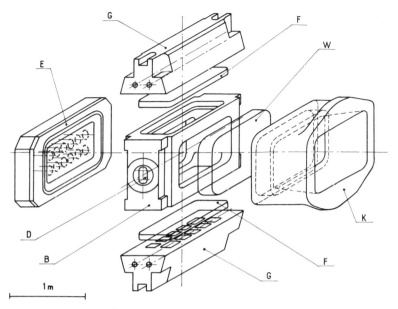

FIG. 6. Main parts of the École Polytechnique chamber. B, chamber body; W, main window; F, flash window; D, beam window; K, main window frame; E, back pole piece with expansion system; G, beam with illumination system.

pieces actually exert a compressive stress on the chamber body. This is obtained by bolting the pole pieces to the upper and lower soft steel slabs of the magnet. Thus, any deformation of the metal of the body due to the pressure in the chamber is eliminated. Heat expansion of the chamber is taken up by Belleville spring washers.

The body was machined out of a single block of nonmagnetic stainless steel alloy containing 18% Cr, 12% Ni, and no titanium. This particular alloy was chosen because of its limit of elasticity, corrosion resistance, and ease of machining and polishing.

4. *Lighting and Photography*

Illumination is provided by four 1-meter-long flashtubes, parallel to the long sides of the chamber. They are lodged above and below the liquid in two stainless steel beams which maintain the rigidity of the chamber. The flash windows are 55 mm thick and rest on a network of ribs that reduce the effective free span to 14 cm. The only precaution taken in the design was to prevent light from the flashtubes from striking the chamber's back wall. To obtain a correct exposure, each tube is flashed with an energy of 100 J.

Parabolic mirrors reflect all of the light into the chamber; the tracks are visible over the whole area (100×50 cm^2) and to a depth of 43 cm from the front window. The illumination system is very effective in lighting the total volume of the chamber.

The main window is 16 cm thick. Compressed nitrogen in the safety tank lowers the pressure differential across the window to a maximum of 10 atm during the expansion-recompression cycle.

The pictures are taken through thick portholes made of three layers of Borosilicate glass. Shielded glass prisms offer further protection in case of rupture of the front window. Three cameras are used to obtain a stereoscopic angle of 40°. The lenses are opened to $f/22$ and give a demagnification of 11.5. The film used is Kodak Plus-X in unperforated rolls 50 mm wide $\times$ 300 m long (2800 photographs). To eliminate any chromatic aberration due to the maximum viewing angle of 25°, the pictures are taken through yellow G-12 Wratten filters.

5. The Expansion System

Expansion and recompression are obtained by compressed nitrogen behind a reinforced rubber membrane. The membrane which forms the rear wall rests on a steel plate in which a grid of more than 8000 holes 3.5 mm in diameter have been drilled. The compressed nitrogen arrives through 12 "Flexflo" pneumatic valves embedded in the iron of the rear pole. Eight valves are used for expansion, four for compression.

The 12 valves are controlled by 6 "Barksdale" electromagnetic pilot valves placed outside the rear pole where the magnetic field is much lower. The "Flexflo" valves (making use of rubber boots) are connected to two 1500 liter tanks, one at the expansion pressure, the other at the recompression pressure. During an expansion cycle, the membrane does not have time to hit the grid; in other words, the expansion pressure can be accurately controlled, and control is important for constancy of the bubble density in a track. Boiling occurs on the membrane when it comes too close to the grid; a minimum cushion of gas prevents this.

Expansion of the chamber takes less than 20 msec. Recompression takes 10 msec and can occur no sooner than 5 to 10 msec after expansion, due to the inertia of the valves. The pressure in the tanks is supplied by a 100 hp compressor and is regulated by a servo system.

6. Temperature Control

The temperatures of the six sides of the chamber can be controlled independently. The two small sides and the main window frame are heated electrically. Part of the back pole piece and the two side beams are heated or cooled by circulating water. To provide temperature control, 28 thermistors are embedded in the chamber body, 4 others are in the liquid at 4 corners of the enclosure.

The control of the temperature is difficult due to the low thermal conductivity of stainless steel. Temperature oscillation can arise with a period of one hour and should be avoided. The body of the chamber must have a vertical temperature gradient of 5°C in order to achieve uniform temperatures in the liquid ($\frac{1}{10}$ to $\frac{2}{10}$°C) and proper operating conditions.

7. Manipulation of the Chamber

The chamber and the magnet weigh a total of 100 tons. Despite this weight, it must be possible to perform the following operations quickly.

(a) Entering the chamber for cleaning, changing the membrane, or installing a hydrogen target. This is done by rolling back the rear pole on ball bearings. The complete operation takes 6 hours, does not necessitate

FIG. 7. General view of the École Polytechnique bubble chamber.

the use of an overhead crane, and could be performed inside a concrete block shield.

(b) Moving from one particle beam to another. This operation takes a few days and has been simplified through use of the following techniques:

(1) Electrical and plumbing connections are easily made through the use of connectors.
(2) The reservoirs and expansion system equipment form a single unit that can be transported by an overhead crane.
(3) The chamber and magnet can move about on rails, a ball bearing platform, or four jacks attached to the magnet.

(c) Small displacements (a few centimeters) and rotations (a few degrees) are obtained by horizontal jacks. For safety reasons, these have never been used while the chamber was in operation.

A photograph of the whole assembly is shown in Fig. 7.

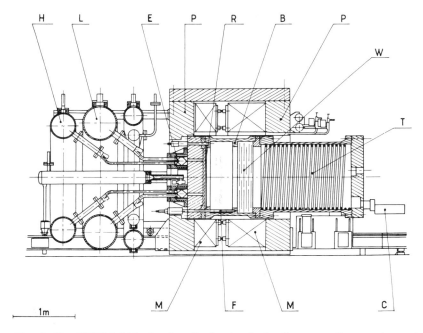

FIG. 8. The CERN bubble chamber. B, chamber body; C, camera; E, expansion system; F, flashtube; H, high pressure reservoir; L, low pressure reservoir; M, magnet coil; P, pole piece; R, rubber membrane; T, safety tank; W, main window.

D. OTHER LARGE CHAMBERS

1. *The CERN Chamber*

The principles of construction of this chamber (Ramm and Resegotti, 1960) are similar to those of the École Polytechnique chamber: thick front window, safety tank, side lighting, expansion cycle through a rubber membrane. It started working in 1961 and is the largest heavy liquid chamber now in use.

The body is a stainless steel cylinder 4 cm thick (Fig. 8), 115 cm in diameter, and 60 cm deep. The cylindrical shape is well adapted to high pressures but requires a thicker front window (25 cm). To prevent a break in the window from projecting pieces against the camera portholes, the pressure in the safety tank is higher than in the chamber. The window rests on a rubber gasket 55 mm wide, 25 mm thick, with a hardness of 92° on the Shore scale. During tests, the window withstood pressures of 35 atm for 1 hour and 60 atm for 1 min.

Expansion and recompression are controlled by a single double action "Flexflo" type of valve, embedded in the rear pole piece and actuated by "Barksdale" pilot valves.

Toroidal tanks located behind the rear pole contain the compressed nitrogen for the operation of the chamber. To avoid a background of a boiling membrane in the photograph, a black metallic plate covering the membrane was recently successfully used. The illumination is supplied by eight flash-tubes parallel to the axis of the cylinder. A series of transverse baffles along each tube protect the camera lenses from direct exposure to the flashes. The magnet gives a field of 27 kG with a power consumption of 4.5 MW. The field is uniform to within $\pm 5\%$ in the useful volume of the chamber.

Water circulation tubes welded to the body of the chamber provide the temperature control, which is fairly easy because of the small thickness of the walls.

An important modification was made in 1965. The length of the chamber was increased to 1 meter. The flashtubes were lengthened and a few elements added to the magnet. The increase in volume to 1 cubic meter is of considerable importance for neutrino experiments or the study of stopping K^+ mesons.

2. *The Columbia University Chamber*

A heavy liquid chamber was built by the Columbia and Brookhaven groups (Prodell and Steinberger, 1962) along the following principles:

(a) safety tank and thick static front window,

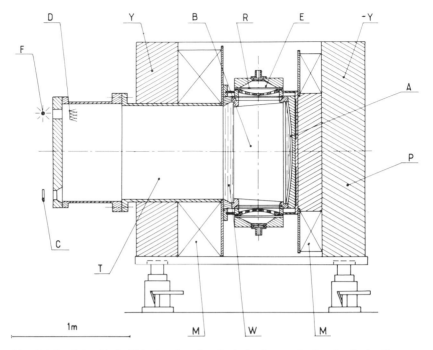

FIG. 9. The Columbia bubble chamber. A, spherical reflector; B, chamber body; C, camera; D, diffusing screen; E, expansion system; F, flashtube; M, magnet coil; P, pole piece; R, rubber membrane; T, safety tank; W, main window; Y, yoke.

(b) bright field illumination, and

(c) cylindrical chamber with lateral decompression through rubber membranes.

The useful volume of the chamber is a cylinder 75 cm in diameter and 35 cm deep (Fig. 9) with a magnetic field of 17 kG.

Construction details:

a. *The Window Mounting.* The window is 10 cm thick and rests on a conical surface inclined at 45°. This arrangement allows a decrease in the size of the window frame, thus increasing the useful volume of the chamber.

b. *The Lighting System.* The critical part of the optical system is the spherical reflector. If a simple spherical mirror were used, the reflections of the tracks in the mirror would also appear in the pictures. To eliminate these reflections, the mirror is made to scatter light through a mean angle of 1 or 2°. Tracks located as close as 2 cm from the mirror have no reflected images. The mirror is made of successive layers of mylar and varnishes of appropriate refractive indices. Also, to avoid the photographing of multiple reflections on the main window, the light sources have been widened by diffusing screens, reducing their brightness.

3. *The Russian Bubble Chambers*

A 2 meter chamber is under construction at Dubna in Russia (Balandin *et al.*, 1962). The dimensions of the useful volume will be $210 \times 65 \times 40\,\text{cm}$, and the magnetic field 15 kG. The principal characteristics are the following.

(a) The sensitive liquid (Fig. 10) is contained in a 2-meter-long volume and viewed through two 1 meter windows. Compressed nitrogen in a safety tank limits the stresses on the windows. Pictures are taken by six cameras.

(b) Twenty-six short flashtubes illuminate the chamber through small

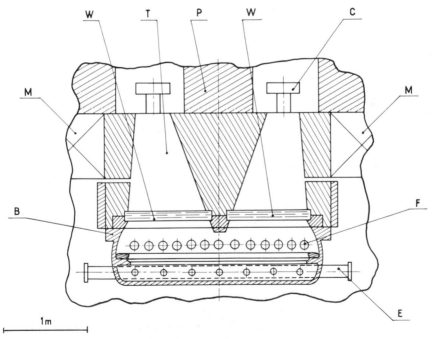

Fig. 10. The 2 meter Russian bubble chamber. B, chamber body; W, main window; F, flash porthole; P, pole piece; E, expansion system; T, safety tank; C, camera; M, magnet coil.

portholes in the side walls. These walls are slightly inclined towards the rear; the lighting is therefore "quasilateral".

(c) Expansion is obtained through a rubber membrane and an intermediate liquid. The pressure of the latter is controlled by two long rubber tubes inflated with nitrogen.

Other chambers constructed in Russia are:

(a) A 24-liter propane chamber with a 13.7 kG field, operating at Dubna since 1959.

(b) A 570 liter freon chamber without a magnetic field (Alikhanian *et al.*, 1959), having a thin front window supported by a volume of water. The expansion system acts directly on the freon through a rubber membrane. Window movement is small, being limited by the compressibility of the water.

(c) A 1 meter chamber very similar to the one at Berkeley, with a volume of $150 \times 50 \times 38$ cm (Budagov *et al.*, 1960). The steady state magnetic field is 15 kG and can be increased to 20 kG when pulsed.

4. *The Chamber of University College, London*

A chamber with a length of 140 cm was built at University College. It greatly resembles the École Polytechnique chamber: thick window, safety tank, expansion through a membrane at the rear, side lighting, and a magnetic field of 20 kG. The dimensions of the chamber are $140 \times 50 \times 45$ cm (Fig. 11).

The illumination is obtained through flashtubes parallel to the magnetic field as in the CERN chamber. Although the "Flexflo" valves are embedded in the rear pole piece, they can easily be changed during an experiment in case of failure. This feature will prove useful because experience has shown that the rubber boots are the parts most likely to fail. The chamber was successfully operated in 1966.

5. *The Michigan–Argonne Bubble Chamber*

The most important characteristic of this chamber is its relatively high magnetic field of 46,000 G. This field is obtained by the classical technique using copper coils (40 tons) and iron pieces to provide the magnetic flux. The electric power necessary is 11 MW.

The illumination and expansion of the chamber are similar in concept to that used by the CERN chamber. A certain amount of effort has gone into collimating the light to a plane parallel to the diaphragm using a system of baffles and toroidal lenses. The volume of the chamber is about $\frac{1}{2}$ m^3.

The biggest advantage of this chamber is its high field which allows precise measurement of momentum. In a mixture of 50% freon, 50% propane ($X_0 \simeq 20$ cm), the accuracy of momentum is $\pm 5\%$ for charged pions and $\pm 20\%$ for electrons.

E. The Xenon Chamber

1. Generalities

Because it has the shortest radiation length, xenon is particularly useful to obtain a maximum photon detection probability. But its extraordinarily high cost ($10,000 per liter) and its rarity have the following consequences:

(a) It is not possible to undertake the construction of chambers larger than 20 or 30 liters.

(b) The utmost precautions must be taken to avoid any loss of the gas by leakage and to minimize the possibility of total loss due to rupture of an element of the chamber.

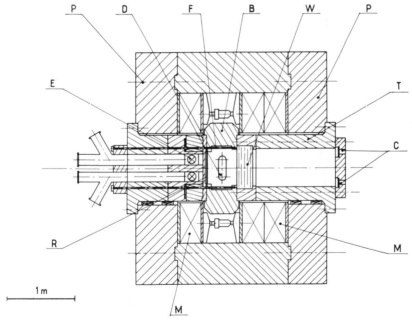

Fig. 11. The University College bubble chamber. B, chamber body; W, main window; F, flashtube; D, beam window; P, pole piece; E, expansion system; T, safety tank; M, magnet coil; C, camera porthole; R, rubber membrane.

There are two such chambers to date: The Berkeley 21-liter chamber built by the group of D. A. Glaser and the Dubna chamber.

2. *The Glaser Chamber*

This chamber uses classical methods: longitudinal lighting with a dark background and a side expansion membrane (Brown *et al.*, 1956; Brown, 1960).

The presence of xenon requires the following techniques:

(a) In case of a membrane rupture, the xenon is retained in the chamber by a metallic piston (Fig. 12).

(b) In case of failure of the window, the xenon is retained in the safety tank. The use of a 45° mirror protects the viewing portholes.

(c) An 18 kW commercial refrigerator is used to cool the chamber to the operating temperature of xenon, −19°C.

(d) Pure xenon is a good scintillator and is therefore transparent to its emitted photons. The energy lost by the particles passing through the liquid

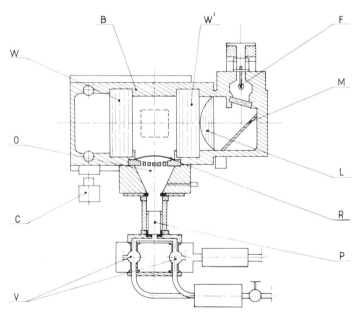

Fig. 12. The Berkeley xenon bubble chamber. B, chamber body; C, camera; F, flashtube; L, lens; M, mirror; O, oil; P, piston; R, rubber membrane; V, Barksdale valve; W, main window; W′, window for illumination.

is immediately dissipated by radiation, and bubbles do not form. The addition of ethylene (2%) absorbs the photons locally, and thus bubbles can be formed.

3. The Dubna Chamber

A similar chamber was constructed at Dubna (Kanarek et al., 1959) with a useful volume of $55 \times 26 \times 16 \text{ cm}^3$. The methods used were also classical: side lighting, expansion cycle through a membrane on the side opposite to the lighting.

A magnetic field of 13 kG is applied to the chamber, but the precision in the measurement is only 50%.

The following points should be noticed:

(a) A system of several membranes is used to control the effective expansion ratio.

(b) Lighting and photography are accomplished through lucite blocks instead of glass.

4. The Tungsten Hexafluoride Chamber

The short radiation length of WF_6 (3.7 cm) places it in the same category as xenon. Much less expensive but highly toxic and extremely corrosive, it has found only limited use. At Pasadena, two such chambers have been constructed (Alyea et al., 1957); one experimental chamber, 4 cm in diameter, and a larger one with a diameter of 30 cm.

Great precautions had to be taken; the windows are made of quartz, the chamber of gold-plated stainless steel, the gaskets of teflon, etc.

Such problems have discouraged construction of larger chambers of this type.

F. Liquids Used in Heavy Liquid Bubble Chambers

1. Various Liquids

To be easily used in a bubble chamber, a liquid must have a low critical pressure and temperature, since the operating conditions are in the region of the critical point. Thus, water cannot be used easily, since the critical point occurs at a temperature of 374°C and a pressure of 218 atm.

The acceptable liquids fit into several categories (see Tables III and IV).

(a) Hydrocarbons: propane, ether, ethylene, pentane.

(b) Nonsaturated hydrocarbon derivatives: methyl iodide, some bromides.

(c) The saturated halogen derivatives: the freon family C_2F_5Cl, C_3F_8, etc.

(d) Isolated elements and compounds such as xenon, sulfur and tungsten hexafluorides (SF_6, WF_6), and tin compounds ($SnCl_4$, $SnBr_4$).

The solubility of these liquids is a rapidly increasing function of temperature, particularly in the region of the critical point. Consequently, they can all be used in mixtures. The choice is therefore quite large.

In the case of xenon and WF_6, the decision to use these liquids must be made before construction of the chamber. On the other hand, propane, most of the freons, sulfur hexafluoride, and their mixtures operate under similar conditions: temperatures between $20°$ and $100°C$ and pressures around 20 atm. Thus, a great number of liquids are acceptable for a propane type chamber; this property makes it a very flexible tool.

The properties of a mixture can be made to suit the needs of the experiment. They are

(a) the radiation length, which controls the measurement precision and the photon detection rate;

TABLE III

PURE LIQUIDS USABLE IN BUBBLE CHAMBERS

Liquids	T (°C)	P (atm)	ρ (gm/cm³)	X_0 (cm)
H^2	−246	4.7	0.06	1145
Propane C_3H_8	58	19	0.43	110
n pentane	155	—	—	—
CF_3Br	30	18	1.50	11
C_2F_5Cl	40	18	1.20	25
CF_2Cl_2	70	18	1.12	21.5
CF_3Cl	15	18	0.95	29
CF_2Br_2	146	18	1.60	8.5
C_3F_8	38	13	1.25	28
C_4F_{10}	75	10	1.25	28
C_4F_8	∼60	—	∼1.25	28
CH_3I	210	31	1.7	5.5
CF_3I	80	17	1.9	6.2
SF_6	15	19	1.42	20.5
WF_6	128	20	2.60	3.7
$Te F_6$	44	15	2.10	6.4
$SnBr_4$	—	—	—	—
$SnCl_4$	270	20	1.4	9
Xe	−19	26	2.3	3.9

(b) the density, which determines the number of reactions per incident particle and the stopping power of the liquid; and

(c) the proportion of hydrogen atoms when reactions on free protons are wanted.

Among the possible liquids, propane offers the highest measurement precision and about the same number of hydrogen atoms as liquid hydrogen.

TABLE IV

MIXTURES USABLE IN BUBBLE CHAMBERS

Mixtures	% volume	T (°C)	P (atm)	ρ (gm/cm³)	X_0 (cm)
$C_3H_8 + CF_3Br$	50%–50%	37	18	0.91	22
$C_3H_8 + CH_3I$	50%–50%	120	35	1.1	10
$C_2F_6 + C_3F_8$	30%–70%	21	14	1.28	27
$SF_6 + C_5F_6Cl$		24	15	1.30	22.8
$SnCl_4 + CClF_3$		20	—	1.70	9
$SnCl_4 + CHClF_2 + CClF_3$		20	—	1.40	14
$C_3H_8 + C_2H_6 + CH_3I$		28	>31	1.05	11.4
$(C_2H_5)_2CO + CO_2$		20	50	—	—
$C_6H_{12} + CO_2$		20	50	—	—
$C_3H_8 + CO_2$		20	30	—	—
$C_3H_8 + CH_4$		20	32	—	—
$C_3H_8 + C_2H_4$		20	27	—	—
$C_3H_8 + C_2H_6$		20	25	—	—

Its low density allows long tracks to be measured since the number of secondary interactions is relatively low.

Freon CF_3Br has a much higher density and shorter radiation length. Propane and freon mixtures therefore cover a wide range of possibilities.

An interesting type of freon, C_2F_5Cl (used by Hahn and at École Polytechnique), offers a good stopping power and a radiation length intermediate between propane and CF_3Br. Noninflammable, it operates at a relatively low pressure and at an ideal temperature. References concerning all these liquids are Hahn *et al.* (1959), Bugg (1958, 1959), Blinov *et al.* (1956, 1957a, b), and Bassi *et al.* (1956).

Among the many possible mixtures two are noteworthy.

a. Methyl Iodide Mixtures. The interest in methyl iodide is due to its short radiation length and high hydrogen content. Unfortunately, at temperatures above 100°C, it is corrosive and unstable; because of the iodine it soon acquires a brown cast, which rapidly makes any further picture taking impossible. The 50–50% (by volume) mixture of propane and methyl iodide operates at the difficult temperature of 120°C (Pless, École Poly-technique; Bullock et al., 1958). The mixture $C_3H_8 + C_2H_6 + CH_3I$ can operate at 30°C while retaining a short radiation length near 11 cm and a high proportion of hydrogen atoms (Bertanza et al., 1958).

b. Dissolved Gas Chambers. Usable liquids have been obtained by dissolving considerable quantities of various gases such as methane or carbon dioxide in ether or propane (Argan and Gigli, 1956; Bullock et al., 1957; Hahn et al., 1957; Henderson et al., 1957; Hahn, 1956; Argan et al., 1957).

Unfortunately, some bubbles do not redissolve in the liquid during recompression, and it is difficult to get rid of the large bubble that often forms at the top of the chamber. This leads to the use of higher recompression pressures which greatly limits the size of the chambers.

2. Determination of the Physical Constants of a Mixture

It is necessary to know the physical constants of a mixture under the conditions existing at the precise moment when the particles pass through it. Most important are the stopping power and refractive index.

The refractive index is determined by measuring on the photographs the position of well known fiducial marks in the chamber.

The stopping power depends on two independent parameters: the density and the mean ionization potential. The most precise method is to *calculate* the ionization potential from the known atomic potentials and a knowledge of the proportions of the constituent elements, and to *measure* in a series of photographs an event particularly sensitive to the stopping power: Q value of Λ° decay with a stopping proton and π^- meson; range of stopping μ or π from the decay of K^+ mesons at rest.

The proportions of the mixture can be determined in two ways.

(a) Before the experiment, the mixture is made up of known quantities of the different constituents. It is important that the measured quantities be introduced into the chamber without altering the proportions because of leakage, residual gases, and the differences of proportions between the liquid and gaseous phases.

(b) During the experiment, a sample of the liquid is taken from the chamber in a small reservoir. The sample is then entirely vaporized to a pressure close to atmospheric. The proportions of the mixture are then determined by comparing the density of this gas with the density of the pure constituents at the same temperature and pressure; the variation of density in the gaseous state with the proportions is assumed to be linear although this is not true for the liquid.

The sample can also be used to measure the compressibility or density of the liquid at the temperature of the chamber. An extrapolation of these quantities into the metastable region gives another direct indication of the density. The error in this method is due to the uncertain knowledge of the exact temperature and pressure conditions that exist at the time of the passage of the particles.

3. *Use of the Liquid as a Scintillator*

The use of the scintillations of the liquid is evident: the flashtubes could be triggered only when at least one charged particle has passed through the chamber. This is useful when cosmic rays are studied or in the case of rare events such as reactions in a beam of neutral particles (neutrino or neutron experiments). For xenon, it was shown that the scintillating character of the liquid was incompatible with the formation of bubbles. But experiments with a solution of 33 gm per liter of naphthaline and 133 mg per liter of PBD phosphor (Pilot Chemicals Inc., Watertown, Massachusetts) in propane have shown the possibility of a liquid being at the same time a scintillator and a producer of tracks (Minehart and Milburn, 1960). It was shown that the phenomenon was in fact due to scintillation and not to Čerenkov radiation, because even low energy protons produced the same effect. When a chamber is used as a scintillator, care must be taken not to introduce a bias in the experiment due to the inefficiency of slightly ionizing events or events that occur in the corners of the chamber (Milburn, 1962).

G. Special Arrangements

1. *Freon Chambers Used to Study Beams*

The ability to determine the position of a trajectory in a bubble chamber with accuracy can be used in the study of beams. Small freon chambers have been built for this purpose.

Freon was chosen because it is very easy to use.

(a) Liquids such as CF_3Br operate very near room temperature; some mixtures even operate at room temperature.

(b) Freon is noninflammable.

(c) Light chambers with a volume of 1 liter can easily be transported during operation.

(d) Connections to the chamber can be limited to a few electrical cables and a flexible hose for compressed air at 25 atm.

Among the many built, the following are noteworthy.

(a) A small chamber built by the Fribourg group (Hahn and Riepe, 1958). It uses a dark field illumination system and was among the first to operate with the CERN Proton Synchrotron, being used to study μ meson fluxes around the machine. It also took part in several experiments, among which was a demonstration of the relativistic rise of the ionization curve.

(b) A similar chamber was constructed at CERN with 90° stereoscopy allowing a study of the cross section of the beam, the axis of the beam being aligned with the optical axis of one of the cameras. This chamber was built to study pencil beams.

(c) A small (5 cm diameter) chamber was built by the Cambridge group; it was used with one camera axis parallel to the beam and thus permitted studying the variation of the convergence of the beam when the beam parameters were varied.

(d) A bubble chamber can also be used to detect weak radioactivity (Brautti et al., 1958).

2. *Rapid Cycling Chambers*

a. Special Problems Encountered in Rapid Cycling Chambers. Most bubble chambers were built to operate at the rate of existing accelerators, that is, one cycle every 1 to 6 sec. There are two reasons for wanting faster chambers:

(1) Construction of accelerators with higher repetition rates (20 to 60 pulses per second).

(2) The possibility of taking several photographs during the acceleration period. This could be realized in a secondary beam of low energy π mesons.

Multiplying the numbers of pictures taken might satisfy ever increasing demands. Several projects of this sort have been realized. The difficulties encountered are of the following nature.

(1) The chamber must be as "clean" as possible, and within each cycle all bubbles must be reliquefied, otherwise an ever increasing volume of gas collects in the chamber making prolonged operation impossible.

(2) During rapid cycling operation, a great amount of heat is produced and must be removed from the top of the chamber. Good thermal contact with the cooling system is therefore necessary.

(3) The energy lost by friction and the viscosity of the fluids must be compensated by a mechanical energy source. In the case of the Princeton chamber these losses reach 20%.

(4) High cycling rates are obtained by a mechanical resonant system, recovering most of the expansion energy. The sudden stopping of the chamber in its recompressed state is always a delicate operation that is difficult to adjust.

b. The Princeton Chamber. This chamber (Blumenfeld *et al.,* 1960) was built to study high rate expansion systems and the reaction of chambers under these new conditions. The expansion system essentially behaves as a mechanical harmonic oscillator, with the freon and compressed gases acting as the spring and a heavy piston acting as the oscillating mass (Fig. 13). The chamber has been operated at a rate of 20 cycles per second.

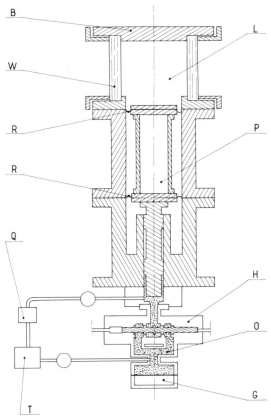

FIG. 13. Rapid cycling bubble chamber (Princeton). B, chamber body; G, gas cushion; H, hydraulic valve; L, liquid in the chamber; O, oil; P, piston; Q, hydraulic pump; R, rubber diaphragm; T, reservoir; W, window.

c. The Pasadena Freon Chamber. Based on a principle similar to that of the Princeton chamber, in this chamber the heavy piston has been replaced by a volume of incompressible liquid (Mullins *et al.*, 1960).

d. The Dubna Chamber. An auto-oscillation expansion system (Budagov *et al.*, 1962) has been studied for a 1 meter propane chamber at Dubna (Budagov *et al.*, 1960). It includes an air pressure stabilizer to eliminate the strong hydraulic impact that occurred during the first trials. The system operates satisfactorily at a rate of 15 cycles per second.

3. Pulsed Magnetic Field Bubble Chamber

a. Generalities. One of the ways of obtaining a very high magnetic field is to apply it in pulses. The method consists of discharging a condenser bank into a field coil with a small number of turns. The resulting field lasts a very short time (from several μsec to several msec), but this time is sufficient to cover the passing of the particles through the chamber. The method can be applied to small chambers only; however, it is well suited to particular experiments that need a high field, such as the measurement of the magnetic moment of hyperons.

The total amount of energy is limited to that required to establish the field, i.e. $\frac{1}{2}Li^2$. The technique has been used extensively to obtain magnetic fields in volumes of a few cubic centimeters. Extension to volumes measured in liters requires very much larger condensers, which is the reason why the technique has not been applied to larger chambers.

b. Russian Chambers. A chamber with a pulsed field of 10 kG was built in Moscow (Mukhin *et al.*, 1959). The condensers with a capacity of 1.6×10^{-2} F discharge into an 18 turn field coil at 3000 V. To prevent strong induction currents from circulating in the chamber body, part of it was made of insulating material. The arrangement, however, was not efficient since only 5% of the magnetic field was concentrated in the useful volume. A plan to increase the efficiency involved a specially shaped pole piece to concentrate the field (Barkov *et al.*, 1959). Another project by the same group involved a 10 kG field with a much larger chamber. In these projects, the main reason for a pulsed field was to reduce the energy consumption.

c. The Munich Chamber. In this chamber (Bergmann *et al.*, 1962), the body itself is the single turn field coil. The useful volume is a cylinder 7 cm in diameter and 10 cm deep. The condenser bank has a capacity of 1.85×10^{-3} F and is charged to 18 kV. The chamber is designed to operate with a field of 300 kG. However, the short duration of the field (3 μsec) prevents its use with the usual beams. It can only be used with beams that last a very short time, such as extracted beams.

The first experiments were performed with a field of 100 kG lasting around 10 μsec. An opaque spot due to a large bubble was observed in the center of the chamber around 100 μsec after the magnetic shock. With a flash delay of 30 to 60 μsec, it was possible to take pictures before the appearance of the bubble.

In such high fields, curvature measurements are accurate even on short tracks. For instance, with 300 kG, on a length of 1 cm in propane, the error due to multiple scattering would be only 2%. The small depth of the chamber and an optic demagnification of $M = 1$ provide small measuring errors ($\sim 10\,\mu$) and accurate momentum measurements.

4. The Hydrogen Target in a Heavy Liquid Chamber

a. Generalities. Interactions in complex nuclei greatly increase the difficulties associated with the analysis of heavy liquid chamber photographs; the Fermi momentum and the nuclear bond prevent the use of a classical production fit: momentum and energy balance, missing mass calculation. Also, secondary particles often interact before leaving the nucleus. There is a simple method to obtain reactions on hydrogen and retain the advantages of a heavy liquid: it consists in placing a liquid hydrogen target inside the bubble chamber. The first such setup was built by I. Pless in a propane and methyl iodide chamber. Subsequently, the École Polytechnique group developed several targets for their 1 meter chamber.

Before liquid hydrogen was used, trials were made with gaseous hydrogen under high pressure in a tube crossing the chamber. The setup was used to study photoproduction (Guerriero et al., 1960).

The main difficulty in the construction of targets is to limit as much as possible the thicknesses of metal and insulating material separating the hydrogen from the sensitive liquid. Interactions in the metal decrease the effectiveness of the target and can lead to false interpretation of events.

Even for small thicknesses of metal (several millimeters), the proportion of undesirable events is between 20 and 30%. Yet in the quest for a minimum thickness, it is important to retain good thermal insulation to keep the hydrogen in the target in a liquid phase.

b. The M.I.T. Harvard Target. In the M.I.T. Harvard system (Chrétien et al., 1962) the pressure envelope containing the target consists of a stainless steel cylinder 5 cm in diameter, 20 cm long, and 1.5 mm thick.

The thermal insulation of the target is a layer of "Microglass" paper under vacuum. Hydrogen fills the target through a gravity feed system (Fig. 14).

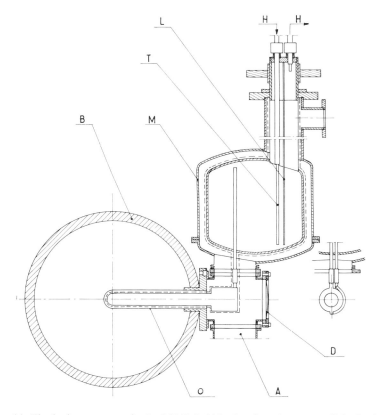

FIG. 14. The hydrogen target in the M.I.T. bubble chamber. A, rupture disk; B, chamber body; D, beam window; H, hydrogen inlet and outlet; L, level indicator; M, multilayer insulation; O, outer tube; T, fill tube.

The thicknesses of metal penetrated by incoming particles are the following:

1.5 mm of aluminum for the window in the hydrogen tank,
0.15 mm of stainless steel to enter the target proper,
0.15 mm of stainless steel to leave the target, and
1.5 mm of stainless steel for the target enclosure.

The target has an obscuring effect on the photographs. An auxiliary light source and a system of mirrors, designed to permit photographing the parts of the chamber hidden by the target, succeeded in eliminating this effect. The system has functioned properly with a liquid hydrogen consumption of about 1 liter per hour. 250,000 pictures have been taken to study π^0 production.

   c. *The École Polytechnique Targets.* These targets have been fitted with an intermediate copper screen cooled by hydrogen gas at atmospheric pressure. The liquid hydrogen is pressurized to about $\frac{1}{2}$ atm. The conical shape of the targets rapidly eliminates any bubbles that might form. Also, argon vapor pressure thermometers are used to monitor the presence of liquid in all parts of the system and in particular at the top part of the target (Fig. 15).

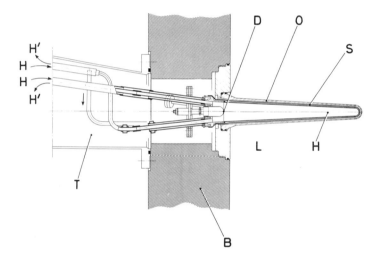

FIG. 15. Hydrogen target inside the École Polytechnique bubble chamber (without beam pipe). B, chamber body; D, internal beam window; H, pressurized hydrogen in the target; H′, hydrogen for refrigeration; L, heavy liquid in the chamber; O, outer container; S, thermal insulation screen; T, vacuum tank.

With a 40 cm target, it is difficult to obtain more than one reaction in the hydrogen per five pictures with about eight input particles per cycle. Increasing the number of particles is useless, since many would react in the heavy liquid and obscure the picture. However, many more particles can be made to pass through the hydrogen if a vacuum tube is used to lead

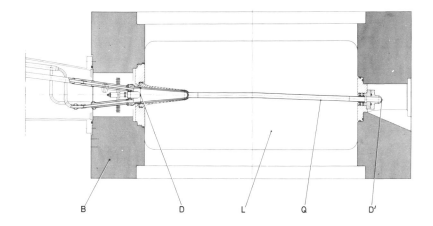

B   D   L   Q   D′

FIG. 16. Hydrogen target inside the École Polytechnique bubble chamber (with beam pipe).
B, chamber body; D, internal beam window; D′, external beam window; L, heavy liquid in
the chamber; Q, vacuum tube for the beam.

them out of the chamber (Fig. 16). This tube should be as small as possible
so as not to obscure the photograph; in other words, a pencil beam must
be used. Furthermore, since there is a magnetic field, the tube must be
slightly curved; this makes its construction particularly difficult.

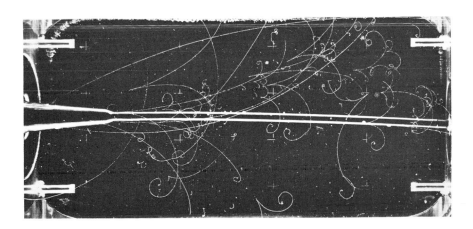

FIG. 17. Example of 8 BeV/c π^- reaction in hydrogen target inside a heavy liquid bubble
chamber (École Polytechnique).

The targets have operated in high energy π beams. The liquids used were C_2F_5Cl freon for the target with vacuum tube, and a low density mixture of propane and CF_3Br freon for the other one. A photograph of a reaction in the target can be seen in Fig. 17.

5. The Combination Chamber

The hydrogen target is not an ideal instrument because the interaction and the first few centimeters of track are not visible. This is a distinct disadvantage when studying low energy protons and strange particles with short lifetimes. It would of course be interesting to replace the target with a hydrogen bubble chamber. The two chambers would have to be separated by as small a distance and as little matter as possible. Also, the hydrogen chamber should be completely surrounded by the propane in order to obtain 4π solid angle detection of π^0 mesons. The first trials were made at Saclay with a 5 cm hydrogen chamber inside a 40 cm freon chamber. The experiment was a success but of not much use to physics because of its small size; it would be more useful if good curvature measurements could be performed in the hydrogen. The machine would then become a big hydrogen chamber enclosed in a still bigger heavy liquid chamber. When magnetic fields in the 100 kG region can be produced over large volumes, combinations with moderate-sized hydrogen chambers, and still reasonable measuring accuracies, will become possible.

For the moment, a hydrogen chamber with lead plates can do most of the experiments that would call for a combination chamber.

6. Future Projects for Very Large Chambers

Future projects involve the construction of chambers with volumes around 10 cubic meters. Since the largest of existing chambers do not exceed a cubic meter, the large increase in volume must be explained.

a. High Energy Neutrino Physics. In the CERN chamber the number of neutrino reactions is 1 to 2 per 10^4 pictures. This rate is very far from saturating the scanning and measuring capacities of a laboratory, as are the rates in most other experiments. Another factor of 50 would correspond to 1 event per 100 exposures, which is better adapted to existing methods.

This would also permit searching for rarer events such as strange particle production by neutrinos. Finally, purer but less intense neutrino beams could be used.

b. Other Physics. A very large chamber is capable of detecting most neutral particles with a very high efficiency:

photons and π^0 mesons by the electron pairs,

neutrons by their interactions, and

K_2^0 mesons by their interactions and production of strange particles.

Such a chamber could also be used to study high energy jets because of the π^0 mesons produced.

Other experiments are also possible such as the photonuclear interactions of μ mesons.

c. *Construction.* Presently, there are three projects for such giant chambers: one at the University of Wisconsin to be used with the Argonne machine, another at Paris to be used at CERN, and one at Serpukhov.

In both first projects, the chamber body is a cylinder roughly 1.80 meters in diameter, and 4.50 meters long. The magnet would surround the chambers and produce a magnetic field of 20 kG. 8 cameras would photograph the chamber through small portholes. The picture quality would suffer because of the great depth of field, wide angle, and varying illumination. However, since it was shown that in present chambers the multiple scattering limits the measurement accuracy, a poorer quality could be tolerated.

III. Special Problems in Data Processing

A. Momentum, Angle, and Range Measurement

1. *Momentum Measurements*

The measurement of momentum by magnetic curvature is equivalent to measuring the sagitta s of a track over an arc of length L.

The momentum (in MeV) is given by

$$p - 0.3\,BR/\sin\theta, \tag{2}$$

where θ is the angle between the track and the magnetic field, R the radius of curvature in centimeters of the projected track, B the magnetic induction in kilogauss.

Taking into account the sagitta s and l, the length of track projected onto a plane perpendicular to the magnetic field, and substituting $R = l^2/8s$, yields the formula

$$p = \frac{0.3\,Bl^2}{8s\,\sin\theta}. \tag{3}$$

The momentum error is due to the error in measuring s, itself dependent on three factors:

(a) the small measurement error due to imperfect measuring equipment.

(b) the multiple scattering error, the most important in heavy liquid because of the heavy nuclei necessary for a short radiation length.

(c) distortion errors due to an imperfect optical system and currents in the liquid. These errors are not always negligible.

Let us examine these three points.

(a) The measurement error is due to the measuring apparatus and the quality of the bubble images. Normally, the machines used for measuring bubble chamber pictures are accurate to $\frac{1}{20}$ mm in actual size. The error is then negligible. But to this must be added the contribution of the human operator. In principle, it is possible to measure to $\frac{1}{10}$ mm but this depends on the quality of the bubble image. Its diameter is around 20 to $30\,\mu$; projected to actual size, it becomes $\frac{5}{10}$ mm.

Finally, the sagitta s can be measured to an accuracy of 0.15 mm. The relative error on p is therefore

$$\left(\frac{\Delta p}{p}\right) = \frac{\Delta s}{s} = \frac{8p\Delta s}{0.3Bl^2}\sin\theta. \tag{4}$$

Introducing the actual length $L\,(= l/\sin\theta)$ of the track gives the formula

$$\left(\frac{\Delta p}{p}\right)_m = \frac{8p}{0.3BL^2\sin\theta}\Delta s. \tag{5}$$

With $B = 20$ kG, $p = 1000$ MeV/c, and $\theta = \pi/2$, the error is only 5% for a length l of 20 cm and only 2.5% for 30 cm. Provided the energy is not too high, this error is negligible compared to the multiple scattering error.

(b) Let us suppose the track is projected onto a plane containing the tangent to the track at a point 0. Δs is now the sagitta due to multiple scattering along a length of track L, and α is the angle through which the projected track has turned (Rossi, 1952):

$$\langle\alpha^2\rangle = \frac{1}{2}\frac{E_s^2}{p^2\beta^2}\frac{L}{X_0}, \tag{6}$$

$$(\Delta s)^2 = \frac{1}{16}\frac{\langle\alpha^2\rangle L^2}{3}. \tag{7}$$

The relative error $(\Delta p/p)_s = \Delta s/s$ is therefore equal to

$$\left(\frac{\Delta p}{p}\right)_s = \frac{E_s}{0.15(6^{1/2})B\,\beta(LX_0)^{1/2}\sin\theta}. \tag{8}$$

E_s is the scattering constant, equal to 21 MeV.

These formulas apply only to small scattering angles and do not hold when the track has a visible angle. It is then necessary to cut the track into smooth sections that do not include a visible angle.

With $E_s = 21$ MeV, the formula becomes

$$\left(\frac{\Delta p}{p}\right)_s = \frac{57}{B\,\beta(X_0 L)^{1/2}\sin\theta}. \tag{9}$$

This error is the most important one. As shown, it is inversely proportional to B, which justifies a strong magnetic field. Furthermore, it is inversely proportional to the square root of the radiation length X_0 and of L. With a given photon detection probability, L is proportional to X_0, which gives

$$\left(\frac{\Delta p}{p}\right)_s = \frac{K}{B\,\beta L \sin\theta}. \tag{10}$$

To improve the accuracy, L and B should be increased and the radiation length adjusted by means of a proper mixture. However, L is limited to the mean distance between interactions or kinks in the track, whether of Coulomb or of nuclear origin. For strongly interacting particles, this length is around 50 cm and, given a certain radiation length, varies little with the liquid used. Therefore, from the point of view of measuring, for strongly interacting particles it is of little advantage to increase the size of the chamber beyond 1 meter. The only way to gain in precision is to increase the field. This explains the interest in possible future 100 kG fields.

(c) The final source of error is due in part to imperfect camera lenses. These have to be carefully chosen to decrease distortions to a minimum. However, chromatic aberration is likely to occur at the edges of the optical field. This is partially reduced by roughly monochromatic filters. Yet the little aberration that remains widens the track images at the edges of the field and thus increases the errors. The imperfections in the front glass window are negligible and do not contribute to the distortion error. However, distortions in the liquid due to temperature differences or turbulence can be important. These effects depend essentially on the construction characteristics of the chamber and its working conditions.

Finally, when the bubble size is greater than several tenths of a millimeter the bright spot in the bubble image (in dark field illumination) is not always at the center.

Let $(\Delta p/p)_d$ be the relative error on the momentum due to these various distortions.

The total error is the root mean square sum of these errors

$$\frac{\Delta p}{p} = \left\{ \left(\frac{\Delta p}{p}\right)_m^2 + \left(\frac{\Delta p}{p}\right)_s^2 + \left(\frac{\Delta p}{p}\right)_d^2 \right\}^{1/2}. \tag{11}$$

Tests were made at the École Polytechnique to evaluate this error by measuring tracks without a magnetic field using 24 BeV protons and 1.15 BeV/c π^- mesons.

The higher energy particles give essentially the distortion and measurement errors while the 1.15 BeV/c π^- mesons give the multiple Coulomb scattering error. The results of these tests are listed in Table V together with the calculated values for the multiple scattering errors.

TABLE V

MEASURED SAGITTA ON TRACKS WITHOUT MAGNETIC FIELD

		Measured sagitta (mm)	Calculated sagitta (mm)
π^-, 1.15 BeV/c	$C_3H_8(X_0 = 110 \text{ cm})$	0.66	0.78
	$C_3H_8 + CF_3Br$ 50% 50% ($X_0 = 22$ cm)	1.55	1.48
Protons, 24 BeV	$C_3H_8 + CF_3Br$ 50% 50% ($X_0 = 22$ cm)	0.07	0.12

These results indicate that the distortion and measurement errors together are around 0.10 to 0.15 mm. It would therefore seem that the distortion errors can be made negligible.

For particles with a momentum p less than a few BeV/c, the error is almost entirely due to multiple scattering. When $\beta = 1$, the error is independent of p. However, for particles with a greater momentum, an error of 0.1 to 0.2 mm in the measurement of the sagitta must be added.

2. Angle Measurements

This section applies to the directions of the tracks. The error on the dip angle φ of a charged track is due to the measurement (including the distortion) and multiple scattering. The influence of the magnetic field can be neglected.

The measurement error on the angle φ is

$$(\Delta\varphi)_m = \frac{2^{1/2}\Delta z}{L}\cos\varphi, \tag{12}$$

with Δz the mean position error on a coordinate z of an element of the track.

The multiple scattering error is

$$(\Delta\varphi)_s = \frac{1}{6^{1/2}}\frac{E_s}{p\beta}\left(\frac{L}{X_0}\right)^{1/2}, \tag{13}$$

with $E_s = 21$ MeV.

There is thus an optimum track length that will give a minimum total error. This value is obtained by minimizing the expression

$$(\Delta\varphi)^2 = (\Delta\varphi)_m{}^2 + (\Delta\varphi)_s{}^2 = \frac{2(\Delta z)^2\cos^2\varphi}{L^2} + \frac{1}{6}\frac{E_s{}^2}{(p\beta)^2}\frac{L}{X_0}. \tag{14}$$

The optimum length is easily calculated as a function of Δz which includes all distortion errors and depends on the stereoscopic angle.

The azimuth angle is measured on a plane perpendicular to the magnetic field; therefore, the effect of the magnetic field is no longer negligible. The error in the azimuth angle θ of a segment of track AB is corrected by the addition of α, the angle between the chord and the tangent to the circle of radius R projected from the trajectory on a plane perpendicular to the magnetic field (see Fig. 18).

The azimuth Φ is given by $\Phi = \theta + \alpha$, where $\alpha = l/2R$ and l is the length AB. Difficulties arise from the fact that θ and R, and therefore θ and α, are not independent quantities. The measurements of θ and R will both be influenced by the scattering error and the error in measuring the point B.

The method which uses the maximum amount of information consists in calculating R from the measured coordinates of many points on the track.

Unfortunately, it is difficult to calculate the correlation terms

$$\left\langle d\theta\, d\frac{1}{R}\right\rangle_m \quad \text{and} \quad \left\langle d\theta\, d\frac{1}{R}\right\rangle_s.$$

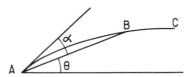

FIG. 18. Azimuth angle measurement.

A simpler method consists in choosing for R the value obtained from only three points A, B, C measured on the track. Points A, B give the angle θ. Under these conditions, it is possible to calculate the term

$$\left\langle d\theta\, d\frac{1}{R}\right\rangle.$$

Let l be the length of the arc AB and l_0 the length of the arc AC; it can be shown that the error on the azimuth is given by

$$\langle\Delta\Phi\rangle^2 = \frac{2(\Delta x)^2}{(l_0 - l)^2}\left(\frac{l^2}{l_0^2} + \frac{l_0^2}{l^2} - 1\right) + \frac{1}{6}\frac{E_s^2}{p^2\beta^2}\frac{l}{X_0}\frac{1}{\sin^3\varphi}. \tag{15}$$

This expression is equal to the one without the magnetic field when l_0 becomes infinite (l and l_0 are projected lengths). Therefore, l_0 should be

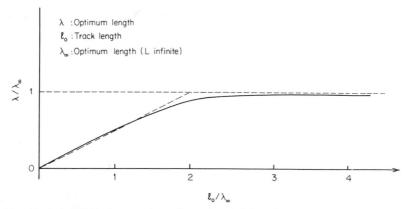

FIG. 19. Relationship between the optimum length λ for azimuthal angle measurements and the track length l_0, in units of the optimum length λ_∞ for an infinite track length.

taken as long as possible, that is, equal to the length of the track. For a given l_0, there is an optimum length λ for l that is given by a sixth degree equation, soluble numerically. Let λ_∞ be the optimum length calculated for infinite l_0, and λ the value calculated with the generalized expression. The value of λ/λ_∞ is shown in Fig. 19 as a function of l_0/λ_∞ for a mixture 50% C_3H_8 50% CF_3Br.

The following simple rules apply:

(1) if the track length is greater than $2\lambda_\infty$, the value λ_∞ is taken as the optimum length λ,

(2) otherwise λ is taken as equal to $l_0/2$.

B. Electron, Photon, and π^0 Measurements

1. Detection of Electrons

One of the advantages of heavy liquid chambers is the ability to identify electrons at the scan table. Over a distance equal to the radiation length X_0, an energetic electron loses by bremsstrahlung radiation a fraction $(1 - 1/e)$ of its energy. The aspect of the track is considerably modified since its potential length is usually several times the radiation length.

Electrons can also be identified by their δ rays. The high density of heavy liquids increases the probability of electron collisions. Furthermore, an energetic electron (100 MeV) has a much higher chance of producing a δ ray several centimeters long than have π or K mesons or protons.

Let us examine these various electron identification methods with their fields of application.

When a particle stops, it is easy to identify an electron. The method can be called a "one look" momentum-range, mass evaluation. An example will illustrate this point. In a 50–50% mixture of C_3H_8 and CF_3Br, the range of a 50 MeV/c π meson is 2 mm. Under the same conditions the range of an electron is 30 cm. The electron has also a distinctive spiraling trajectory.

On the other hand, this method can only identify the end of a track. The beginning of the track might be a μ, a π, or a K meson that has decayed into an electron along its trajectory. Usually, this type of decay is visible because of a kink in the track or a change in ionization. But sometimes it is not. This type of background can easily be accounted for, because the mean lives of the particles and the branching ratios of decays are well known.

The probability of an electron stopping in the chamber is quite high. It can be calculated if the properties of the liquid, the shape of the chamber, and the energy of the electron are known. The problem has been solved numerically by applying a Monte Carlo method.

A more delicate problem arises when the electron does not stop in the chamber. In the case of an energetic electron (i.e. >1 BeV), a characteristic shower is produced; in theory, the probability of seeing this shower can be calculated, the laws of electron radiation and photon materialization being well known. But, in practice, it may be preferable to use an empirical method. It consists of measuring this probability in the photographs of the experiment. There is always a great number of electron pairs at all energies. Beforehand, criteria defining an electron shower must be selected. Then for each electron of a pair, the length of track necessary for its identification as an electron, according to the set criteria, must be measured.

In this way, it is possible to calculate various identification probabilities according to the energy of the electron, its length, and its position in the chamber. In practice, this is done at the scan table on the projected lengths. The energy of the electron does not need to be known accurately and can be evaluated by a rapid curvature measurement. This empirical method gives the best results and can be applied to all identification procedures.

The problem is more difficult when an intermediate energy electron (a few hundred MeV) does not stop in the chamber. In this case, one must examine the variation in curvature of the electron, which is much greater than for other particles. The method used by Six (1962) was to measure the projection of α in the center photograph of three stereo views between the chord AB of an electron arc and the tangent at the point B. A is the origin of the electron and B the point where it leaves the chamber (see Fig. 20). There is a region where α is much greater for an electron than for a π meson.

A 200 MeV/c π meson has an α of 38° after a trajectory of 40 cm ($C_3H_8 + CF_3Br$, 50–50%, B = 17.4 kG). The choice of a large angle, say 90°, eliminates almost all particles other than electrons. Of course, some electrons are also eliminated. It is therefore necessary to know the probability of identification of electrons by this method.

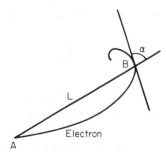

Fig. 20. Electron track in a heavy liquid bubble chamber.

Two solutions exist. A theoretical one consists in generating electron tracks by a Monte Carlo method using the radiation and ionization laws; an experimental one consists in measuring electron tracks that come from known sources such as electron pairs. The results of these measurements are given in Fig. 21 (Six, 1962) where the identification probability is

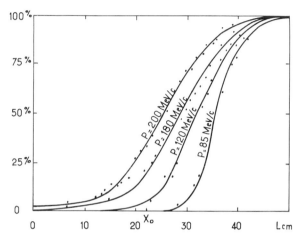

FIG. 21. Probability of recognizing an electron versus potential length for various electron energies: Mixture, 50% CF_3Br 50% C_3H_8; radiation length, $X_0 = 22$ cm (Six, 1962).

expressed as a function of the available length of track, for four different energy ranges. The results show that the method is useful when the available electron track length is greater than the radiation length. However, for higher energies it does not apply, but then the probability of seeing an electron shower or at least an associated pair of electrons is much greater.

The theoretical problem of δ ray identification has long been solved (Rossi, 1952). It is easily shown that the maximum energy transferred to an electron by a particle of mass M and momentum p is given by

$$E_{\max} = \left(\frac{p}{M}\right)^2, \qquad (16)$$

with all quantities expressed in MeV.

Thus a π meson with an energy of 300 MeV gives electrons with a maximum energy of 4 MeV and a range of 2 or 3 cm, according to the liquid used.

Furthermore it is possible to calculate that there is a negligible chance of a transfer with an energy close to $E_{\max}$. But due to its low mass, an electron has a much better chance of ejecting an energetic electron. For example, in a 50–50% mixture of CF_3Br and C_3H_8 the probability of a 30 MeV electron creating a δ ray at least 2 cm long is 70%. The probability of identifying an intermediate range electron is thus fairly high.

2. Detection of Photons

This problem is fairly simple. Knowing the energy of the photon, the radiation length of the liquid, and the available length of trajectory, it is easy to calculate the probability of materialization of the photon into an electron pair. These calculations are done at length in textbooks (Rossi, 1952). The simple rule to remember for high energy photons (>100 MeV) is that the probability of not seeing the pair after a distance L is $\exp(-7L/9X_0)$, where X_0 is the radiation length.

For lower energy photons (less than 100 MeV), the detection probability by Compton effect is no longer negligible. These photons are recognized by an isolated negative electron with an energy of around 50 MeV.

A positive electron can be annihilated; this introduces a certain bias in the scanning. It suddenly disappears and sometimes the materialization of a produced photon can be seen.

Photons can also manifest themselves in the form of a Dalitz pair. In the case of a π^0 production, an electron pair is seen at the interaction itself. This occurs in 1 case out of 80. The phenomenon is, of course, independent of the medium in which it occurs. The only advantage of the heavy liquid in this case is the direct identification of the electrons.

In the case of ordinary pairs, as in the case of Dalitz pairs, the energy of the photon can be unevenly distributed between the two electrons. In 0.5% of the cases, one of the electrons is not visible (this can introduce a scanning bias).

It is important to determine the probability of photon detection for a given experiment. Two methods are used. The first consists in calculating this probability, knowing the exact composition of the liquid, the energy spectrum of the photons, the angular distribution of their directions, and the distribution of their emission points. This can be done numerically by a Monte Carlo method. The only difficulty is to avoid introducing a bias into the above information.

The second method consists in measuring the detection probability on the photons that have already been detected. Let us suppose first the photons have the same energies: an exponential law describes the decrease in the number of photons materialized with distance. The argument of the exponential can be measured in the same way as the mean life of other particles, using, for example, the Bartlett method (Bartlett, 1958). The number of undetected photons can be deduced easily. If the photons are not mono-energetic, which is usually the case, the argument of the exponential is a function of energy. The same measurements can then be repeated in different energy ranges.

This method is usually sufficient because the radiation length varies little with the energy and almost not at all for energies above 100 MeV. It has the advantage of determining the detection probability on the same photons that are used in the experiment. For example, it is useful when counting the absolute number of Ξ^0 hyperons, or K^0 mesons that have decayed into three π^0.

3. *Electron Measurements*

The measurement of electron energies is important in many experiments: determination of photon or π^0 meson energies, spectrum of electrons in K or Λ decays, etc. (See Table VI.)

The two methods described complement one another. The first is useful when the length of the electron is of the same order as the radiation length. The second applies better when the potential length of the electron is several times greater than the radiation length.

TABLE VI
PHENOMENA INFLUENCING THE MEASUREMENT OF THE ENERGY OF ELECTRONS

Phenomenon	Mean value	Deviation about the mean value
Magnetic curvature	sagitta: $s = \dfrac{0.3Bl^2}{8E \sin \theta}$	$\Delta s \sim 0.015$ cm
Multiple scattering	$\langle \Delta s \rangle = 0$	$\langle \Delta s \rangle^2 = \dfrac{1}{96} \dfrac{E_s^2}{p^2} \dfrac{L^3}{X_0}$
Energy loss by ionization	ΔE, calculable as function of l	≈ 0 (negligible)
Energy loss by radiation	?	? increases with L

a. First Method (Behr *et al.*, 1963). This method was developed at the École Polytechnique. A given electron with an energy E is submitted to four different almost independent electromagnetic effects. They are: magnetic curvature, multiple scattering, loss of energy by ionization, loss of energy by radiation (bremsstrahlung). Each phenomenon has a mean effect and a deviation about that mean.

In the bremsstrahlung case, the mean energy loss and the deviation about that mean must be calculated as a function of L. Given these two quantities, it is possible to calculate the initial energy of the electron from a curvature measurement over a projected distance l.

The error due to curvature measurements is negligible for electrons with energies lower than 400 MeV. The two important contributions to the total error are the error due to multiple scattering that decreases as L increases (see Eq. (8)) and the error due to radiation that increases with L. The result is an optimum length for the measurement of electrons by curvature. For more energetic electrons, the measurement error is no longer negligible, but it can easily be accounted for as its effect is to increase the optimum length. The following description will therefore be limited to the lower energy range where curvature measurements are neglected.

The probability of emission of a photon of energy e by an electron of energy E is given as a function of $v = e/E$;

$$dP = \frac{K}{v} dv, \qquad (17)$$

where K is a constant.

According to Heitler (Quantum Theory of Radiation), it is preferable to use the following formula

$$dP = \frac{K}{\log 2} \frac{1}{\log (1 - v)} dv. \qquad (18)$$

Let E_0 be the initial energy of an electron. After a distance L the energy becomes E. If $E = E_0 e^{-y}$, it is shown (Quantum Theory of Radiation) that

$$P(y) \, dy = \frac{e^{-y} y^{\frac{L}{X_0 \log 2} - 1}}{\Gamma\left(\frac{L}{X_0 \log 2}\right)} dy. \qquad (19)$$

This formula depends on the ratio E/E_0 and not on E. Furthermore, it is independent of the magnetic field and of X_0 if L is expressed in units of X_0.

Let s_r be the sagitta of the track due to the magnetic field and the losses of energy by radiation, s_v the sagitta due to the magnetic field alone (sagitta in vacuum). These two quantities are functions of L. Formula (19) then gives

$$\frac{\langle s_r \rangle}{s_v} = 1 + \frac{L y_0}{X_0 \log 2}, \qquad (20)$$

where y_0 is a quantity defined by

$$\frac{hv_{max}}{E} = 1 - e^{-y_0}.$$ (21)

hv_{max} is the maximum energy of the emitted photon.

It is natural to choose such a cutoff because eliminating the tracks that have heavy radiation losses reduces the fluctuations. This is evident in the following formula giving the deviation around the mean

$$\frac{\Delta s_r}{s_v} = y_0 \left(\frac{1}{6} \frac{L}{X_0 \log 2} \right)^{1/2}.$$ (22)

Several remarks should be made.

(1) The cutoff is applied at the scan table by rejecting those electrons with an energy loss greater than the cutoff value after a certain distance.

(2) The optimum length can be determined from the value of the deviation, by minimizing the total error, the quadratic sum of this deviation, and the error due to multiple scattering.

(3) The optimum length is independent of X_0 and of the energy, but it is a function of the magnetic field and of the chosen cutoff.

(4) For the more energetic electrons, the term due to the measurement error must not be forgotten. This has the effect of increasing the optimum length.

(5) A Monte Carlo calculation has shown that the energy distribution about the mean is compatible with a Gaussian distribution when all the error sources are taken into account.

(6) Finally, if φ is the dip angle, the dispersion due to radiation must be divided by $(\sin \varphi)^{1/2}$.

Table VII gives the errors and the optimum lengths for different radiation lengths and for different cutoffs.

TABLE VII

OPTIMUM LENGTH IN ELECTRON ENERGY MEASUREMENTS

Radiation length	110 cm (propane)	50 cm	22 cm
Cutoff $\dfrac{hv_{max}}{E}$	0.33	0.39	0.50
Length	15 cm	11 cm	7 cm
Expected errors	11%	19%	33%

In particular, this method has been applied to the determination of the masses of the η^0 and the π^0 by measuring the energies of the decay photons in the modes $\eta^0 \to 2\gamma$, $\pi^0 \to 2\gamma$ (see Section IV,B).

b. *Second Method* (Burmeister *et al.*, 1963). This method was developed at CERN for the neutrino experiments. It applies to the cases where the potential length available for an electron shower is several times the radiation length. This is the case for the neutrino experiments where $X_0 = 11$ cm,

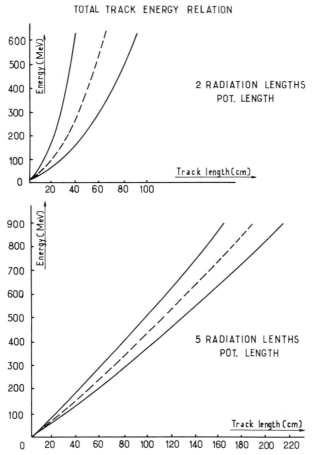

FIG. 22. Total track length of an electron shower versus the energy of the primary electron. The dotted line is the mean value of the visible track length and the solid curves include $\frac{2}{3}$ of the showers (Burmeister *et al.*, 1963).

i.e. one-tenth of the length of the chamber. The method consists of measuring the total track length of the shower. The magnetic field does not influence this quantity but is a considerable aid in separating the tracks of the shower.

To test the method, the chamber was exposed to a separated beam of 600 MeV/c electrons. A mean value was found for the total track length by measuring 82 showers. The value was 131 cm with a spread of only 15%.

To compare the results with theory, an experiment was simulated numerically by generating electron showers by a Monte Carlo method. The theoretical results gave a value of 128 cm, consistent with the measured results. Also, the calculated length of the primary electron agreed to within 5% with the measured value. Finally, the total length of visible shower for a given potential length was found to be consistent with the measured value.

These results show the validity of the Monte Carlo method. It was applied to different energy ranges and potential lengths. The results are listed in Fig. 22 for potential lengths between 2 and 5 times the radiation length. The dotted curve represents the mean value of the total visible portion of the shower whereas the solid lines include only $\frac{2}{3}$ of the events. It can be seen that the method applies best when the potential length is several times the radiation length.

4. Photon and π^0 Measurements

Let E' and E'' be the measured energies of each electron of a pair. If the energy of one of the electrons is small, then

$$\frac{\Delta E}{E} = \frac{\Delta E'}{E'}, \tag{23}$$

where E is the energy of the photon.

On the other hand, when the energy is evenly distributed between the photons,

$$\frac{\Delta E}{E} = 2^{-1/2} \frac{\Delta E'}{E'}. \tag{24}$$

In general, the energy is randomly distributed between the electrons. In this case, the relative error in the measurement of the photon energy is

$$\frac{\Delta E}{E} = 0.85 \frac{\Delta E'}{E'}. \tag{25}$$

The precision in measuring a photon is better than in the case of an electron.

Let a π^0 (or η^0) emit two photons at an angle θ between them. Let E_1 and E_2 be the energies of the photons and m the mass of the π^0, then

$$m^2 = 2E_1 E_2 (1 - \cos \theta). \tag{26}$$

In general, the decay point of the π^0 is known. This makes the error on the measurement of the angle negligible,

$$\frac{\Delta m}{m} \sim \frac{\Delta E_1}{E_1}. \tag{27}$$

If it is certain that the particle is a π^0 meson, then there are two equations for determining its energy, i.e. the sum of the energies of the two photons. A one constraint fit can then be applied to increase the precision. In general, the error on the energy of the π^0 is half as small as the error on the energy of the electrons.

The following table gives an idea of the errors encountered in a chamber with a magnetic field of 17.5 kG and 22.5 cm of radiation length.

Electron	Photon	Mass of two photons	π^0 energy
30%	25%	25%	15%

These are average values, and in the particular case of the π^0 the error can vary considerably depending on the direction of emission of the photons. Also, the energy of the π^0 meson is measured with an accuracy equal to that of other particles measured by curvature.

C. Ionization Problems: Relativistic Increase, Range Measurements, Other Problems

1. Ionization

No systematic study has been made, to date, of the measurement of ionization in the large heavy liquid chambers. On the other hand, interesting studies have been made in smaller chambers (Blinov et al., 1957; Argan et al., 1958a, b). This section will discuss the results of a more recent study by the Fribourg group (Hahn et al., 1960a, b).

A small two-liter chamber filled with CF_3Br was exposed to a beam of 16 BeV π^- mesons and 24 BeV protons at CERN. The ionization was measured by the bubble density and the gap length distribution methods.

The results were examined as functions of the parameter $\gamma = (1 - \beta^2)^{-1/2}$. 16 BeV pions have a γ of 115.

The chamber did not have a magnetic field. Points corresponding to values lower than $\gamma = 115$ were determined by strange particle decays. The nature and energy of the secondary tracks were identified by angle and multiple scattering measurements. The results plotted in Fig. 23 show a

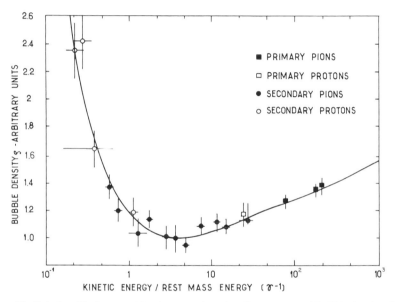

FIG. 23. Relationship between kinetic energy in units of rest mass and bubble density along the track (Hahn *et al.*, 1960).

definite relativistic rise from the minimum of ionization to a γ of 100. The increase is $30 \pm 5\%$. The implications of this result on the theory of bubble formation are discussed in Chapter II, this volume.

The results were further confirmed in the following manner. The bubble density along the 16 BeV/c π^- tracks was compared with the bubble densities of the tracks of particles resulting from interactions of the π mesons. The density of the π tracks is 24% higher than the density of the secondary tracks. This result is in complete agreement with the result found by measuring neutral V's.

This method was also used to measure any variations in the relativistic increase with the temperature of the liquid and with the pressure differential of the expansion cycle. The parameter used was the ratio of the bubble densities of the primary $16 \, \text{BeV} \, \pi^-$ tracks to the bubble densities of the secondary tracks. The results showed that the ratio seemed to be independent of the conditions in the chamber.

This property can be applied to the study of energetic particles produced in very high energy reactions (jets). In principle, it should be possible to distinguish π mesons, K mesons, and protons through the measurements of bubble density and momentum.

In practice, the reliability of bubble density measurements for the poorer pictures of the large bubble chambers remains to be proven. No systematic study has been made yet.

2. Range Measurements

The high stopping power of heavy liquids permits energy measurement and identification of a particle by its range. The energy range curves for the different particles are well known. However, there is uncertainty on the density of the liquid at the time of the passage of the particles. This value can be determined by measuring the range of particles of known energies such as the π or μ mesons from the decays of stopping K^+, $K^+ \rightarrow \pi^+ + \pi^0$, and $K^+ \rightarrow \mu^+ + \nu$.

The error in the determination of the energy by range measurements is usually negligible. However, as the multiple scattering increases towards the end of a trajectory, it is often necessary to measure the track in several segments. The error due to fluctuations in the range (or straggling) has been studied by Symon (1948). The spread about the mean value can be determined from a simple known curve (Ritson, 1961). The resulting errors are around 2 or 3%. It is therefore an excellent method for energy determination.

3. Scattering Measurements

When a bubble chamber does not have a magnetic field, the value of $p\beta$ can be determined by measuring the multiple scattering with the methods described by several authors (Goldschmit-Clermont et al., 1948; Annis et al., 1953). The nature and energy of a particle can in principle be determined by measuring $p\beta$ and the range or the ionization of the track. With this method, in a small propane chamber (Kirillov-Ugryumov et al., 1960; Pershin et al., 1959; Pershin and Golubchikov, 1960), the mass of a π meson could be measured to no better than 25% for a track length of 25 cm. In the case of larger chambers, this method has not been applied since the quality of the pictures is poorer and the magnetic curvature method gives better results.

However, it can be advantageous for the xenon chamber. Brown (1960) and Karatsuba *et al.* (1960) have discussed this. The error on the quantity $p\beta$ for nonstopping particles in the Berkeley chamber is at least 20%. The Russian authors have shown that the variable cell length method can be used for stopping particles and permits a 10% accuracy on the mass determination.

IV. Examples of Experiments

This section contains a description of several heavy liquid bubble chamber experiments. They were chosen because they demonstrated the particular qualities of heavy liquids and their possible applications.

A. Electron Identification

The ability to identify electrons at the scan table is one of the essential properties of heavy liquid chamber pictures.

(1) The method has been applied to the study of the β decay of the Λ^0 hyperon:

$$\Lambda^0 \rightarrow p + e^- + \nu.$$

The difficulty of the experiment lies in the very low branching ratio of this disintegration, namely 0.1%.

First of all, the greatest possible number of Λ^0 hyperons must be produced. The first experiments were done with π mesons. Then, when properly separated beams were available, K^- mesons were used (Crawford *et al.*, 1958; Aubert *et al.*, 1962; Ely *et al.*, 1963; Baglin *et al.*, 1963).

The method consists of choosing the Λ_β^0 events directly at the scan table by recognizing the electrons (Section III). This avoids having to measure all the Λ^0 hyperons, i.e. 100,000 events.

The liquid used had a medium radiation length (20 to 25 cm) to combine measurement accuracy with direct electron identification.

The different methods do not have the same probability of electron identification for all the energies. Corrections must therefore be applied, using the fact that the electron energy spectrum in the Λ^0 rest system is not very sensitive to the ratio of the vector and axial vector coupling constants C_V/C_A. The electron energy spectrum is almost the phase space spectrum.

One difficulty remains in all experiments where the absolute rate of a type of event must be measured. To establish proper statistics, the scanning efficiency must be accurately known. This can be obtained by repeated scanning of one portion of film, for example, but the calculated value rests on a false assumption: that the scanning efficiency is the same for any event. Of course, the error introduced is not greater than a few percent but it certainly limits the accuracy of the experiment.

Another problem is that of possible background events. The desired events are so rare that it is necessary to make a complete study of all possible "pseudoevents" that may simulate them. Among these pseudoevents the most important are the normal decays of Λ^0 into a proton and π^- with subsequent π-μ-β decay. Also included are the decays of the K^0 into an electron, π, and neutrino, when the π is highly energetic and can simulate a proton. Other types of background can also be found, such as neutron stars and wide angle electron pairs. However, it is usually possible to determine the number of these background events for a particular experiment. It is better to minimize these effects by a proper choice of cutoff values on track lengths, angles, etc. Figure 24 shows a Λ_β decay in freon.

The physicists of the European collaboration went further in trying to measure the ratio of the coupling constants C_V/C_A. A method used was to study the angular correlation between the neutrino and the electron, since the Λ^0 hyperon was unpolarized. But for practical purposes it was simpler to study the energy spectrum of the proton in the rest system of the Λ^0. There is one difficulty; the Λ^0 hyperons having been produced in complex nuclei, only their directions are known and not their energies. By measuring the electron and the proton, it is possible to calculate the velocity of the Λ^0 and thus deduce the energy of the proton in the Λ^0 system. However, the velocity of the Λ^0 is given by a quadratic equation that has two roots. Often, one of the roots can immediately be eliminated, but this is not always the case. Two methods were used to overcome this difficulty. The first consisted in using the projected momentum of the proton in a plane perpendicular to the Λ^0 trajectory. In this case, the two solutions are identical. In the second method, the two solutions are treated as two half events. This distorts the expected spectra, but it is possible to account for this effect by using a Monte Carlo method.

(2) Direct identification of the electrons was used in another similar type of experiment: the study of the β decays of K^0 mesons.

K^0 mesons are produced in K^+ charge exchanges with a well determined strangeness equal to $+1$. As the K^0 advances into the chamber, the K_1^0 component of the wave decays to zero, leaving after a few centimeters an almost pure K_2^0 wave containing K^0 and $\overline{K}^0$ with equal amplitudes.

The experiment (Ely *et al.*, 1962; Aubert *et al.*, 1963) consists of measuring the β decay rates as a function of the time of flight of the K^0 meson. For

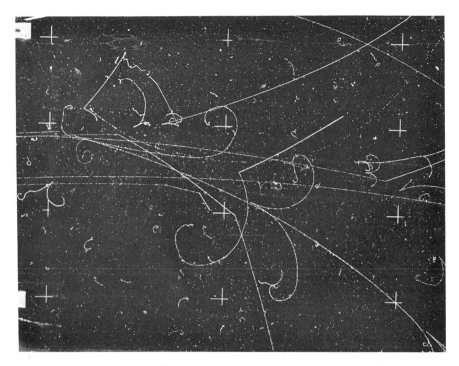

Fig. 24. Λ_β decay in freon C_2F_5Cl. The Λ^0 is produced by a K^- at 1.5 BeV/c. The proton from the Λ_β decay stops in the liquid (École Polytechnique Bubble Chamber).

the $\Delta S = \Delta Q$ rule to hold, the only K_β^0 decays observed close to the decay point must have positive electrons. It was shown that the best method was to measure the total rate of positive and negative β decays as a function of time. The spectra obtained were then compared to theoretical curves containing a parameter K. The parameter K is equal to the ratio of β decay rates of K_1^0 mesons and K_2^0 mesons. For $\Delta S = \Delta Q$ to hold, this ratio must be equal to 1.

In this experiment, the advantage of the heavy liquid chamber is twofold. Due to the presence of complex nuclei some of the target nucleons are neutrons, and the following reaction is observed: $K^+ + n \rightarrow K^0 + p$. Furthermore, the radiation length of the liquids allows an easy identification of the K_β^0 events without having to measure hundreds of thousands of K^0 decays.

The experiment is difficult and must be done carefully. It consists of comparing the number of K_β^0 decays having K_1^0 lifetimes with the number having much longer lifetimes (or $K_2{}^0$ lifetimes). There are several critical points. First, care must be taken to separate the possible sources of background, such as a $K_1{}^0$ decay having a π^- meson that decays in flight followed by a stopping μ decay. The flux of $K_1{}^0$ components is quite high near the charge exchange point; this constitutes therefore a dangerous background source. Then, the probability of detecting a $K_\beta{}^0$ decay decreases strongly at the longer lifetimes because of geometrical losses or losses by nuclear absorption. All these effects must be carefully accounted for. Finally, care must be taken to avoid sources of $K_2{}^0$ mesons outside the liquid. This would increase the background for the longer lifetimes. If a great number of events were available, these difficulties could be easily overcome by applying strong cutoff criteria.

B. PHOTON DETECTION

The good photon detection of heavy liquid chambers allowed the proof of the decay of the η^0 meson into two photons. The experiment (Chrétien *et al.*, 1962) was performed at Brookhaven in a 1.4 BeV/c π^- beam. The chamber used was the relatively small, 50 liter Cambridge chamber, with a mixture of methyl iodide and ethane for an X_0 of 8.2 cm.

The reaction studied was

$$\pi^- + p \rightarrow \pi^0 + n.$$

But an important background came from the reaction

$$\pi^- + p \rightarrow N \pi^0 + n.$$

The method was original in that only the directions of the photons were used, and not their momenta. These directions were given by the directions of the materialized electrons and not by the measurement of the photon momenta which is much less precise with such a short radiation length.

The method consists in searching for events where an incident π^- meson stops without giving any visible branches. This selects events on hydrogen or on protons that are almost free. The directions of the photons in the center-of-mass system are obtained by a Lorentz transformation in the following reaction: $\pi^- + p \rightarrow X^0 + n$, where X^0 is any particle that decays into two photons. It is easy to calculate that the distribution of the angle between the photons has a distinct minimum for a given mass of the X^0 particle. The results obtained are represented in Fig. 25. There is an important peak corresponding to the expected distribution of the π^0 mass. A careful analysis shows that the accumulation of points to the right of the peak is due to a particle with a mass of 550 MeV that disintegrates into two photons. This value is consistent with that found for the η^0 mesons in hydrogen chamber experiments using the $(\pi^+\pi^-\pi^0)$ decay mode.

The angular distributions were corrected for the background due to the mode of decay into several π^0 mesons where only two photons were visible

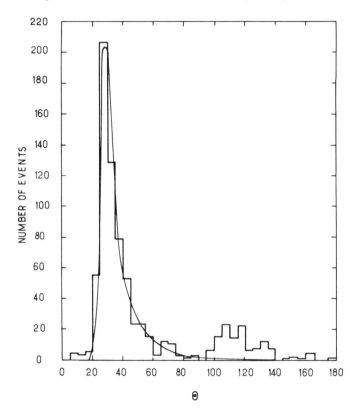

FIG. 25. Number of events versus the angle Θ between two photons in the center-of-mass system, in the reaction $\pi^- + p \rightarrow X^0 + n$, $X^0 \rightarrow \gamma + \gamma$ (Chrétien *et al.*, 1962).

in the chamber. The correction was evaluated by studying pairs of photons in events where three photons are visible.

A second experiment was performed (Behr *et al.*, 1963) by directly measuring the electron energy. This was made possible through use of a liquid with a greater radiation length ($X_0 = 215$ cm). Thus, with a knowledge of the energy of the two photons and the angle between them, it is possible to calculate their effective mass, i.e. the mass of the original particle that created them.

As in the previous case, the events producing several mesons and only two visible photons must be taken into account. The correction factor is evaluated in the same way.

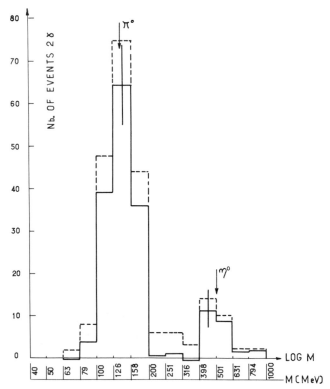

FIG. 26. Number of events versus the relative mass of two photons, in the reaction $\pi^- + p \rightarrow X^0 + n$, $X^0 \rightarrow \gamma + \gamma$ (Behr *et al.*, 1963).

The histogram of the masses is represented in Fig. 26. Two peaks are apparent, one corresponding to the π^0 meson, the other to the η^0 meson. The values obtained were

$$M_{\pi^0} = 138.5 \pm 3.7 \, \text{MeV/c}^2, \quad M_{\eta^0} = 573 \pm 26 \, \text{MeV/c}^2.$$

The mass obtained for the π^0 meson shows that the method described in Section III,B for evaluating the energies of electrons is correct. The width of the distribution is narrower than expected, showing that the electrons were measured with an error of 26% rather than 33%. This is probably so because the choice of measured electrons was stricter than the experiment would have called for.

The second peak is made up of 21 ± 6 events and has a width equal to that of the π^0 peak. This proves the existence of another particle giving two photons. The value for the mass is consistent with the results of the hydrogen chamber experiment.

C. π^0 MESON DETECTION

The ability to detect π^0 mesons being one of the main qualities of heavy liquid chambers, an experiment was undertaken at CERN to determine the properties of the Ξ^0 hyperon produced in the reaction (Jauneau et al., 1963):

$$K^- + p \to \Xi^0 + K^0.$$

The chamber was filled with C_2F_5Cl for a radiation length of 25 cm. The decay mode of the Ξ^0 hyperon is

$$\Xi^0 \to \Lambda^0 + \pi^0.$$

The Λ^0 is identified and measured by its decay π^- and proton, the π^0 by the materialization of the two decay photons. Furthermore, the Ξ^0 with a strangeness of -2 is accompanied by a K^0 meson. The distinctive aspect of the event is shown in Fig. 27, and a photograph in Fig. 28.

The π^0 meson is reconstructed by measuring the energies of the two decay

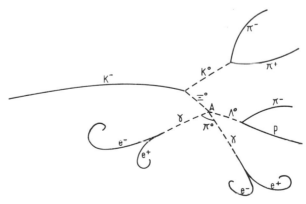

FIG. 27. Ξ^0 production followed by Ξ^0, K^0, Λ^0, π^0 decays in a heavy liquid chamber. $K^- + p \to K^0 + \Xi^0$, $\Xi^0 \to \pi^0 + \Lambda^0$, $\pi^0 \to \gamma + \gamma$, $\Lambda^0 \to \pi^- + p$, $K^0 \to \pi^+ + \pi^-$.

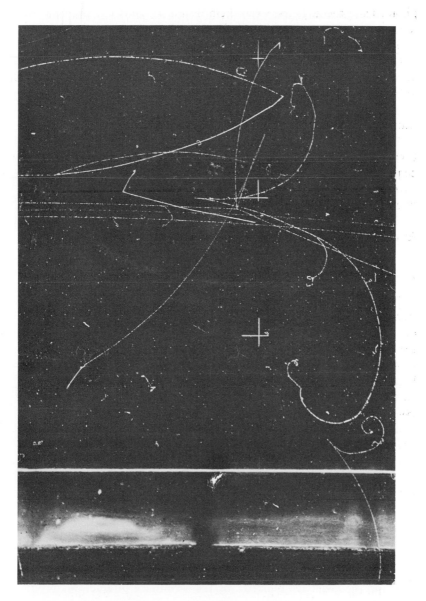

Fig. 28. Example of reaction $K^- + p \rightarrow \Xi^0 + K^+ + \pi^-$. The Ξ^0 decays into a Λ^0 and a π^0. The Λ^0 decays into a proton and a π^- and is visible. The π^0 decays into two γ's giving two visible e^+, e^- pairs. The K^+ stops in the liquid and decays (École Polytechnique Bubble Chamber).

photons and the angle between them. Point A, the decay point of the Ξ^0, is found by measuring the Λ^0 and the π^0. Thus the energy, time of flight, and mass of the Ξ^0 can be evaluated.

Precautions must be taken: only a small number of events have all these elements visible or usable. It is necessary to eliminate the possible back-grounds. For example, a Ξ^0 hyperon can react in the nucleus and result in two Λ^0 hyperons. One might decay into a π^- and a proton, and the other into a π^0 and a neutron. This event might simulate a Ξ^0 decay.

Also, when a Ξ^0 hyperon has a very short trajectory, it must be eliminated because the π^0 mesons seem to come from the interaction. These difficulties can be avoided by a suitable choice of cutoff values; for example, rejecting events where the π^0 seems to originate from a point closer than 2 cm to the interaction.

Once the event has been reconstructed, all the parameters concerning the Ξ^0 can be determined: mass, lifetime, asymmetry parameter α_{Ξ^0}.

D. π^0 DETECTION: JET EXPERIMENTS

The π^0 detecting quality of heavy liquid chambers can be applied to the study of the reactions of higher energy particles (> 6 BeV). Until now, the only high energy beams available were π^- mesons and protons. But with the radio frequency separators, it will be possible to obtain beams of anti-protons and K mesons with energies greater than 10 BeV. The problem of high energy reactions or jets is the study of the reaction of the incident particle on a single proton and the identification of all the reaction products. No instrument exists yet that is able to do this perfectly.

Hydrogen chambers have free protons but cannot detect π^0 mesons. The technique of measuring the missing mass of the neutral particles by a pro-duction fit cannot be used in this case for two reasons: the number of π^0 mesons is often greater than one and the value calculated will therefore be the effective mass of the group. Then the precision decreases rapidly with increasing energy and, even in the case where only one π^0 is produced, one cannot properly apply this method.

The heavy liquid chamber bypasses this difficulty but another appears: most reactions occur on a single nucleon, even in complex nuclei, but, while the Fermi momentum has little effect, the number of particles produced is high and the event is "blurred" by the secondary interactions produced in the nucleus.

One solution is to place lead plates in a hydrogen chamber to materialize the photons. The method will certainly be used in future jet experiments.

Unfortunately, thick plates must be used to obtain a high detection probability; this reduces the precision in the electron energy measurement.

Another method is to use a hydrogen target in a heavy liquid chamber (see Section II,G). The setup is being used in the École Polytechnique chamber at CERN to study $\pi^0\pi^0$ reactions of the type: $\pi^+ + p \to \pi^0 + \pi^0 + n$.

Another possibility of this technique is the ability to select interactions where no π^0's are produced, by eliminating the events giving electron pairs. Such an experiment (Veillet *et al.*, 1963) with 6 BeV π^- mesons permitted a study of the f^0 particle in the reaction

$$\pi^- + p \to \pi^+ + \pi^- + n.$$

It was important to be able to distinguish this type of event from the more frequent π^0 producing reactions. The relative mass spectrum of the two π mesons showed two peaks: one due to the ρ meson; the other, at a mass around 1260 MeV/c^2, due to the f^0 meson. The equivalent histogram for the π^0 producing events is quite different. As these events are three or four times more frequent, it was important to distinguish them in order to reveal the f^0 peak.

Another typical example of jet experiment is the study of the dissociative diffraction of an incident pion into three pions by a carbon nucleus:

$$\pi^- + \text{carbon} \to \pi^- + \pi^- + \pi^+ + \text{carbon}.$$

E. High Density Experiments: Neutrino Detection

The neutrino experiment makes full use of the qualities of heavy liquid chambers.

An experiment took place at CERN using the 500 liter chamber filled with freon CF_3Br. The $\frac{3}{4}$ ton of detecting medium is small when compared with the 10 ton spark chambers, but the advantages of a better track quality and a 27 kG field far outweigh this drawback. Also, because of the short radiation length ($X_0 = 11.5$ cm), it is possible to identify almost all of the electrons and photons; it is sometimes possible to distinguish between π and μ mesons because the interaction length of the π is 60 cm.

The reactions studied are the following:

$$\nu_\mu + n \to p + \mu^- \qquad\qquad \text{``elastic'' reaction,}$$

$$\left.\begin{array}{l} \nu_\mu + n \to n + \mu^- + \pi^+ + N\pi^0 \\ \nu_\mu + n \to p + \mu^- + N\pi^0 \\ \nu_\mu + p \to p + \pi^+ + \mu^- \end{array}\right\} \text{``inelastic'' reactions.}$$

The neutrinos come from the decays of π mesons and sometimes of K mesons focused onto the direction of the chamber by a magnetic horn (van der Meer, 1961). By reversing the polarity of the field, positive or negative particles can be selected. With the negative particles antineutrinos are produced and the expected elastic reaction is

$$\bar{v}_\mu + p \rightarrow n + \mu^+ .$$

The analysis is based on the identification of particles produced in the reactions.

(1) The photons and π^0 mesons are detected and measured because of the short radiation length $X_0 = 11.5$ cm.

(2) The electrons are also easily detected.

(3) The μ mesons are identified by their lack of reactions or their decays into electrons (half of the cases).

(4) The π mesons are identified by their reactions, as 60% react in the chamber.

(5) Protons are recognized because they usually stop in the chamber or have more heavily ionized tracks.

In most of these cases, the detection efficiency is not 100% but is enough to be useful. An inelastic neutrino-induced reaction is shown in Fig. 29.

FIG. 29. An example of a high energy inelastic neutrino event of the type $v + p \rightarrow \mu^- + p + \pi^+ + \pi^0$ found in the CERN heavy liquid chamber. The π^0 produced decays instantly into two γ rays which convert and produce a large electron shower.

Finally the 27 kG field gives a fairly good accuracy despite the short radiation length.

The first results of the experiment seem to be consistent with the theoretical predictions for the elastic cross section (Lee and Yang, 1960). Furthermore, the following points were proven.

(1) First of all, the results confirmed the fact shown by the Brookhaven experiment that two kinds of neutrinos exist (Danby *et al.*, 1962). The result is based on the absence of the following type of reaction

$$v + n \rightarrow p + e^-.$$

Actually, a few negative electrons were observed in inelastic reactions but they were probably due to v_e neutrinos from electrons of the K_β^+ decay.

(2) The lepton number is conserved, as was proved by the absence of the following reactions.

$$v_\mu + n \rightarrow n + \pi\text{'s} \quad \text{and} \quad v_\mu + n \rightarrow \mu^+ + \text{etc.}$$

(3) The question of a neutral leptonic current was considered. Existence of the current would lead to the following elastic reactions: $v_\mu + p \rightarrow p + v_\mu$, in addition to the normal: $v_\mu + n \rightarrow p + \mu^-$. These would appear as isolated protons in the chamber.

(4) It has been calculated that approximately 20% of the neutrinos come from K decays: $K \rightarrow \mu + v$. The uniformity of the results shows that K produced neutrinos are identical to π produced neutrinos. This rejects the spin flip hypothesis (Feinberg *et al.*, 1961).

(5) An investigation was made for the intermediate boson $W^\pm$. A few events of the following type would prove its existence: $v_\mu + p \rightarrow p + \mu^- + W^+$ followed by the decay $W^+ \rightarrow e^+ + v_e$. In this case a positive electron would accompany a μ^- candidate when the primary is a neutrino.

These results show the importance of the heavy liquid chamber in neutrino physics. There is no doubt as to the future usefulness of this chamber, and larger size chambers will probably play an essential role in this new field.

ACKNOWLEDGMENTS

Our gratitude is due to Professor L. Leprince-Ringuet for his sustained interest and encouragement. We also wish to extend our thanks to the heavy liquid bubble chamber group of the École Polytechnique for their suggestions and help in the preparation of this chapter.

REFERENCES

ALIKHANIAN, A. I., *et al.* (1959). *Proc. Intern. Conf. High Energy Accelerators and Instrumentation, CERN, Geneva*, p. 512.

ALYEA, E. D., Jr., GALLAGHER, L. R., MULLINS, J. H., and TEEM, J. M. (1957). *Nuovo Cimento* **6**, 1480.

ANNIS, A., BRIDGE, H. S., and OLBERT, S. (1953). *Phys. Rev.* **89**, 1216.

ARGAN, P. E., and GIGLI, A. (1956). *Nuovo Cimento* **3**, 1171; **4**, 953.

ARGAN, P. E., GIGLI, A., PICASSO, E., TOMASINI, G., and GONELLA, L. (1957). *Proc. Intern. Conf. Mesons and Recently Discovered Particles, Padova-Venezia 17th*, p. 17.

ARGAN, P. E., CONTE, M., GIGLI, A., PICASSO, E., and GONELLA, L. (1958a). *Nuovo Cimento* **10**, 182.

ARGAN, P. E., GIGLI, A., PICASSO, E., and TOMASINI, G. (1958b). *Nuovo Cimento* **10**, 177.

AUBERT, B., *et al.* (1962). *Nuovo Cimento* **25**, 479.

AUBERT, B., BEHR, L., BLOCH, M., LOWYS, J. P., MITTNER, P., and ORKIN-LECOURTOIS, A. (1963). *Sienna Conf.* To be published.

BAGLIN, C., *et al.* (1963). *Phys. Letters* **6**, 186.

BALANDIN, M. P., *et al.* (1962). *Proc. Conf. Instrumentation High-Energy Phys., CERN, Geneva*, p. 110.

BARKOV, L. M., MUKHIN, K. N., and SHLYAPNIKOV, R. S. (1959). *Proc. Intern. Conf. High Energy Accelerators and Instrumentation, CERN, Geneva*, p. 640.

BARTLETT, M. S. (1958). *Phil. Mag.* **44**, 1407.

BASSI, P., LORIA, A., MEYER, J. A., MITTNER, P., and SCOTONI, I. (1956). *Nuovo Cimento* **4**, 491.

BEHR, L., and MITTNER, P. (1963). *Nucl. Instr. Methods* **20**, 446.

BEHR, L., MITTNER, P., and MUSSET, P. (1963). *Phys. Letters* **4**, 22.

BERGMANN, W. H., *et al.* (1962). *Proc. Conf. Instrumentation for High-Energy Phys., CERN, Geneva*, p. 116.

BERTANZA, L., FRANZINI, P., MANNELLI, I., and SILVESTRINI, V. (1958). *Nuovo Cimento* **10**, 403.

BLINOV, G. A., KRESTNIKOV, IU. S., and LOMANOV, M. F. (1956). *Zh. Eksperim. i Teor. Fiz.* **31**, 762.

BLINOV, G. A., KRESTNIKOV, IU. S., and LOMANOV, M. F. (1957). *Soviet Phys. JETP* **4**, 661.

BLINOV, G. A., KRESTNIKOV, IU. S., LOMANOV, M. F., and SHALAMOV, IA. IA. (1957a). *Proc. Intern. Conf. Mesons and Recently Discovered Particles, Padova-Venezia, 17th*, p. 27.

BLINOV, G. A., KRESTNIKOV, IU. S., LOMANOV, M. F., and SHALAMOV, IA. IA. (1957b). *Soviet Phys. JETP* **5**, 1281.

BLOCH, M., *et al.* (1959). *Proc. Intern. Conf. High-Energy Accelerators and Instrumentation, CERN, Geneva*, p. 499.

BLOCH, M., LAGARRIGUE, A., RANÇON, P., and ROUSSET, A. (1961). *Rev. Sci. Instr.* **32**, 1302.

BLUMENFELD, H. A., BOWEN, T., and MCILWAIN, R. L. (1960). *Proc. Intern. Conf. Instrumentation High-Energy Phys., Berkeley*, p. 100.

BRAUTTI, G., CESCHIA, M., and BASSI, P. (1958). *Nuovo Cimento* **10**, 1148.

BROWN, J. L. (1960). *Proc. Intern. Conf. Instrumentation for High-Energy Phys., Berkeley*, p. 110.

BROWN, J. L., GLASER, D. A., and PERL, M. L. (1956). *Phys. Rev.* **102**, 586.

BUDAGOV, JU. A., DZHELEPOV, V. P., DJAKOV, N. I., FLYALIN, V. B., and SHATET, T. (1960). *Proc. Intern. Conf. Instrumentation for High-Energy Phys., Berkeley*, p. 135.

BUDAGOV, YU. A., DZHELEPOV, V. P., IVANOV, V. G., LOMAKIN, YU. F., FLYAGIN, V. B., and SHLYAPNIKOV, P. V. (1962). *Proc. Conf. Instrumentation for High-Energy Phys., CERN, Geneva*, p. 128.

BUGG, D. V. (1958). *Rev. Sci. Instr.* **29**, 587.

BUGG, D. V. (1959). *Progr. Nucl. Phys.* **7**, 1.

BULLOCK, F. W., DODD, C., HENDERSON, C., and KALMUS, G. (1957). *Nuovo Cimento* **6**, 334.

BULLOCK, F. W., DODD, C., and KALMUS, G. E. (1958). *Nuovo Cimento* **10**, 718.

BURMEISTER, H., VAN DARDEL, G., and SCHULTZE, K. (1963). *CERN, NPA* 63–22.

CHRÉTIEN, M., *et al.* (1962). *Phys. Rev. Letters* **9**, 127.

CHRÉTIEN, M., FIRTH, D. R., YAMAMOTO, R. K., PLESS, I. A., and ROSENSON, L. (1962). *Proc. Conf. Instrumentation for High-Energy Phys., CERN, Geneva*, p. 120.

CRAWFORD, F. S., Jr., CRESTI, M., GOOD, M. L., KALBFLEISCH, G. R., STEVENSON, M. L., and TICHO, H. K. (1958). *Phys. Rev. Letters* **1**, 377.

DANBY, G., *et al.* (1962). *Phys. Rev. Letters* **9**, 36.

ELY, R. P., *et al.* (1962). *Phys. Rev. Letters* **8**, 132.

ELY, R. P., *et al.* (1963). *Phys. Rev.* **131**, 868.

FEINBERG, G., GÜRSEY, F., and PAIS, A. (1961). *Phys. Rev. Letters* **7**, 208.

GLASER, D. A. (1952). *Phys. Rev.* **87**, 665.

GOLDSCHMIDT-CLERMONT, Y., KING, D. T., MUIRHEAD, H., and RITSON, D. M. (1948). *Proc. Phys. Soc. (London)*, **A61**, 183.

GUERRIERO, L., *et al.* (1960). *Rev. Sci. Instr.* **31**, 1040.

HAHN, B. (1956). *Nuovo Cimento* **4**, 944.

HAHN, B., and FISHER, J. (1957). *Rev. Sci. Instr.* **28**, 656.

HAHN, B., and HUGENTOBLER, E. (1960). *Nuovo Cimento* **17**, 983.

HAHN, B., and RIEPE, G. (1958). *Rev. Sci. Instr.* **29**, 184.

HAHN, B., RIEPE, G., and KNUDSEN, A. W. (1959). *Rev. Sci. Instr.* **30**, 654.

HAHN, B., HUGENTOBLER, E., and STEINRISSER, F. (1960a). *Proc. Intern. Conf. Instrumentation for High-Energy Phys., Berkeley*, p. 143.

HAHN, B., KNUDSEN, A. W., and HUGENTOBLER, E. (1960b). *Nuovo Cimento* **15**, Suppl. 2, 236.

HENDERSON, C., and KALMUS, G. (1957). *Nuovo Cimento* **6**, 925.

JAUNEAU, L., *et al.* (1963). *Phys. Letters* **4**, 49.

KANAREK, T. I., *et al.* (1959). *Proc. Intern. Conf. High-Energy Accelerators and Instrumentation, CERN, Geneva*, p. 508.

KARATSUBA, A. P., MALTSEV, E. I., NAGY, T., and NAGY, J. (1960). *Proc. Intern. Conf. Instrumentation for High-Energy Phys., Berkeley*, p. 113.

KIRILLOV-UGRYUMOV, V. G., KOTENTO, L. P., KUZNETOV, E. P., and SAMOILOV, A. V. (1960). *Instr. Exptl. Tech. (USSR)*, p. 47.

KUZNETSOV, E. V., LOMANOF, M. F., BLINOV, G. A., CHUAN, C.-N., and KHUAN, S.-N. (1957). *Soviet Phys. JETP* **4**, 773.

LEE, T. D., and YANG, C. N. (1960). *Phys. Rev. Letters* **4**, 307.

LORIA, A., MITTNER, P., SCOTONI, I., and ZAGO, G. (1959). *Nuovo Cimento* **11**, 718.

MILBURN, R. H. (1962). *Proc. Scintillation Counter Symp., March*, p. 16.

MINEHART, R. C., and MILBURN, R. H. (1960). *Rev. Sci. Instr.* **31**, 173.

MUKHIN, K. N., SHLYAPNIKOV, R. S., and BARKOV, L. M. (1959). *Proc. Intern. Conf. High-Energy Accelerators and Instrumentation, CERN, Geneva*, p. 514.

MULLINS, J. H., ALYEA, E. D., Jr., and TEEM, J. M. (1960). *Proc. Intern. Conf. Instrumentation for High-Energy Phys., Berkeley*, p. 106.

PERSHIN, I. I., and GOLUBCHIKOV, V. M. (1960). *Instr. Exptl. Tech. (USSR)*, p. 382.

PERSHIN, I. I., BARMIN, V. V., KANAVETS, V. P., and MOROZOV, B. V. (1959). *Instr. Exptl. Tech. (USSR)*, p. 555.

POWELL, W. M., FOWLER, W. B., and OSWALD, L. O. (1958). *Rev. Sci. Instr.* **29**, 874.

POWELL, W. M., OSWALD, L. O., GRIFFIN, G., and SWARTZ, F. (1963a). *UCRL 10861*.

POWELL, W. M., OSWALD, L. O., GRIFFIN, G., and SWARTZ, F. (1963b). *Rev. Sci. Instr.* **34**, 1426.

PRODELL, A. G., and STEINBERGER, J. (1962). *Rev. Sci. Instr.* **33**, 1327.

RAMM, C. A., and RESEGOTTI, L. (1960). *Proc. Intern. Conf. Instrumentation High-Energy Phys. Berkeley*, p. 127.

RITSON, D. M. (1961). "Techniques of High Energy Physics," pp. 23–24. Wiley (Interscience), New York.

ROSSI, B. (1952). "High Energy Particles," pp. 13–15; Chapter II, p. 82. Prentice-Hall, Englewood Cliffs, New Jersey.

ROUSSET, A. (1960). *Proc. Intern. Conf. Instrumentation High-Energy Phys., Berkeley*, p. 140.

SHALAMOV, Y. Y., and SHEBAMOV, V. A. (1960). *Instr. Exptl. Tech. (USSR)*, p. 501.

SIX, J. (1962). Thesis, Faculté des Sciences de Paris, No. 4753.

STRAUCH, K. (1959). *Proc. Intern. Conf. High-Energy Accelerators Instrumentation, CERN, Geneva*, p. 505.

SYMON, K. R. (1948). Thesis, Harvard University.

VAN DER MEER, S., (1961). *CERN Report*. 61–7.

VEILLET, J. J., *et al.* (1963). *Phys. Rev. Letters* **10**, 29.

CHAPTER V

Illumination and Photography of Bubble Chambers

W. T. WELFORD

Department of Physics
Imperial College of Science and Technology, London, England

The main problems in making a track of bubbles "visible" to a camera arise from the fact that a bubble in a transparent liquid does not absorb light, but removes it from an incident pencil by a process which can be considered as a mixture of reflection, refraction, and scattering. Then a bubble can be "seen" by a camera either because it scatters light out of a beam and appears dark against a light background (bright field photography) or because it scatters light into a lens placed so as not to receive the direct beam (dark field photography). Thus the light scattering properties of bubbles must first be studied. We then discuss systems for illuminating the bubbles and the geometrical problems of making the most of the available chamber volume. The remainder of the chapter is concerned with the photography proper, and the questions of focal depth, magnification, light power, and overall precision of measurement are treated.

At the time of writing several chambers in the size range 1–2 meters have been successfully run and the optical principles are well understood. Some new chambers of roughly spherical shape and about 4 meters diameter are being constructed but many of the optical aspects are as yet untried; these newer optical proposals are mentioned briefly in this chapter but it must be stressed that they have not all been tested under operating conditions.

I. Light Scattering by Bubbles

The problem of scattering of electromagnetic waves by spherical obstacles was first solved by Mie in 1908. A good exposition of the Mie theory was given by van de Hulst (1957), who considered also the various approximations which can be made to the exact electromagnetic theory for certain ranges of the parameters; these parameters are n, the refractive index of the particle relative to the medium; $2r$, the diameter of the particle; λ, the wavelength of the radiation; and α, the scattering angle. Van de Hulst distinguished in particular the geometrical optics approximation, for which $r \gg \lambda$, $\alpha \gg \lambda/r$, and the Fraunhofer diffraction approximation, for which $r \gg \lambda$, $\alpha \sim \lambda/r$. These two, particularly the first, apply to bubble chambers, since the bubbles are usually more than $100\,\mu$ in diameter and the scattering angle is several degrees.

In the geometrical theory, the scattering process is treated by considering reflection and refraction of incident rays which are assumed not to interfere with each other but which are suitably modified by the Fresnel reflection and transmission coefficients for oblique incidence at refracting media. In the Fraunhofer theory, the bubbles are treated as circular thin diffracting obstacles; the result does not depend on whether they are taken to be opaque or transparent and phase shifting.

A. GEOMETRICAL BUBBLE SCATTERING THEORY

A detailed description of the computation of geometrical scattering by bubbles, illustrated by numerical results for bubbles in water, was given by Davis (1955).

Let light of flux density or illumination E be incident on a bubble of radius r in a medium of refractive index n. We have first to determine all possible ray paths which give the same emergent direction α; some of these are shown in Fig. 1a, which illustrates the notation. Let θ be the angle of incidence of the light and I the angle of refraction inside the bubble; then all possible paths are governed by the relation

$$\pm \alpha = 2\theta - 2NI + \pi(N - 1), \tag{1}$$

where N is the number of times the ray traverses the bubble; thus N can be 0, 1, 2, ..., the first value corresponding to reflection at the first surface.

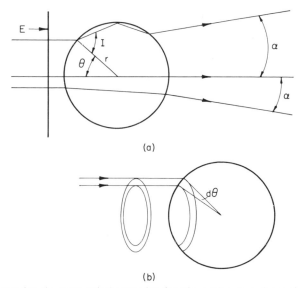

(a)

(b)

FIG. 1. Computing the geometrical scattering function: (a) rays and notation, (b) annulus of incident flux.

The total flux incident in the annulus shown in Fig. 1b is

$$E2\pi r^2 \sin \theta \cos \theta \, d\theta, \tag{2}$$

and this is reflected and refracted through the bubble into a hollow cone of semiangles $\alpha, \alpha + d\alpha$, where, from Eq. 1,

$$d\alpha = 2(1 - N \, dI/d\theta) \, d\theta. \tag{3}$$

Thus, at a (large) distance R, this flux is spread over an area

$$2\pi R^2 \sin \alpha \, d\alpha, \tag{4}$$

and the flux density over this area is

$$\frac{E2\pi r^2 \sin \theta \cos \theta \, d\theta}{2\pi R^2 \sin \alpha \, d\alpha}. \tag{5}$$

Substituting the value of $d\alpha/d\theta$ from Eq. (3) and using Snell's law to find $dI/d\theta$, we have for the scattered flux

$$E\left(\frac{r}{R}\right)^2 \frac{\sin 2\theta}{4 \sin \alpha(1 - nN \cos \theta/\cos I)}. \tag{6}$$

This expression was obtained on the assumption that all the light in the incident annulus is transmitted to the final annulus, so we now have to allow for reflection losses. Let $f(\theta)$ be the reflection factor for angle of incidence θ; then we have to multiply Eq. (6) by $f^{N-1}(1 - f)^2$ if $N \neq 0$ or by f if $N = 0$. The two polarizations should be considered separately; for the electric vector in a plane containing the center of the sphere, the Fresnel formula gives

$$f_p(\theta) = \frac{\tan^2(I - \theta)}{\tan^2(I + \theta)}, \tag{7}$$

and for the other polarization

$$f_s(\theta) = \frac{\sin^2(I - \theta)}{\sin^2(I + \theta)}, \tag{8}$$

so that the overall factor for reflection losses is

$$\tfrac{1}{2}\{f_p^{N-1}(1 - f_p)^2 + f_s^{N-1}(1 - f_s)^2\}. \tag{9}$$

Such a calculation is made for all paths ending in a given scattering angle and the results are summed; clearly, there are an infinite number of paths, but the reflection losses increase rapidly with N and only the lower values

$(N \leqslant 3)$ are usually significant. The scattered flux is then expressed in the form

$$E_s = E\left(\frac{r}{R}\right)^2 G(\alpha), \tag{10}$$

where G is the geometrical scattering coefficient.

B. FRAUNHOFER SCATTERING

The Fraunhofer theory for small angles and large diameters may be most simply explained as an application of Babinet's principle of complementary diffracting screens. The bubble, considered as a diffracting obstacle, gives the same distribution of light at infinity as a hole of the same diameter in an opaque screen. This diffraction pattern is, by the classical formula (Born and Wolf, 1959),

$$\left(\frac{\pi r}{\lambda}\right)^2 \{2J_1(z)/z\}^2 E\left(\frac{r}{R}\right)^2, \tag{11}$$

where

$$z = 2\pi r\alpha/\lambda \tag{12}$$

and the other symbols are as in Section I,A. It is not simple to relate this directly with the geometrical scattering formula Eq. (10). In Eq. (11), the term

$$F(\alpha) = \left(\frac{\pi r}{\lambda}\right)^2 \{2J_1(z)/z\}^2, \tag{13}$$

which is the coefficient of $E(r/R)^2$, is analogous to the geometrical scattering coefficient $G(\alpha)$ and it could thus be called the Fraunhofer scattering coefficient. However, $F(\alpha)$ contains the ratio of the radius of the bubble to the wavelength and would thus have to be plotted for particular bubble sizes, whereas $G(\alpha)$ is independent of bubble size. The discrepancy is, of course, a consequence of the very crude approximations inherent in geometrical optics calculations of this kind.

The Fraunhofer scattering coefficient has very large values near $\alpha = 0$ for typical bubble sizes on account of the factor $(\pi r/\lambda)^2$; the Bessel function has its first zero at the celebrated value $z = 3.83$, and we may take this as representing the region near which the geometrical approximation should take over, i.e. we use $F(\alpha)$ for $\alpha < \lambda/2r$ and $G(\alpha)$ for greater values of α. To get a more precise estimate, if we assume $r \sim 100\mu$ we find from Eqs. (12) and

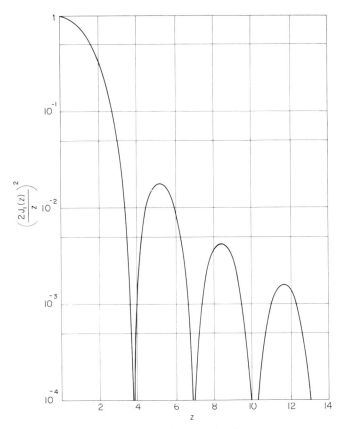

FIG. 2. The Fraunhofer scattering function.

(13) that $F(\alpha)$ has fallen to about 10 for $\alpha \sim 2°$, so that some contribution to the scattering would be expected from the Fraunhofer term up to this point.

Figure 2 shows the form of the function $\{2J_1(z)/z\}^2$ with an indication of the region of importance for our purposes. Of course, neither $F(\alpha)$ nor $G(\alpha)$ represents the scattering exactly, but taken together they give enough indication of the order of magnitude of the scattering and its derivatives with respect to α for our purposes.

C. Refractive Indices of Bubble Chamber Liquids and Numerical Results of Geometrical Scattering Computations

Table I gives approximate values for the refractive indices of liquids used in bubble chambers. Since the liquids are in a condition of superheat at the

TABLE I

REFRACTIVE INDICES OF BUBBLE CHAMBER LIQUIDS

Liquid	Refractive index
Hydrogen	1.1
Deuterium	1.1
Helium	1.025
Propane	1.25
Freons[a]	
Xenon	1.2

[a] Freons are halogenated hydrocarbons such as CF_3Br and $C_2Cl_3F_3$. Their refractive indices vary over the range 1.25 to 1.40 (private communication from A. Tamosaitis).

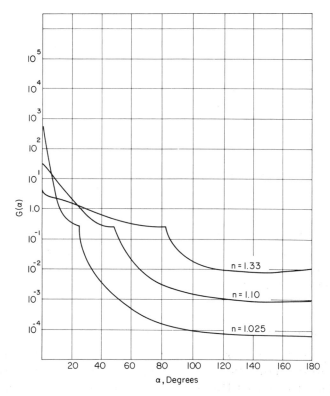

FIG. 3. Geometrical scattering function for $n = 1.33$, 1.1, and 1.025, logarithmic ordinates.

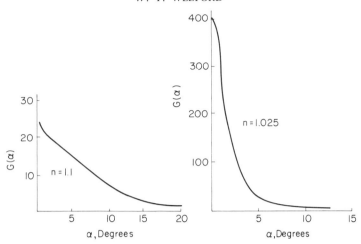

FIG. 4. Geometrical scattering function for $n = 1.1$ and 1.025 for small angles.

instant of exposure, the precise values are critically dependent on the temperature and pressure. Also, it is found that the optimum operating conditions have to be found by trial for every chamber, so that a given liquid will have slightly different refractive indices in different chambers. As far as the scattering properties are concerned, it is only necessary to know the refractive index approximately, so that the general shape of the scattering function is determined. We show in Fig. 3 the values of $G(\alpha)$, the geometrical scattering function, for $n = 1.025$, 1.10 and 1.33, corresponding roughly to the three cases of helium, hydrogen (or deuterium), and heavy liquids such as propane and the freons. The values of $G(\alpha)$ are plotted logarithmically to show the full range up to $\alpha = 180°$. Figure 4 shows $G(\alpha)$ for the light liquids on linear scales for refractive indices 1.025 and 1.1 and for ranges of α of importance in bubble chamber optics. It is seen that the form of $G(\alpha)$ changes quite rapidly with refractive index. The sharp angle in the curve for hydrogen at 50° is an artefact introduced by the geometrical approximation; it corresponds to the angle of incidence $\sin\theta = 1/n$ at which total internal reflection occurs. Similarly for the other curves.

II. Modes of Illumination: Contrast in Dark Field and Bright Field Systems

It will appear from Section V that for all except the smallest chambers it is necessary to stop down the camera lenses to secure adequate focal depth through the liquid to an extent which means that the bubbles appear as unresolved point objects; thus their diameters are below the resolution limit and no details of their shapes can be photographed. This considerably simplifies the discussion of illumination since the bubble images will be bright diffraction disks on a dark background in dark field illumination and vice versa in bright field illumination, with certain reservations about contrast.

The alternatives may be discussed by reference to Fig. 5 which shows schematically (a) dark field with small angle scattering, (b) dark field with 90° scattering, and (c) bright field. Considering first (a) and (b), we may note

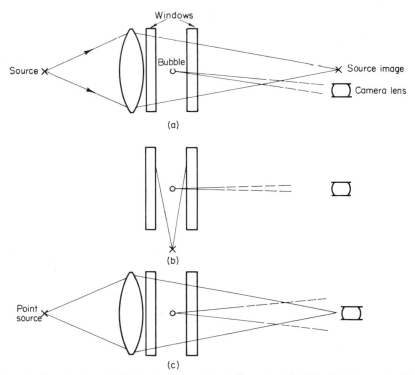

FIG. 5. Illumination of bubble chambers: (a) small angle dark field, (b) right angle dark field, (c) bright field.

that for large bubble chambers with light liquids an order of magnitude calculation of the light energy needed (Section VI,A) gives a result in the region of 100 J (i.e. flashtubes in which 100 J is dissipated) on the assumption of 100 μ diameter bubbles, and a geometrical scattering function of about 10. From the graphs of Fig. 3, it is immediately clear that small angle scattering must be used for the light liquids since flashtube powers exceeding about 1000 J are probably impracticable. On the other hand, for heavy liquids it can be seen that 90° illumination is quite practicable, particularly since here the direction of the light need not be so strictly collimated, and consequently larger and more powerful sources can be used. It is to be noted that even if the light energy could be increased indefinitely, it would be disadvantageous to use 90° illumination with light liquids: this is because the so-called dark field is never perfectly dark; there is always some background of stray light from imperfections in and dirt on the optics. Also, the smaller the value of $G(\alpha)$, the less will the bubbles stand out against this background; the contrast can only be recovered by allowing a longer bubble growth time.

The principle of bright field illumination (Fig. 5c) as applied to this case involves a source small enough for its image to fall within the camera lens aperture; the bubble scatters some of the incident light outside the aperture and thus appears dark against the bright field. The optimum conditions for good contrast in bright field are complicated and they depend in detail on the condenser system or its equivalent. This is discussed in detail in Section II,C.

In the subsections which follow, we describe in more detail the systems that have been proposed and used for small angle dark field illumination and for bright field illumination. We shall not discuss 90° illumination systems any further since they have been dealt with in Chapter IV, this volume; they are used only for heavy liquids and the problems involved are not specifically optical in character. We shall, however, distinguish between small angle dark field systems in which the sources and cameras are on opposite ends of the chamber (through illumination) and those in which sources and cameras are on the same side (retrodirective illumination).

A. Through Illumination in Dark Field

The basic system for through illumination in dark field is as in Fig. 5a. The (small) scattering angle is equal to the distance from the camera lens to the image of the source divided by the distance from the bubble to the camera lens, with corrections to take account of refraction in the liquid. More specifically, let all the windows between the liquid and the camera lens be lumped together as one thickness d_g with refractive index n_g as in Fig. 6, let z be the distance of the bubble from the inner window surface, let l be the distance of the camera lens from the outer window surface, and let η be the distance from the source image to the camera lens. Then, within the Gaussian optics approximation, we have

$$\alpha = \frac{\eta}{nl + (n/n_g)d_g + z}. \tag{14}$$

Obviously the scattering angle varies with the position of the bubble, a point to which we return in Section III,B.

The lens system which forms an image of the source near the camera lens is in principle only a condenser, but since the scattering angle has to be small (values from 2 to 14° are used), it has to be rather well corrected as

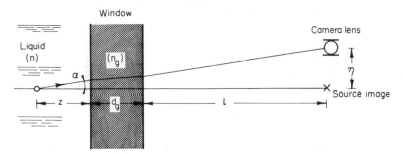

FIG. 6. Notation for calculating scattering angle.

condensers go, to ensure that no direct light enters the camera lens. Since the scattering coefficient varies rapidly with angle, it is also desirable that the image should be quite well corrected for aberrations, so that the scattering angle is nearly the same in different parts of the chamber. Figure 7 shows how spherical aberration in the condenser gives a greater scattering angle on one side of the chamber than on the other. Thus, it is clear that some approach should be made to aberration correction in the condenser, to the extent that the angular aberrations should not exceed, say, 1°. Optical designs of corrected condensers are described in Section II,A,1.

The geometry of the light sources is bound up to some extent with that of the camera lenses. An array of three or, in some large chambers, four cameras may be used and the simplest arrangement is to have a single concentrated source focused at a point symmetrically placed between the

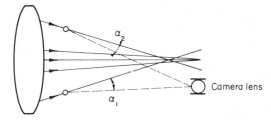

FIG. 7. Effect of spherical aberration on scattering angle.

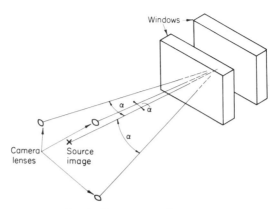

FIG. 8. Stereo array of cameras.

lenses (Fig. 8). This relatively simple arrangement leads to a scattering angle in the range 7 to 14° with the average layout of bubble chambers.

Large bubble chambers intended to be used with beams of very high energy particles are naturally rectangular in shape, with length three or four times the width (length and width are dimensions seen directly by the cameras); in such a case, it is natural to split the condensers into three or four roughly square aperture sections, as in Fig. 9. This reduces condenser cost considerably, since the central thickness of a lens is roughly proportional to the square of its diameter for given power. The individual sections would in fact probably be doublets or triplets but they are shown as single lenses for simplicity in Fig. 9 and elsewhere in this section.

Stray light in dark field systems presents serious problems. For our purposes there are three kinds of stray light: (a) ghost reflections of the

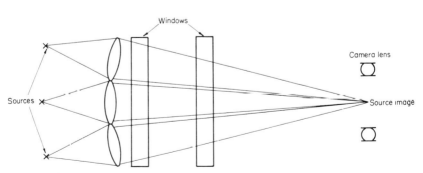

FIG. 9. Three channel condenser system for a rectangular chamber.

sources from optical surfaces; (b) general background from optical surfaces due to poor polish and surface dirt, e.g. dust, grease, frozen nitrogen, or diffusion pump oil; and (c) general background from nonoptical surfaces which happen to be in the field of view of the cameras. Of these, (c) is easily dealt with by suitably choosing the geometry of light shields so that illuminated surfaces are not seen by the cameras. As for (b), the general question of surface polish is discussed in Section IV,B and the prevention of frozen vapors is a matter of cleanliness and high vacuum technology; however, the scattering of most kinds of dirt increases rapidly at small scattering angles, so cleanliness is particularly important in small angle systems. There remains the problem of ghost reflections. Since the reflection factor of an uncoated glass surface is 4%, the luminance of the brightest ghost images in a through-illuminated system will be 0.0016 of the directly viewed condensers; this would usually be much brighter than the bubble images, as can be seen by the following calculation.

Let E be the incident illumination (watts per square meter, say) on the bubble and suppose this comes from a source which subtends a solid angle Ω. Let r be the bubble radius, let R be the distance from the bubble to the camera, and let the camera lens aperture be $2a$ in diameter. The camera lens collects from the bubble a total scattered flux

$$F_s = E\left(\frac{r}{R}\right)^2 G(\alpha)\pi a^2 , \tag{15}$$

where $G(\alpha)$ is the scattering function (Section I,A). If the camera lens were moved so as to be covered by the image of the source, it would collect, from an area equal to that subtended by the bubble, the flux

$$F_d = \frac{E\pi r^2}{\Omega}\pi\left(\frac{a}{R}\right)^2 . \tag{16}$$

Thus

$$F_s/F_d = G\Omega/\pi . \tag{17}$$

As order of magnitude values, we may take $G = 10$, $\Omega = 10^{-3}$, indicating that the bubble images will be about as bright as ghost images produced by two reflections from uncoated surfaces. In fact, the situation is rather worse because the flux F_s is spread into a diffraction pattern in the image formed by the camera lens, since the bubble cannot be resolved, whereas F_d would be used in forming an image of an extended object and so would, in effect, all fall within a circle of the diameter of the geometrical image of the bubble.

Three ways of minimizing effects of ghost images have been used. First, we may reduce their brightness by antireflection coatings on the optics. This is almost always done on large through-illumination systems; the theory and practical details are discussed in Section IV,C below. Secondly, we may decrease the scattering angle, which has the effect of increasing the scattering function $G(\alpha)$ and so improving the ratio F_s/F_d. Thirdly, we may increase the angle subtended by the source.

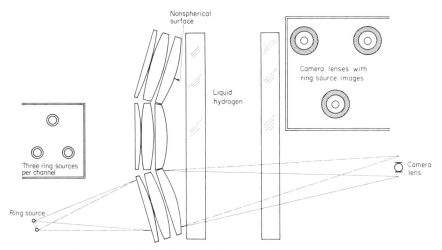

FIG. 10. Optics of Rutherford Laboratory 1.5 meter hydrogen chamber; the precondensers are not shown.

The use of a small scattering angle necessarily involves more complicated source geometry; there must be a source image near each camera lens, so that if there are n camera lenses and m sections to the condenser array, we have altogether mn sources. We gain the most advantage if the individual sources are in the form of rings of which the images encircle the camera lenses. Figure 10 shows how the illumination optics is arranged for the 1.5 meter hydrogen chamber of the Rutherford High Energy Laboratory.

The alternative of increasing the solid angle Ω subtended by the source seems to have been used only on small and medium size chambers. It evolves as a large area of ground glass at the object plane of the condenser which is illuminated by the flashtubes; black patch stops are fixed to the ground glass in positions such that their images fall on the camera lenses. Clearly the source has low luminance and large area so as to get the required total flux through the chamber. A disadvantage is that the parts of the ground glass at great distances from the patch stops are used with large scattering angle and they therefore contribute little to the flux scattered into the lens by the bubble image, although they contribute to the background from dirt on the optics. This drawback is particularly serious with helium, for which $G(\alpha)$ drops rapidly with increasing α. Several systems of this kind and hybrid types have been made and some are described in a review of bubble chamber optical systems (Welford, 1963a); they are mainly suitable for smaller chambers because in a large chamber, the loss of light power due to scattering from the diffusing material and to the effectively larger scattering angle is a serious disadvantage. Furthermore, cylindrical or toroidal lens shapes are frequently involved and these are made of plastics, which do not take such a scatterfree polish as glass.

1. *Optical Design of Condensers*

The power (reciprocal of focal length) of a condenser section is determined in the usual way by the two conjugates, i.e., distances to source and to camera lens. The latter depends on the geometry of the camera and on the field angle of the camera lens: it must be as short as possible to give a large stereo angle but if it is very short the field angle becomes too large. We discuss this in more detail in Section III but here we may say that for the current type of large chamber the camera side conjugate is of the order of 2 meters. As will be seen in Section II,A,2, there is usually an auxiliary collecting optical system between the light source and the main condenser, the so-called precondenser. The light-gathering power of the system is determined by the solid angle which the precondenser subtends at the source. The angular aperture of the main condenser on the light side is thus immaterial from the optical point of view, but there are nonoptical considerations concerned with the design of the various vacuum vessels which usually make it desirable to have this conjugate as short as possible. A practical limit which is dictated by glass thicknesses and aberration corrections is that the condenser can work at a relative aperture of about $f/0.9$ on this side, i.e. the conjugate distance is about 90% of the diagonal of the condenser aperture. A shorter f ratio leads to great difficulties in design, construction, and alignment.

Supposing the conjugates and therefore the power to have been fixed, it will be found that a very thick and heavy condenser system is needed. It will usually be better to split this into two or three components both for ease in handling and to facilitate aberration correction, since, as we saw, some approximate aberration correction is desirable. If a lens of positive power K has an aperture of diameter $2h$ then its central thickness must be approximately $\frac{1}{2}h^2K/(n-1)$, where n is the refractive index of the glass, or, with a further approximation, $n \approx 1.5$, it is h^2K. Putting $K = 1\,\text{meter}^{-1}$ and $h = 0.5\,\text{meter}$, we find a central thickness of 25 cm; if the lens is split into two or more components, this will be the total central thickness.

This excludes the possibility of correcting two of the aberrations, namely longitudinal chromatic aberration, since an equivalent bulk of dense flint glass and even more crown would be needed to obtain the same total power with cancelling dispersions, and astigmatism. In order to correct astigmatism it is necessary to have an aperture stop remote from the lens and components of negative power, if spherical aberration correction is also to be obtained, and again the extra bulk of glass needed would be too great.

The remaining point-imaging aberrations, spherical aberration, coma and transverse chromatic aberration can be corrected to the approximation necessary for our purpose. Of these, transverse chromatic aberration is negligible since condensers are used with their effective aperture stop at the lenses and transverse color only arises if the stop is remote from a lens component. Also, quite frequently a restricted wavelength range is used, by filtering and choice of film sensitivity, so that both longitudinal and transverse color are negligible; this is done partly in order to minimize chromatic aberration effects but mainly in order to improve the efficiency of anti-reflection coatings (Section IV,C) and, by using the blue end of the spectrum, to gain resolving power in the camera lens.

Spherical aberration and coma can both be corrected by choice of the curvatures and shapes of the lens surfaces, without increasing the total bulk of glass beyond that needed to obtain the power. It would not be possible

TABLE II

PROPERTIES OF K50 AND BK7

	BK7	K50
n_d	1.5168	1.5226
V^a	64.2	60.2
Density	2.51	2.61
Thermal expansion coefficient	8.2×10^{-6}	7.6×10^{-6}
Transformation temperature °C	547	560
Young's modulus (kg/cm^2)	8.2×10^5	7.3×10^5
Bubble cross section (mm^2 per 100 mm^3 of glass)	0–0.1	0–0.029
Transmission at 3650 Å in 25 mm thickness	0.945	0.960

[a] The quantity V measures the dispersion and is defined by $V = \dfrac{n_d - 1}{n_f - n_c}$.

here to give full details of the design process because of lack of space but we indicate briefly the principles.

The glass would naturally be the cheapest optical glass that could be made in large pieces reasonably free from defects such as bubbles and stones. The only manufacturer seriously in the market at the time of writing is Jenaer Glaswerk Schott u. Gen., Mainz, W. Germany, and they recommend either their K50 or their BK7. The optical and other relevant properties of these are summarized in Table II. BK7 is a pot-melted borosilicate crown and is of the highest quality as regards homogeneity. K50 is made by a continuous tank process and is probably not so homogeneous as BK7 but it is amply good enough for condensers; it is claimed to be somewhat freer from bubbles and stones than is BK7.

In the case of condensers with a diameter or diagonal of order 1 meter, it will almost invariably be advisable to use two components in order to

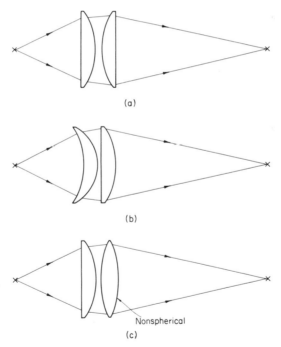

(a)

(b)

Nonspherical

(c)

FIG. 11. Stages in the optical design of a doublet condenser: (a) uncorrected system, showing central thickness required for given aperture and power, (b) system with spherical surfaces corrected for coma and spherical aberration, (c) system with a nonspherical surface corrected for spherical aberration and coma.

have reasonable central thicknesses (Fig. 11a). Then it is in principle possible
to choose bendings of the components to make the Seidel spherical aberration and coma both zero, but it will then be found that this involves deep
meniscus shapes (Fig. 11b) and this adds further weight to the raw glass and
to the finished lens. It is better therefore to choose shapes without concave
surfaces; but since the spherical aberration cannot be made zero with this
limitation, we have to make one surface nonspherical. It is then best to
make one component planoconvex, since the flat surface is easy to work, to
choose the bending of the other to give zero coma, and, then, to asperize
one surface to eliminate spherical aberration (Fig. 11c).

The aspheric figuring could be chosen in the first instance to eliminate
the Seidel spherical aberration and it could then be improved by tracing

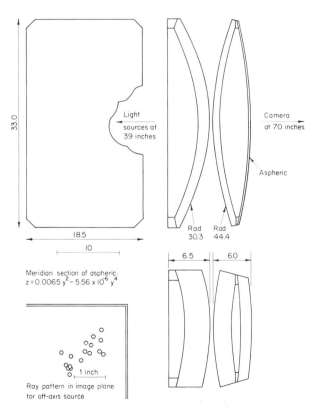

FIG. 12. Doublet condenser for a helium chamber; the chamber aperture, 16 by 32 in., is
covered by the one condenser.

exact rays. In practice, the author has found that if the aspheric surface is represented by a meridian section with an equation of the form

$$z = a_2 y^2 + a_4 y^4,$$ (18)

the coefficient a_4 being found from the Seidel approximation, the aberration correction is amply good enough as judged by ray tracing.

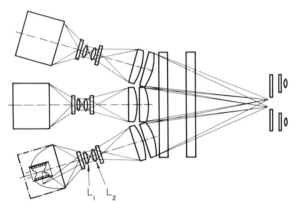

FIG. 13. Illumination system of the CERN 2 meter hydrogen chamber. The precondenser mirrors around the flashtubes have a crinkled surface to distribute the light flux evenly over the main condenser apertures.

If the condenser is to be used off axis, as in systems with small scattering angle where each camera lens has its own source, then rays should be traced off axis to check that the astigmatism is within a suitable range and to allow for field curvature. The results will indicate whether the aberrations are low enough.

Multicomponent condensers of this kind have been used in the Rutherford Laboratory 1.5 meter hydrogen chamber (operating at CERN at the time of writing). Figure 12 shows the author's design of a two component condenser for use with a helium chamber (window aperture 80 × 40 cm); there are four cameras arranged at the corners of a rectangle and four point sources focused near them to give a mean scattering angle of 4°. The ray intersection diagram shows the residual aberrations. Details of a system for a 2 meter hydrogen chamber consisting of 3 doublets, each with 1 aspherized surface, were given by Früngel et al. (1963); this system is shown complete in Fig. 13; it will be noticed that the last surfaces of the condensers are steeply convex and this is also the case with the condenser array of the

Rutherford Laboratory 1.5 meter chamber. It is advantageous to have this so because the pencils then gain a considerable increment of convergence at this last surface; this means that the rays can be kept clear of the chamfered edges along which the three sections of the condenser array touch, and these edges do not show up as bright patches.

2. Precondensers

In low temperature bubble chambers, there are two vacuum jackets, an outer tank at ambient temperature and an inner one at the temperature of the chamber, and there is often an intermediate heat shield at liquid nitrogen temperature. In order to avoid having excessively large windows in all these tanks, it is usual in large chambers to form a real image of the light source near the surface of the inner tank; thus, the innermost windows can be kept small and radiation losses minimized. It is the collecting angle of the precondenser which determines the light-gathering power of the whole system, assuming that the convergence angles between the precondenser and main condenser are matched. A field lens can be placed at or near the real image; its power is chosen so as to form an image of the precondenser aperture in the aperture of the main condenser lens.

Figure 14 shows the precondenser system used with ring sources for the 1.5 meter Rutherford Laboratory hydrogen chamber. The source is imaged by the precondenser onto the annular stop, which is then the effective source for the main condenser and is imaged by it around the camera lens.

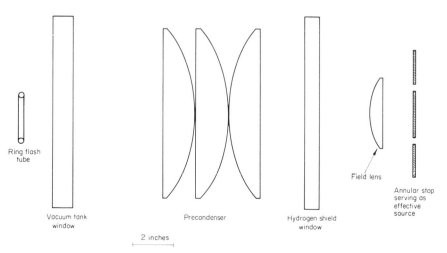

Ring flash
tube

Vacuum tank
window

Precondenser

Hydrogen shield
window

Field lens

Annular stop
serving as
effective
source

2 inches

FIG. 14. Precondenser system for the Rutherford Laboratory 1.5 meter hydrogen chamber.

The field lens images a plane near the midpoint of the precondenser into the main condenser, so as to give uniform illumination. It should be emphasized that such a system should not be completely designed on paper; it is safest to set up the optics and light source, and find by trial the optimum lens positions for uniform illumination. In the present case, the separation shown between the annular stop and the field lens was not in the original design but it was found to give better results in practice!

For the system of the CERN 2 meter chamber (Fig. 13), the light sources are "point" flashtubes, and they are focused by the ellipsoidal mirror precondensers into the field lenses (the doublets L_1, L_2). The ellipsoidal mirrors have slightly corrugated surfaces to ensure that rays diverge from all points of the field lens apertures at all angles; thus, a central gap in the illumination which would have resulted from the use of mirror precondensers is avoided.

B. Retrodirective Illumination in Dark Field

Through-illumination systems require large and elaborate condenser arrays, two main chamber windows, and considerable extensions to the vacuum tank and cryogenic shields on the illumination side. For these reasons, it is useful to consider retrodirective illumination, in which the light sources are on the same side of the chamber as the cameras. The general principle is as in Fig. 15; a large concave mirror forms one wall of the chamber, and a light source at or near the center of curvature of the mirror is reimaged back on itself; the cameras are arranged round the light source image. This is clearly very simple in principle, since only one window is needed and the condenser optics reduces to a single large concave mirror.

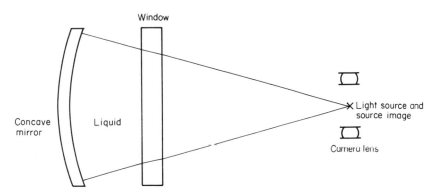

FIG. 15. Principle of retrodirective illumination.

The space behind this mirror can be filled with iron, giving a useful gain in magnetic field although possibly at the expense of some uniformity.

The camera lenses have to be stopped down enough to ensure that tracks are reasonably in focus throughout the depth of the chamber and this means that slightly out-of-focus images of the tracks will be seen reflected in the concave mirror; these are dark field images formed by light scattered before the illuminating beam meets the mirror. These out-of-focus tracks could not be tolerated since they would confuse the pictures too much. The chief complications and problems of retrodirective illumination arise in eliminating them. Subsidiary problems arise in eliminating ghost reflections; these images are, of course, much brighter than in through-illumination systems, since only one reflection in the window is needed to produce a ghost image which can be seen by the camera lenses.

Many methods have been proposed for eliminating the reflected track images, but only one seems to have been used on large chambers, namely the "coathanger" system (see Section II,B,1). We review here briefly the other possibilities; further details and references are given by Welford (1963a). If the concave mirror is simply moved far enough back, the reflected track images will go far enough out of focus to be not visible in the photographs; however, this involves a second window and a large space behind it, and nearly all the advantages of retrodirective illumination are lost. Another proposal was to make the concave mirror very thick, with the reflecting surface at the back, thus again putting the track images further out of focus; again many advantages are lost and it is rather difficult to be sure of the level of background due to the reflected tracks which might remain. None of these systems seems to have been tried.

The second class of system is based on the venetian blind or slat principle; the mirror is covered with slats placed edgeways so that the illuminating beam can be reflected back but the mirror surface is not visible to the cameras. The sizes and positions of the slats are worked out on obvious geometrical principles. The principal drawback to this system is that the edges of the slats are directly illuminated and are seen by the cameras; it is well known that even the best optical blacks reflect quite an appreciable proportion of light and thus one may doubt whether the dark field would have enough contrast to permit the bubbles to be seen. Improvements on this scheme which appear to have considerable promise have been proposed by Palmer (1963). He first suggested making up the slats as a solid matrix of black and clear glass slats aluminized on the rear (Fig. 16a); the system is polished on both sides as a whole. The black glass, the clear glass, and the cement have the same refractive index, so there is no reflection at the joins.

Palmer's second proposal was for clear glass fibers fused together with black glass of the same refractive index (Fig. 16b). Provided the refractive indices match and provided the joins do not disturb the polishing process, this would seem to be a very promising idea and well worth following up. The limit on performance would be set by the far field diffraction pattern of the ends of the fibers. If as a first approximation these are assumed to behave

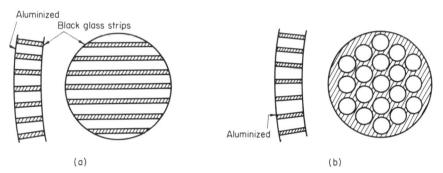

(a)   (b)

FIG. 16. Developments of the venetian blind or shutter principle proposed by R. B. Palmer for retroreflectors; (a) slats, (b) glass fibers about 1 mm diameter in a black glass matrix.

like circular diffracting apertures, the diffracted intensity as a fraction of that in the main beam from one fiber is

$$(2J_1(z)/z)^2,\tag{19}$$

where

$$z = (2\pi/\lambda)na\beta,\tag{20}$$

n is the refractive index of the liquid, a the radius of the fiber, and β the angle of the diffracted beam with the main beam. We have to put β equal to the illumination scattering angle, say 0.1 rad; then, if the fiber diameter is 0.5 mm, we have $z \sim 300$; and the scattered intensity is about 10^{-7} times the direct intensity, which is well below the danger level. There are, however, non-negligible technical problems in making such a system and it could be quite expensive.

Another type of retrodirective system depends on spoiling the reflected bubble images by suitable irregularities on the concave mirror; this is the so-called "wobbly mirror," where the mirror surface is distorted, as in Fig. 17. The changes in slope must be limited to a maximum of less than half the scattering angle, so that no direct light enters the camera lens. Also, the

wobbles must be rapid enough to ensure that one complete wobble subtends an angle at the nearest bubble which is less than that subtended by the
camera lens aperture; this condition ensures that the light scattered by the
bubble from the illuminating beam before it strikes the mirror is spread
over a wide angle and cannot form a bright bubble image. The wobbles
could be on the mirror surface or on a sheet of transparent material in front
of it. This system has not been used in dark field illumination but a similar
scheme has been applied in a bright field system (see Section II,C).

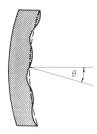

FIG. 17. The wobbly mirror retroreflector.

Finally, we come to retrodirective systems in which the scattered light is
trapped optically near an intermediate image of the light source. The
principle is illustrated in Fig. 18. Each unit of the retroreflector is a solid
lens of glass or plastic of such a thickness that an image of the light source
is formed at its rear surface; a patch on this surface of the same size as the
image is aluminized and the rest of the surface is painted with absorbing

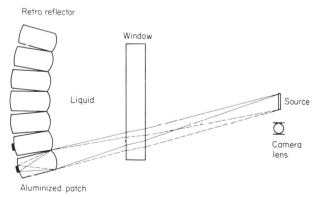

FIG. 18. Lens-mirror retroreflectors; the aluminized patches correspond exactly to the size
of the source images.

black paint. The main illuminating beam is thus reflected back to form an image of the light source at the same position as the source itself, but any light scattered by bubbles when the light is travelling to the left misses the reflecting patch; thus, no reflected images are seen. The reflecting surface is made concave to the incident light with a radius of curvature equal to the thickness of the solid lens; thus this surface acts as a field lens in that it forms an image of the front (right-hand) surface on itself and so prevents the rays from spreading at this surface after returning from the reflecting patch. This point is illustrated in detail by the lowest retroreflector in Fig. 18.

Many realizations of this principle are possible but only one seems to have been used, namely the coathanger system, described in the next section.

1. *The Coathanger Retrodirective Illumination System*

Systems of the kind shown in Fig. 18 would require a large number of solid lens units and would probably be prohibitively expensive to make and adjust for a large chamber. This disadvantage was overcome by the coathanger system, which was developed at the Lawrence Radiation Laboratory (Bradner, 1960). The array of lenses is made in the form of a row of curved cylindrical lenses (Fig. 19) each with an aluminized strip along its back. The radius of curvature in the side view is equal to the distance from the light source, allowing for refraction in the liquid. The radius in the other view is determined as before to form an image of the source on the aluminized strip, one-dimensionally. It can be seen that this system eliminates all but a very small proportion of the light scattered by a bubble from the illuminating beam going to the left.

The coathangers themselves have been made of plastic, "Homolite" in the case of the Berkeley 72 in. hydrogen chamber and "Plexiglass" for the Brookhaven 80 in. chamber. Great care is needed to obtain good polish, and these items cannot be expected to be much cheaper than large glass condensers for through illumination. The absorbing optical black is "Luxorb"; this is a paint which is applied in two or three coats and which can be specified to match any refractive index between 1.48 and 1.62. It is thus much blacker when applied to glass or plastic as seen from the inside than are conventional blacks.

The coathanger system can only be used with a single light source, i.e. it is not practicable to have a source imaged near each camera lens, so that the scattering angle cannot be less than about 7°. Very careful work is needed in the manufacture and adjustment of the coathangers to ensure that they do not scatter light into the camera lenses. However, the system has advantages of flexibility in light control over the through-illumination systems;

thus, it is in principle possible to grade the widths of the reflecting strips
so as to ensure uniform illumination all over the mean plane of the chamber,
although this does not seem to have been done so far.

Belonogov *et al.* (1963) mention a system of retroreflectors which are

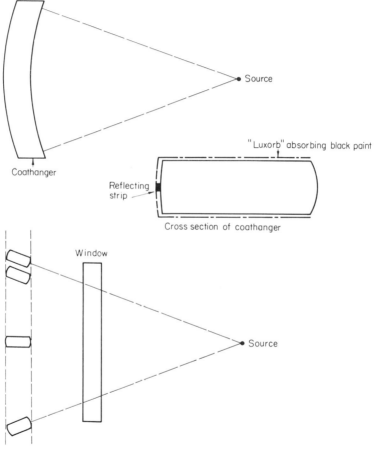

FIG. 19. The coathanger retroreflector.

"prismatic glass elements with one toroidal and two conical surfaces"; no
further description is given and there is no diagram, but one assumes that
the device is a quasi-coathanger with a 90° roof edge as the reflecting
surface.

2. *Precondensers for Retrodirective Dark Field Illumination Systems*

Precondensers are necessary in the retrodirective systems for the same reasons as in the case of through illumination systems. The Berkeley 72 in. hydrogen chamber uses an array of three sources and precondensers which produce superposed images of the sources at the hydrogen shield window. The whole of the Berkeley 72 in. chamber optical system is shown in Fig. 20. The coathanger system can be seen at the bottom of the chamber. One of the main drawbacks to retrodirective systems is the presence of bright flares in the field of view, due to reflections of the sources in the window surfaces. In the Berkeley chamber, these are avoided by setting the light sources and cameras away from the central normal of the window. For a full description of this chamber, see Bradner (1960).

A similar method of avoiding back reflections from the main window is used in two large retrodirectively illuminated hydrogen chambers described briefly by Nikitin (1963) and by Belonogov *et al.* (1963); in both these chambers, the window is actually tilted with respect to the horizontal.

The precondensers shown in Fig. 20 are simply condensers of high

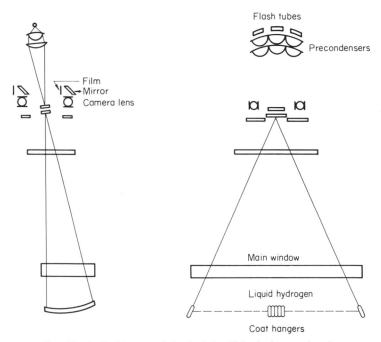

FIG. 20. Optical layout of the Berkeley 72 in. hydrogen chamber.

numerical aperture of the type used in slide and film projectors. They are aplanatic, i.e. corrected for spherical aberration and coma; the spherical aberration correction ensures that a sharp image of the source is formed at the window and the coma correction ensures that the luminance is constant over the whole of the precondenser aperture, i.e. over all the field of the chamber. In fact, exact coma correction is not necessarily the ideal condition for uniform illumination; there are small modifications depending on the nature of the polar diagram of the source and the convergence angle of the beams on the image side. We discuss this further in Section III,B.

The Brookhaven 80 in. hydrogen chamber also uses a coathanger retrodirective system; the source window is on the central normal of the window, and a more elaborate system is used to eliminate flares from the reflected source images. The precondenser system, designed by Rosin (1963), uses cylindrical optics in an ingenious way to make the maximum use of a linear flashtube. This system is shown in outline in Fig. 21; two linear flashtubes near the axis of a cylindrical mirror form effectively a solid source of four

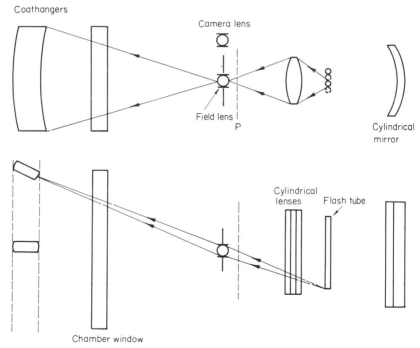

FIG. 21. Principle of the cylindrical precondenser system of the Brookhaven 80 in. hydrogen chamber.

tubes one above the other. The cylindrical lens forms an image of this (in vertical planes) at the chamber window, where there is a spherical lens. The spherical lens images the source (in horizontal planes) at the coathangers. Thus, the whole array of coathangers is uniformly illuminated. The camera lenses would see in the front and back surfaces of the window reflected images of the source which would be too bright to be eliminated by coating; to eliminate these, patch stops are put in the plane P which is conjugate with the camera lenses. Figure 21 is schematic only and does not show many elegant details in the design of this system; for these we refer to Rosin's original paper. This use of patch stops to eliminate flares depends on careful ray tracing through all possible light paths.

C. Bright Field Illumination Systems

The conditions for a bright field illumination system to give good contrast are rather restricted. A reasonable proportion of the light from the source must enter the camera lens aperture to give a bright field and the bubble must then scatter most of the light going in this direction *out* of the aperture. If too much of the direct light misses the camera lens, this will produce a dark field illumination of the bubble and will reduce the contrast.

We treat below two cases; the first is that in which the bubble is too small to be resolved by the camera lens, when it is found that, in general, the contrast is poor and it drops rapidly with bubble radius; in the second case the bubble is easily resolved and then the contrast is good.

Using the same notation as in Section I, let the bubble radius be r and let the distance from the bubble to the camera lens be R; let the diameter of the camera lens aperture be $2a$. To simplify the formulas, we ignore the slight refraction effects due to the chamber liquid. A small aperture in an opaque screen in the plane of the bubble would produce an image in which the light distribution takes the form

$$k^2(2J_1(z)/z)^2 E,\tag{21}$$

where E is the illumination (light power per unit area) at the bubble,

$$z = (2\pi/\lambda)(a/R)\eta,\tag{22}$$

η is a radial coordinate in the bubble space, and

$$k = \frac{\pi a r}{\lambda R}.\tag{23}$$

We now assume that when a bubble is photographed all the direct light from the source enters the lens but all the scattered light misses it, a condition which will be approximately fulfilled if

$$r \ll 0.61 \lambda R/a. \tag{24}$$

This is the condition that the lens aperture is well inside the main maximum of the Fraunhofer scattering function; it is assumed that most of the scattered light falls in this region, which is true for light liquids and small bubbles.

Then we can say that the bubble image would take the form

$$E\{1 - (2kJ_1(z)/z)^2\} ; \tag{25}$$

the fractional drop in intensity at the center of this image is a reasonable measure of contrast, which is simply equal to k^2, i.e.

$$\text{Contrast} \sim \left(\frac{\pi a r}{\lambda R}\right)^2. \tag{26}$$

It can be seen that if we assume that the largest bubble radius for which Eq. (24) is fulfilled is, say, $0.2\lambda R/a$ the maximum contrast is, from Eq. (26), only about 0.4, so that the bubble radius must be controlled rather carefully to ensure this condition.

It should be emphasized here that this theory is very approximate; it corresponds roughly to the assumptions that the bubbles are opaque and that they are incoherently illuminated, and neither of these is true. In particular, it should be noted that if the source size is increased beyond the point at which its aberration-free image would just fill the camera lens aperture, this must result in a drop in contrast, since there is no increase in intensity of the bright field but on the other hand more light is scattered into the lens from the bubble image. Also, it should be noted that the above discussion applies only to the case where the bubbles are small enough to appear unresolved; if the light delay time were long enough, the bubbles would grow to a size (≈ 1 mm) such that their actual shapes could be resolved, and then the mechanism of bright field image formation would be quite different and even more complicated. A bubble image would consist of a dark ring with a bright center, this center being the image of the source formed by the bubble acting as a negative lens; in general, there would be adequate contrast, always provided the source image did not fall outside the camera lens aperture.

We can obtain an approximate expression for the contrast in bright field for large (i.e. resolvable) bubbles by considering a bubble as a negative lens of power $-2n(n-1)/r$, where r is the bubble radius and n the refractive index of the liquid. Thus, in Gaussian approximation, an incident parallel pencil is spread by the bubble into a cone of semiangle $2(n-1)$ in the liquid or $2n(n-1)$ in air. This cone has a solid angle $4\pi(n-1)^2$ ($=\omega_1$, say). Suppose the camera lens subtends a solid angle ω_2 at the bubble and let the bright field illuminating system form an image of the source at the camera lens which subtends a solid angle ω_3 at the bubble. Then, if all the source image falls within the camera lens ($\omega_3 < \omega_2$), the ratio, brightness of bubble divided by brightness of field, will be ω_2/ω_1; if the source image more than covers the camera lens aperture ($\omega_3 > \omega_2$), but if $\omega_3 < \omega_1$, this ratio will be ω_3/ω_1; if the source image is so large that $\omega_3 > \omega_1$, then the ratio will be unity. From these approximate formulas, it follows that bright field illumination with heavy liquids and large bubbles should give excellent contrast; with hydrogen, adequate contrast should be obtainable if the illumination is carefully collimated so as to produce a source image a few degrees or less across, but with helium, the practical difficulties in obtaining adequate contrast would be very great.

The finite resolution and granularity of photographic emulsions may be expected to degrade contrast in bright field still further. Firth (1963) reported some simulation experiments in which fused silica spheres suspended in carbon disulphide were photographed under various bright field conditions. Qualitatively his results confirm the above conclusions, but he found that "bubbles" even larger than the formulas predict could not be photographed. A $330\,\mu$ diameter bubble could not be adequately photographed at $54\,\text{in}$. distance with camera lens apertures of $f/8$ and $f/45$ unless very high contrast process film was used and the exposure was carefully controlled; a $200\,\mu$ bubble could not be photographed even with high contrast film.

Bright field illumination has been used on a few heavy liquid chambers. The geometrical scattering function is then broad enough to ensure that the condition that a good proportion of the scattered light falls outside the camera lens is fulfilled even if Eq. (24) does not hold. In order to have a small source image lying within each camera lens aperture, it is necessary to have extremely good aberration correction on the main condenser system; this is difficult with a through-illumination system, because there will have to be an off axis image of one source for each camera; the most practical system seems to be that in which a concave spherical mirror is placed at the rear of the chamber and the light sources and camera lenses are in conjugate positions near the center of curvature. The reflected images of bubbles which would be seen in the mirror must then be eliminated. In a chamber which was constructed by Pless at M.I.T., it was proposed to accomplish this by covering the mirror with a corrugated plastic sheet which would make it equivalent to the "wobbly mirror" (Fig. 17); the corrugations must be adjusted so that they destroy the reflected images but yet do not spread the source images much beyond the camera lens apertures.

Perhaps the most serious disadvantages of the bright field system as described above are the low contrast and the difficulty of obtaining an optical system which will ensure uniform illumination of the bright field without too much spread of the source images. A further snag is that the developed film will be black except for the tracks; it will thus absorb a lot of energy in the scanning and measuring process, which will cause heating and distortion. Having large heavily exposed areas may also cause distortion of the emulsion during development, but it is difficult to estimate the magnitude of these effects.

On the other hand, bright field illumination has certain very attractive features. Very little light power is needed; consequently, it is possible to use a very slow emulsion, with a gain in resolution; also the negatives with bright tracks on a dark ground would be expected to give better performance on some kinds of automatic measuring machines. The illumination system would not be troubled much by stray light, and it would probably be unnecessary to put antireflection coatings on the windows.

A recent development in bright field illumination is the use of Scotchlite as a retroreflecting surface by Powell et al. (1963) in a heavy liquid chamber. This material is well known for its use in road signs, etc. It consists of a layer of spheres of refracting material (sometimes embedded in a matrix of lower refractive index) with a reflecting coating at the back. Recently an experimental version called Scotchlite SPR-704 was produced which returns light incident at any angle along the same direction within one or two degrees. The mode of action is indicated diagrammatically in Fig. 22a; it is easily shown that the condition for the rays to focus at the back of the sphere is $n_2 = 2n_1$, so that the spheres must have a very high refractive index. SPR-704 returns 10 to 15% of the incident light for wavelengths down to 5000 Å but below this there is rapid attenuation. The polar diagram of the returned beam has an angular width at half intensity of $\pm 0.6°$. These properties hold good with little change for angles of incidence from $0°$ up to about $60°$. At Brookhaven a 30 in. hydrogen chamber has been used with SPR-704, and the tracks show excellent contrast. The method of use is to line all the inside of the chamber with Scotchlite and to have ring sources round the camera lenses; various methods including cylindrical diaphragms and the use of polarizers have been proposed to reduce reflections from the camera port windows; in this connection, it may be noted that if the light

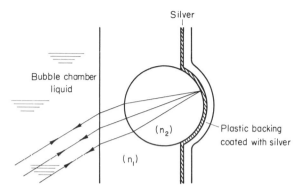

FIG. 22a. Action of "Scotchlite."

source and camera lens are covered with crossed polarizers so as to eliminate these window reflections, the light returned from the Scotchlite can be effectively depolarized by covering the Scotchlite with Mylar, which is strongly birefringent.

A considerable advantage of Scotchlite is a great gain in usable volume, since, if the sides as well as the rear of the chamber are lined with Scotchlite, all the liquid will show tracks. The Scotchlite along the sides must be arranged so as to avoid angles of incidence exceeding 60°. This may be contrasted with the relatively poor volume utilization of older systems (see Section III). Scotchlite as a retroreflective material will be of the utmost importance for the large circular chambers now being planned.

Recent experiments at Argonne have indicated that it is possible to get reasonable contrast in dark field using Scotchlite type FE 582, which has an open beaded structure (Bougon and Tamosaitis, 1966). The camera lens and light source are set up so that the lens is about 10° to 15° away from the main retro-reflected beam. This has interesting possibilities, but it is not known whether the optimum geometrical conditions could be obtained all over a large chamber.

Figure 22b shows the main optical properties of FE 582 Scotchlite. The ordinate of the graph is the relative scattered intensity, normalized to unity at zero angle to the incoming beam. The total amount of light actually returned by the Scotchlite in a cone of about 20° semiangle is rather small, 10–20% of the incident flux.

Figure 22c shows the results of a ray trace through a Scotchlite bead, assuming a relative refractive index of 1.9; a wavefront of the returned pencil is also shown. Clearly for this index the bead returns an approximately

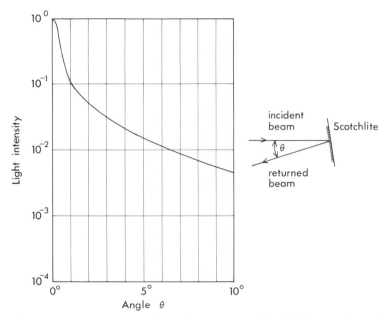

FIG. 22b. Light returned near the incident direction by Scotchlite FE582, in air. The ordinates are arbitrary units and the values are averages from different samples. The total flux returned within a cone of 20° semiangle is about 20% of the incident flux, for wavelength 0.54 μ.

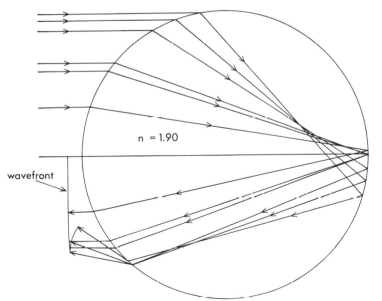

FIG. 22c. Rays traced through a sphere of refractive index 1.90 and the shape of the returning wavefront.

plane wavefront over a good proportion of its aperture and the form of the returned light intensity curve near the origin must be determined chiefly by Fraunhofer diffraction theory. This is confirmed experimentally by SPR704, since the beads were between 40 and 60 μ in diameter in one sample and the main peak had a half intensity width of about 0.5° ($\sim \lambda$/diameter).

D. OTHER ILLUMINATION POSSIBILITIES

We have examined in some detail the specific systems which have been used for illuminating bubble chambers, in particular those using the light liquids. From a more general point of view, it is worth surveying the whole field of optical techniques to see if any other possibilities have been missed. The most frequently proposed methods are interference and phase contrast, since both of these have had considerable success in the study of phase objects, i.e. those objects which do not absorb light but merely refract it by virtue of a refractive index difference. Both interference and phase contrast are essentially most suited to the case where (a) the total phase change ($2r(n - 1)$ in our case) is only a fraction of a wavelength or a few whole wavelengths at most and (b) the lateral dimensions of the object are clearly resolvable by the image-forming system to be used. Neither condition holds in our case, and in particular the violation of condition (b) means that no gain is obtained. However, if an attempt is made to use phase contrast with very small objects, one is led naturally to reduce the light intensity in the main light beam by using a heavily absorbing phase retarding plate and this tends in the limit to dark field illumination. Interference contrast is suited to showing up, by an interference fringe structure, the details of the phase changes in the object, but if the object cannot be resolved the system loses all sensitivity. We may add also that it would be very difficult to make a system for either interference or phase contrast on the dimensional scale needed for bubble chamber work.

Occasionally, it is proposed to utilize polarization effects due to reflection and refraction of light at very oblique incidence in the bubble. This is impossible because the magnetic field in the liquid causes a large Faraday rotation of the plane of polarization, which would completely muddle the fine details of such effects.

The use of image storage tubes (e.g. image orthicon) has been proposed in which each frame would be recorded and stored on magnetic tape without the intermediate photographic process. Present day techniques are certainly not adequate here because the storage tubes do not have the resolution required, about 10^5 lines, and they fall short of this by some two orders of magnitude.

Illumination and photography in collimated light, as in Fig. 23, has been suggested; this would simplify reconstruction calculations, utilize the liquid volume more efficiently, and make the bubble images more uniform in brightness (Section III,B,1). However, the technical problems in making the big lens on the camera side, which is in effect part of the camera lenses, seem insuperable for large chambers. Campbell and Pless (1956) described such a system for a small chamber with a 90° stereo angle, two cameras photographing through different windows and different field lenses.

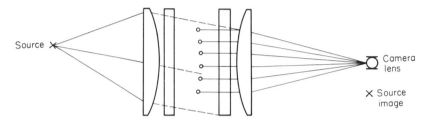

FIG. 23. Photography by collimated pencils; the camera lens is at the focus of the second condenser lens, and the source and its image are off axis. All rays which enter the lens are parallel inside the chamber. The aberrations of the second condenser would cause large deviations from collimation if the camera lens were put off axis.

Welford (1966) has proposed a system of holographic photography of which the advantage would be the greatly increased focal depth. Such a system is in principle possible and Ward and Thompson (1967) report experimental confirmation on simulated "tracks" consisting of coils of wire. There are, however, many technical problems in applying such a system to an actual chamber and in modifying the scanning and measuring equipment to deal with the results.

III. The Illuminated Volume

The shape and size of the volume of liquid in which tracks can actually be photographed depends on the distance of the camera lenses, their separation (i.e. the stereo angle), the scattering angle of the illumination system, and the depth-to-length ratio of the chamber. There is no obviously best arrangement and the choice of geometry depends on the relative importance to be attached to such factors as stereo sensitivity and distortions due to turbulence and optical effects; in particular, there is the dilemma that a roughly rectangular chamber gives optimum conditions for obtaining a uniform volume expansion without turbulence but is wasteful in that a large part of the volume is not fully used, whereas a chamber of a shape which can be economically illuminated is difficult to expand uniformly.

A. Dependence of Illuminated Volume on Stereo Angle and Scattering Angle

The geometrical relationships differ markedly in the two cases (a) large scattering angle with one source image for all cameras and (b) small scattering angle with a source image for each camera. We consider case (a) first because it is simpler.

1. *A Single Source Image*

In Fig. 24 is shown a general arrangement which could apply to either through or retrodirective illumination by any of the systems described in Sections II,A and B. The source image is common to perhaps several actual sources and the volume which is illuminated is in the form of a truncated cone with roughly rectangular base. Shutt (1963) has stated that a stereo angle of at least 30° is desirable in order to make depth measurement errors comparable in importance to others; in fact, a few chambers have a stereo angle as large as this between certain pairs of cameras but, in general, other conflicting considerations restrict the angle to be about 14°, so that for a single source system the scattering angle is about 7°. The arrangement of cameras is very much a matter of individual choice in such a system. It seems now to be customary to use three or four cameras to ensure good stereo perception of tracks in all directions and positions, but it is not yet known whether all views would necessarily be measured as a routine; experience with large chambers in the next few years will clarify this point.

Figure 25 illustrates the effect of varying R, the distance from the chamber to the cameras. In order to keep the vacuum vessels short, it is desirable to keep R as small as possible. For constant stereo angle, shown in the figure as 14°, the lower limit to R is set by the available field angle of camera lenses, which is about $\pm 30°$ (see Section V,C). This arrangement then gives a short vacuum case which can be coned down at the camera end; part of the liquid volume (shown shaded in Fig. 25a) which is not illuminated is also not used to photograph through, so that if desired the chamber can be shaped so as to exclude this volume. If, on the other hand, we make R very large (Fig. 25b), the lens field angle becomes smaller but the vacuum tank becomes longer and wider and also the shaded area of Fig. 25a vanishes; however, the illuminated volume is actually larger, since the cone of light from which it is cut is more acute-angled. In practice, the considerations of vacuum tank

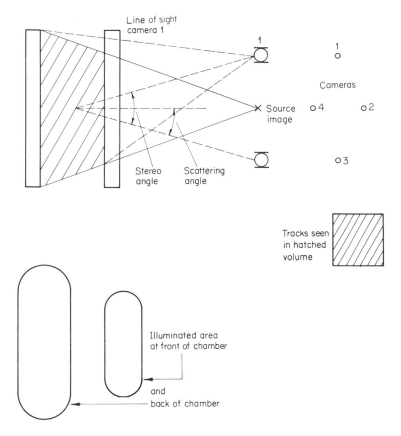

FIG. 24. Geometry of the illuminated volume for a single source image.

size affecting the efficiency of the magnet seem to weigh most strongly and most large chambers are designed with as short a value of R as possible.

Figures 24 and 25 are drawn with the camera lens axes normal to the chamber window but it can be seen that, if the axes were toed in, the effective field angles would become smaller, resulting in a further possible decrease in R. This does not seem to have been done on any existing chamber, probably because of the great increase in complexity of the geometry reconstruction programs; it would also cause optical distortions which would complicate scanning. We can see from Figs. 24 and 25 that the effect of increasing the depth of the chamber, keeping other factors constant, is to lower the proportion of used to total volume.

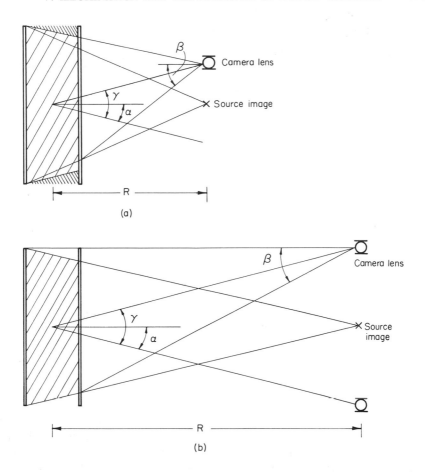

FIG. 25. Effect of choice of chamber-camera distance R on used volume and camera lens field angle β. The stereo angle, γ, is the same in both drawings; (a) small R, giving large β and leaving wasted liquid volume (heavily shaded) which is not illuminated and not used for photographing through; (b) large R, giving small β and no wasted volume. The lightly shaded volume is illuminated.

We can obtain relatively simple formulas expressing these properties by assuming a circular chamber and neglecting refraction effects, as in Fig. 26; let the diameter of the chamber be $2b$ and its depth $2d$; let the distance from the center of the chamber to the cameras be R, let the mean stereo angle be γ, and let the semifield angle of the camera lenses be β. We consider for simplicity only two lenses, arranged symmetrically about the source

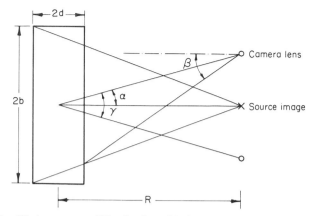

FIG. 26. Simplified geometry of illumination with single source image: α is scattering angle, β is field angle, γ is stereo angle.

image, so that the scattering angle is $\alpha = \gamma/2$. Then in linear approximation we have

$$\frac{\text{volume in which tracks are seen}}{\text{total chamber volume}} = q_1 = 1 - 2d/R \qquad (27)$$

and for the field angle,

$$\beta = \gamma/2 + \frac{b}{R}(1 - 2d/R). \qquad (28)$$

If $b \geqslant \gamma R/2$, so that the camera lens axes still fall within the chamber volume, we can also consider the ratio of the volume in which tracks are seen to that which must be kept clear for photography if the chamber is coned down to exclude the shaded part in Fig. 25; calling this q_2 we have, again in linear approximation,

$$q_2 = 1 - \frac{\gamma d}{b}. \qquad (29)$$

This ratio is independent of R, so that if the maximum used volume were the sole desideratum it would pay to increase R to the point at which $b = \gamma R/2$, i.e. the camera axes touch the rim of the chamber; then we should have $q_1 = q_2$, and the maximum available volume would be obtained for a cylindrical chamber of given dimensions and given stereo angle. In practice, the matter is complicated by the fact that the chamber is usually rectangular, but similar reasoning can be applied in discussing the geometry.

The CERN 2 meter hydrogen chamber is a recent example in which the chamber has been kept rectangular in the interests of uniform expansion; the geometry is described by Früngel *et al.* (1963). In the Brookhaven 80 in. chamber, on the other hand, the chamber shape has been coned to fit the volume actually photographed in order to economize on magnet costs and chamber liquid; the paper by Rosin (1963) already cited gives details of the optical layout. See also Androulakis *et al.* (1963) for a description of this chamber.

2. *Multiple Source Images*

The geometry of case (b) in which each camera has its own source image, is more complicated; the point of this arrangement is to be able to use a very small scattering angle, as is essential for liquid helium, so that to a sufficient approximation, we can assume that each camera sees tracks in a volume which is a truncated cone with its apex at the camera lens. Then it follows that different cameras see different illuminated volumes which partly overlap, as in Fig. 27. The same general relationships between chamber shape, illuminated volume, and stereo angle are valid, and conclusions similar to those for case (a) can be drawn but with reservations because of the difference between the volumes seen. This difference can be turned to advantage because it is possible to have a better coverage of the chamber volume, provided we are satisfied to choose a suitable pair of cameras for measurements on a given track, i.e. we do not require a track to be measurable

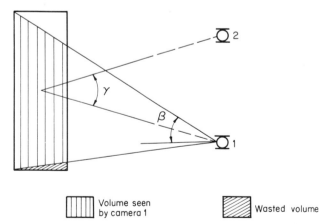

FIG. 27. Geometry of illumination for small scattering angles when a source image is focused near or around each camera lens.

on all four views. Consider a rectangular chamber with four cameras, 1, 2, 3, 4, opposite the four corners, as in Fig. 28; the volume seen by cameras 1 and 4 is bounded by the rectangle formed by the rear window and by the rectangle *ABCD* at the front window, but cameras 2 and 3 see a volume bounded at the front window by the rectangle *A'B'C'D'*. If we take account of the pairs 1, 2 and 3, 4 then almost the whole volume is seen by at least two cameras, a much more efficient utilization of volume than in case (a). However, this presupposes that the measuring and computing techniques can take advantage of this by suitable selection of pairs of views; there are clearly some disadvantages in measuring a complex event which extends over a large part of the chamber partly on some views and partly on others.

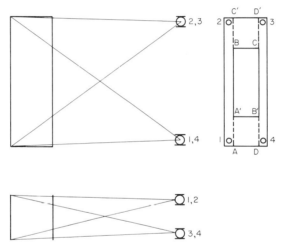

FIG. 28. Volumes seen by a chosen pair of cameras with small scattering angles.

What has been said for multiple source images and small angle scattering applies equally to the case of bright field illumination; here one is forced to accept the situation that the volumes in which bubbles are seen by different cameras only partly overlap and this can be turned to advantage as explained previously in increasing the volume utilization of the chamber.

B. FACTORS AFFECTING UNIFORMITY OF ILLUMINATION THROUGHOUT THE CHAMBER

So far, in discussing the illumination of bubble chambers, we have not considered in any detail possible variations in brightness of the bubble images except insofar as these may be caused by changes in scattering angle due to lens aberrations. We now consider such variations both in depth and across the chamber in dark field systems.

1. Variations of Illumination in Depth

Let the distance of the midplane of the chamber from the cameras be R_0 and let the illumination at this plane be E_0; then at any other distance R from the cameras the illumination is $E_0(R_0/R)^2$, so that a bubble of radius r at this distance produces a scattered illumination E_s at the cameras, given by

$$E_s = E_0(R_0/R)^2 G(\alpha)(r/R)^2, \tag{30}$$

where $G(\alpha)$ is the geometrical scattering function (Section I,A) and α is the scattering angle. Since α is proportional to $1/R$, we have

$$\frac{dE_s}{dR} = -\frac{r^2 R_0{}^2 E_0}{R^5}\left(4G(\alpha) + \alpha G'(\alpha)\right) = -\frac{E_s}{R}\left(4 + \frac{\alpha G'(\alpha)}{G(\alpha)}\right). \tag{31}$$

The condition for this function to be zero is

$$\alpha G'(\alpha)/G(\alpha) = -4 \tag{32}$$

but in fact this condition is not attainable for reasonably small values of α, as can be seen from Fig. 29; thus the bubble images are brighter in the tracks which are nearer to the cameras according to the inverse power $(4 + \alpha G'(\alpha)/G(\alpha))$ of R, and this in practical cases would be about 2. There seems to be no way of overcoming this in principle, although some improvement is possible by suitable adjustment of the plane of focus and the focal range of the camera lenses, as explained in Section V,A.

2. Lateral Variations of Illumination

We discuss lateral variations of illumination by specific reference to a through-illumination system but the argument is applicable, *mutatis mutandis*, to retrodirective systems. Consider, as in Fig. 30, a small source of luminance B at one conjugate of a condenser; the flux in a hollow cone of angles U, $U + dU$ is $2\pi B \sin U \cos U \, dU$, on the assumption that the source has a Lambertian polar diagram, and this flux, after transmission through the condenser, falls within the hollow cone U', $U' + dU'$. The illumination in the region of the median plane of the chamber is therefore obtained by

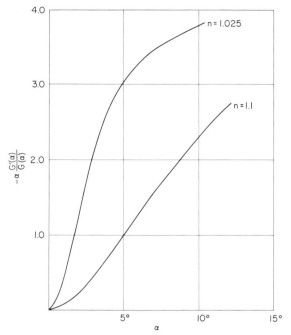

FIG. 29. The function $\alpha G'(\alpha)/G(\alpha)$ which governs the dependence of bubble brightness on depth in the chamber.

dividing this by $2\pi R^2 \sin U'\, dU'/\cos^2 U'$, i.e. it is

$$\frac{B}{R^2} \frac{\sin U \cos U \cos^2 U'}{\sin U'} \cdot \frac{dU}{dU'}; \tag{33}$$

since the projected area of the entrance pupil of the camera lens will be proportional to $\cos U'$, we see that the light flux which goes to form a bubble image should vary as

$$\frac{\sin U \cos U \cos^3 U'}{\sin U'} \cdot \frac{dU}{dU'}. \tag{34}$$

Putting this equal to a constant m^2 and integrating, we obtain as a condition of constant illumination over the width of the chamber[1]

$$\sin U = \pm\, m \tan U', \tag{35}$$

where m is clearly the transverse magnification of the condenser. The

[1] The constant of integration vanishes since U and U' vanish together.

condition Eq. (35) was ascribed by Rosin (1963) to R. K. Luneberg. Its applicability is somewhat doubtful since it depends on the assumption that the source is Lambertian, which is almost certainly not true for flashtubes.

We have, moreover, neglected to take account of the effect of varying scattering angle and distance, but, as we shall now see, this is rather small. The scattered illumination at the camera lens due to incident flux E at bubbles in the median plane is

$$E \cos^2 U' \left(\frac{r}{R_0} \right)^2 \cdot G(\alpha_0 \cos U'), \tag{36}$$

where α_0 and R_0 are the scattering angle and distance for a bubble at the center of the median plane (P, Fig. 30). Expanding the cosine and also expanding $G(\alpha)$ as a Taylor series about α_0, we find this expression becomes for small U',

$$E \left(\frac{r}{R_0} \right)^2 (1 - U'^2) \{ G(\alpha_0) - \tfrac{1}{2}\alpha_0 U'^2 G'(\alpha_0) \},$$

$$= E \left(\frac{r}{R_0} \right)^2 G(\alpha_0) \left\{ 1 - U'^2 \left(1 + \frac{\alpha_0 G'(\alpha_0)}{2 G(\alpha_0)} \right) \right\}. \tag{37}$$

As we saw in Section III,B,1, the function $\alpha G'(\alpha)/G(\alpha)$ would be equal to -2 for $\alpha \approx 3°$ in the case of helium and $\alpha \approx 9°$ in the case of hydrogen, so that we are justified in ignoring this effect. The main lateral variation in bubble brightness then comes from nonfulfillment of the condition Eq. (35) or the corresponding condition for a non-Lambertian source.

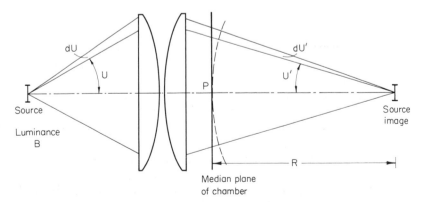

FIG. 30. Lateral variation of illumination in a through illumination system.

In practice, this condition is not aimed at; most condensers are designed to fulfill the condition

$$\sin U = m \sin U', \tag{38}$$

which, if there is also good spherical aberration correction, is the Abbe sine condition for absence of coma. This is desirable if the condenser is to form a reasonably compact image of an extended light source; if there is more than one light source, as in systems with small scattering angle, it is an essential condition for good off axis images.

Thus, comparing Eq. (38) with Eq. (34), we see that a falling off in brightness of bubbles proportional to $\cos^4 U'$ may be expected across the field. Both this and the longitudinal effects described in Section III,B,1 are clearly minimized by placing the cameras as far from the chamber as possible.

It is in principle possible to correct the lateral brightness variation by graded absorbing filters in the precondensers or, in the case of retrodirective systems, by grading the geometry of the retroreflectors (coathangers, etc.) across the field, but so far this does not seem to have been attempted.

IV. Windows

In this section, we shall be mainly concerned with the actual chamber windows but most of what is said will also apply to the smaller windows on the vacuum chambers. For a general discussion on choice of materials and surface finishing, we refer to Welford (1963b) and to Reitmeyer and Deeg (1963).

A. CHOICE OF GLASS. HOMOGENEITY AND ANNEALING

Most large bubble chamber window blanks seem to have been cast by Schott, and this firm has undoubtedly put considerable effort into improving the quality of castings over the past few years. The choice of the kind of glass depends on cost, durability of surface, optical homogeneity, freedom from bubbles, striae and stones (inclusions of unmelted foreign material from the batch), and frequency of melting; all these point clearly to the Schott type BK7, a borosilicate crown of which the optical properties are listed in Table II (Section II,A,1). We may note that mechanical strength is not considered in the choice of glass type, since this is not an intrinsic property of the type of glass but depends mainly on the nature of the heat treatment which the glass has received and the state of the surface, i.e., whether ground, polished, fire-polished, etc. The thermal expansion coefficient is not taken into consideration because the only optical glass type for which this is sensibly lower than the average is a zinc crown, ZK7, which cannot be made without a much higher bubble content than BK7. The new glass K50 (see Table II) was at first suggested by Schott as suitable for windows but it has been found (Reitmeyer, 1962) that the method of manufacture does not allow the attainment of as high a degree of homogeneity as BK7, although K50 is actually freer from bubbles and stones than BK7. The refractive index and dispersion are not very important, the only purely optical requirements being that the glass should not absorb light from the spectral region used for photography, which is usually the blue end of the visible spectrum, and that the dispersion should be low to minimize transverse chromatic aberration (Section IV,D).

Inhomogeneity in a window between the camera lenses and the liquid causes apparent distortion of the tracks, and it is desirable to have a figure for the maximum permissible distortion on which to base tolerances for inhomogeneity and lack of parallelism of the window. It is unfortunately very difficult to obtain such a figure from bubble chamber physicists, presumably because it would depend on the nature of the experiment, and figures ranging from $\pm 10\,\mu$ to $\pm 50\,\mu$ have been quoted to the writer. Shutt (1963) quotes the overall error due to optical distortions, turbulence, finite bubble size, film distortion, and errors in the measurement process as ranging from ± 35 to $\pm 70\,\mu$ in the chamber and suggests that $\pm 50\,\mu$ is a reasonable figure. We should bear in mind that distortions resulting from inhomogeneity and lack of surface flatness in the optics cause systematic errors, which cannot be eliminated by simply taking more measurements, whereas errors due to turbulence and the measurement process are random and can be so reduced. It is therefore perhaps best to keep to a figure in the $10\,\mu$ to $20\,\mu$ region. If this dimension is denoted by $\pm\rho$, we have an angular tolerance of $\pm\rho/2d$ for deviations caused by inhomogeneity and errors of optical figure in the window, where $2d$ is the depth of the chamber, since this would cause a displacement $\pm\rho$ to tracks at the rear of the chamber, the worst case. In practice, this is of order of magnitude 10^{-4} (20 seconds), depending on the values of ρ and d. If the window has a refractive index gradient dn/dx in a direction x parallel to the glass surface, this will deviate a normally incident ray by the angle $t\, dn/dx$, where t is the thickness of the window. The vacuum tank windows are further from the tracks and should therefore have a smaller deviation tolerance.

The manufacturers specify homogeneity in terms of absolute variation in refractive index and claim that in large castings of astronomical quality, the refractive index can be kept within 5×10^{-6} of a mean value. This can still, in principle, be consistent with considerable *gradients* of refractive index, but the writer has found that in fact the refractive index gradients in windows 16 cm thick cause deviations *less than* 2×10^{-5}, which is an angular tolerance adequate for the largest chambers so far built. This corresponds to a refractive index change of less than 5×10^{-6} in about 50 mm, so it appears that the homogeneity is adequate for bubble chamber windows, whether or not it conforms to the highest astronomical standard. It is not possible to check slow gradients of refractive index before the window has been polished reasonably flat and parallel but rapid gradients, i.e. striae or *schlieren*, can be detected in a blank which has been only "inspection polished." The glass is set up a few meters away from an intense point source of light, e.g. a high pressure mercury or xenon arc, and a white screen is placed some distance behind the glass as in Fig. 31; as can easily be seen, a nonzero value of the second derivative of refractive index in any direction will cause a change in the illumination on the screen, so that a vein will show as a dark shadow with bright edges. The depth of the vein in the glass can be found by marking points in line with the shadow on both surfaces with a chinagraph pencil and then repeating with light incident at a different inclination; the joins of the marks would intersect in the vein inside the glass so that a simple graphical construction gives its position. This technique is useful in determining whether a vein will be removed when the glass is reduced to its final thickness. The shadow test is very sensitive and can detect veins which cause deviations of 10 sec or perhaps less.

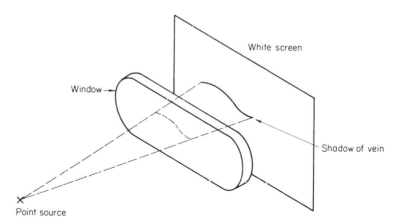

Fig. 31. The shadow test for veins in a window. The point source can be a carbon arc or a high pressure mercury lamp at a few meters distance from the window; the distance of the screen from the window is not important.

The same setup can also be used to check on the distribution of stones and bubbles in the glass. Recent BK7 window blanks have shown only 1 or 2 bubbles per liter and 1 or 2 stones in a window of some 20 liters. These windows, made for a helium bubble chamber, are also completely free from veins, although in earlier windows it was not possible to avoid several large veins.

The annealing process serves two purposes. The first, to reduce internal stresses, is well known. The second purpose is to "normalize" the glass, i.e. to bring it to the same refractive index throughout; it is known that the final refractive index at room temperature depends on the fictive temperature of the glass (Jones, 1956), which is, roughly speaking, a measure of the state of disorder of the glass which is frozen in when the glass is cooled. It is thus important that the blank be heat soaked at a uniform temperature in the annealing range for some time so as to ensure that it is all at the same fictive temperature when cool.[2]

The residual stresses at the end of the annealing process appear as stress birefringence; this may be measured by standard techniques and an annealing tolerance expressed as so many millimicrons stress birefringence per centimeter path through the glass; the usual figure for fine annealed glass is about 25 mμ/cm. In fact, the stress does not always lie in the same direction, so that such a measurement made through the thickness of a plate is an average; but, as a matter of experience, this figure seems amply good enough for bubble chamber windows.

In connection with annealing, we have to consider the question of tempering or toughening glass. An excellent description of tempering and its effects on windows was given by Reitmeyer and Deeg (1963). The process produces a smooth gradation of stress through the thickness of a window, compressive near the surfaces and tensile at the center; the surfaces can be reground and polished with care after tempering. The optical effects of tempering are changes in refractive index, causing nonuniform deviation of rays traversing different parts of the window, and birefringence, causing image doubling. These effects are shown by experimental results given by Reitmeyer and Deeg; in particular, their Fig. 4 shows deviations due to refractive index gradients in a 56 mm thick window of 5 to 10 sec in the central area and 10 times this near the edge. Image doublings of 25 to 50 sec were observed near the edge. In view of this, there is much to be said for not using tempered windows, in spite of the lower thickness needed because of the increased mechanical strength.

---

[2] One firm of optical glass makers actually quotes a range of refractive indices for each glass type which can be made by suitable annealing.

The actual thickness of window needed is decided from the generally agreed figure of 1000 psi as the maximum safe tensile stress in untempered glass. Various approximate and empirical formulas are then available from engineering handbooks from which the required thickness of untempered glass can be calculated. For long rectangular shapes which are simply supported at the edges, most formulas are equivalent to

$$t = c(Wl/SL)^{1/2}, \qquad (39)$$

where W is the total distributed load due to the pressure in the chamber, L and l are the dimensions of the rectangle, S is the permitted tensile stress, t is the thickness, and c is a constant between 0.75 and unity if t is in inches (Welford, 1963b).

The manufacturers should be consulted about the permitted reduction in thickness by tempering. Tempered windows are, of course, quite suitable for use in the parts of the optical train between the light sources and the chamber.

Little is known about effects of temperature gradients in windows although it is quite likely that there is a radial gradient in vacuum tank windows under operating conditions. Let α be the thermal expansion coefficient and β the temperature coefficient of refractive index, i.e. β is dn/dT, where T is the temperature. Then a temperature gradient dT/dx parallel to the surface of the glass will produce a ray deviation

$$[\beta + (n - 1)\alpha]t \, dT/dx,$$

where t is the thickness of the window. For BK7, α is 82×10^{-7} and β is 15×10^{-7} relative to vacuum (about twice this relative to air). These figures were supplied by Jenaer Glaswerk Schott u. Gen.

B. SURFACE FINISHING OF WINDOWS

The main chamber windows are traversed by image forming pencils of light which have very small diameters and convergence angles; thus the main aberration which can be introduced by a window is distortion, and the optical polishing tolerances must be set to correspond with the deviation tolerance that was explained in Section IV,A. If this deviation tolerance is $\pm\theta$, the two surfaces of the window must be parallel to $\pm\theta/(n - 1)$ where n is the refractive index; this corresponds to a wedge on either surface with respect to a mean plane of one test plate fringe per $(n - 1)\lambda/2\theta$ run along the surface (λ = wavelength of light used). A detailed discussion of the tolerances was given by Welford (1963b) and a method of testing for deviation was described.

It is usual to finish the nonoptical surfaces (edges, chamfers) by deep etching in hydrofluoric acid after grinding to shape. This process improves the mechanical strength, possibly by widening and smoothing the minute cracks which are considered to be starting points for fracture; whatever the explanation, the tensile strength of etched glass rods has been found to be as great as or even greater than that of fire-polished glass (Reitmeyer, 1962).

The specification of the quality of polish, aside from the question of flatness, for glass surfaces in a dark field illumination system is difficult. In general very slight scratches of the kind which are offensive to the eye of the optical worker are not too serious except at very small scattering angles, but incomplete polish, i.e. residual "grey" from grinding, can cause heavy background even if it cannot be seen on casual inspection; the surface must be inspected carefully with oblique illumination against a dark background. It is best to set up a photographic test in which a test surface is illuminated with the same energy per unit area and photographed in dark field at the same exposure as planned for the bubble chamber in operation. While this may be inconvenient to carry out on the actual window or condenser surfaces, it can be done on smaller samples which can then be used as standards for visual comparison under critical lighting conditions.

C. Antireflection Coating

Antireflection coatings on optics in general serve three purposes: (a) to increase transmission; (b) to reduce the intensity of ghost images caused by multiple reflections at optical surfaces; and (c) to reduce stray background illumination from reflections of illuminated nonoptical surfaces, i.e. blackened metal, in optical surfaces. In bubble chambers, we are chiefly concerned with (b) and (c), although the reduction in light power obtained through (a) is not to be ignored.

From Section II,A Eq. (17), we see that bubble images may be expected to be of the same order of brightness as ghost images produced by two reflections (as in a through-illumination system) at uncoated surfaces. The reflectivity of an uncoated surface is about 4%; this may be reduced to about 1.4% by a single quarter-wavelength coating of magnesium fluoride, the usual commercial process, and to about 0.1% (in theory zero) by means of a two-layer coating. This figure of 0.1% is obtained at a specific wavelength, the design wavelength, which can be specified arbitrarily within a considerable wavelength range, and at normal incidence; at oblique incidence and at other wavelengths, the reflectance is higher. Figure 32 shows the measured reflectance at normal incidence of a plate of glass with two-layer

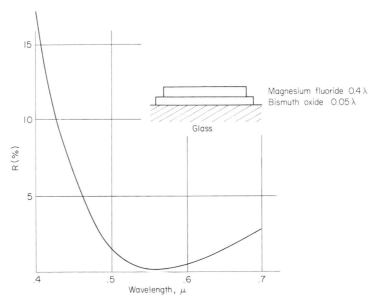

FIG. 32. Reflectance at normal incidence of glass coated with two-layer antireflection coating. The minimum can be set at any wavelength by suitable choice of the film thicknesses.

coatings on each surface. Figure 33 shows a plot of equireflectance contours as a function of angle of incidence and reciprocal of wavelength, computed by Catalán (1962). It can be seen that there is quite a useful range of angle of incidence and wavelength over which the coating is efficient; but, in order to obtain the best performance, it is desirable to restrict the wavelength range somewhat.

Such coatings can be made with any available materials of high and low refractive index within wide ranges. Catalán (1962) gave a theoretical solution for the thicknesses required with given refractive indices; this can be adapted for the case when the film is in contact with the chamber liquid, when slightly different thicknesses are needed. Thetford (1964) described in detail coating techniques for windows and also for deeply curved condenser surfaces, using magnesium fluoride and bismuth oxide as the two materials. Früngel et al. (1963) use magnesium fluoride and tantalum oxide as the two materials. The coatings made according to Thetford's techniques have been found to be extremely durable and they are, of course, proof against repeated cooling to liquid hydrogen temperature; dust can be removed by gentle brushing but cleaning with liquids is inadvisable and if the coatings become contaminated with grease they have to be cleaned off and redeposited.

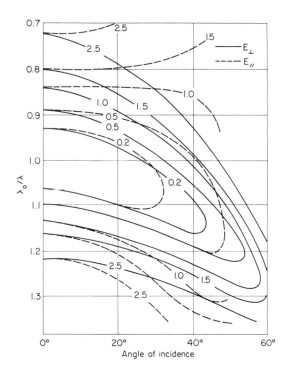

FIG. 33. Contours of equireflectance of a two layer antireflection coating (after computations by Catalán (1962)). The contours are labeled in percentage reflectance; the full lines refer to s polarization and the broken lines to p polarization of the electric vector. The quantity λ_0 is the design wavelength, i.e. the wavelength for which the coating has zero reflectance at normal incidence.

D. Optical Distortions due to Windows and Chamber Liquid

The question of the precision with which the windows must be aligned parallel to each other and perpendicular to the camera lens axes arises because relative tilts of these elements cause optical distortions. In this section, we give the formulas for these distortions.

Consider a window of thickness t and refractive index n, as in Fig. 34; a camera lens on the right sees a point P on the left of the window as being at P' in a plane displaced a distance $t(n - 1)/n$ to the right from the original plane of P. Let the angle of incidence of the principal ray from P to the lens be I and let the angle of refraction, inside the plate, be I'.

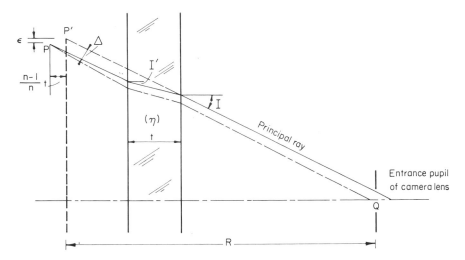

FIG. 34. Notation used in calculating distortion due to a plane-parallel plate.

The principal ray is displaced a distance Δ, perpendicular to itself, given by

$$\Delta = t \sin I \left(1 - \frac{\cos I}{n \cos I'} \right) \tag{40}$$

and P' is displaced vertically above P a distance ε given by

$$\varepsilon = \frac{t}{n} \tan I \left(1 - \frac{\cos I}{\cos I'} \right). \tag{41}$$

Thus ε may be taken to represent the radial distortion of the image of P as seen through the window. In fact, this is not strictly true because the principal ray meets the axis at a point displaced slightly to the right of the pupil point for principal rays close to the axis, Q in the diagram, so that the actual principal ray of the pencil used to photograph the bubble would be that shown chain dotted; this has a slightly greater angle of incidence I, so that the value of ε should be slightly greater, but the difference between the two values of I is only of order of magnitude ε and so for all practical purposes Eq. (41) is adequate.

Now consider a straight line, i.e. a track, passing through P normal to the plane of the diagram; since ε depends on I the line seen through the plate will appear curved convex to the lens axis, i.e., the plate produces pincushion distortion. Let I and I' refer to the angles of incidence of the principal ray in the plane of the diagram and let the plane of P' be at a distance R from the lens, i.e. R is the apparent distance of the track from the lens. Then the curvature of the track near P is given by

$$c = \left(\frac{n^2 - 1}{n^3}\right)\frac{t}{R^2}\tan I\left(\frac{\cos I}{\cos I'}\right)^3 G^{-1}, \tag{42}$$

where

$$G = 1 - \frac{t}{nR}\left(1 - \frac{\cos I}{\cos I'}\right) - \left(\frac{n^2 - 1}{n^3}\right)\frac{t}{R}\tan^2 I\left(\frac{\cos I}{\cos I'}\right)^3. \tag{43}$$

In most cases, it can be seen that G may be put equal to unity as a sufficient approximation and then we have

$$c \sim \left(\frac{n^2 - 1}{n^3}\right)\frac{t}{R^2}\tan I\left(\frac{\cos I}{\cos I'}\right)^3. \tag{44}$$

Thus, in linear approximation, the curvature is proportional to the field angle and to the thickness of the plate, and it is inversely proportional to the square of the distance of the track from the lens. The actual position of the plate between the lens and the track has no effect on the curvature. The curvatures due to several windows with possibly differing refractive indices are simply added; also, the effect of a thickness of bubble chamber liquid is to produce a similar curvature which can be calculated by the same formula.

The actual shape of the track image is given by an algebraic curve of the fourth degree, so that Eq. (42) gives the curvature only at the point of symmetry closest to the camera lens axis. Also, it should be pointed out that this formula has been deduced simply by considering displacements of the principal ray projected onto the plane shown chain dotted in Fig. 34; actually, the plate introduces other aberrations in the pencil of rays from any point of the track, the largest being astigmatism and transverse chromatic aberration. Of these, astigmatism is below the Rayleigh limit in practice and may be neglected. The effect of transverse chromatic aberration can be seen by taking I and I' as small in Eq. (40), i.e. neglecting I^2 and differentiating with respect to n; we find

$$\delta\Delta = \frac{t\delta n}{n^2}\sin I. \tag{45}$$

If δn is taken to correspond to the wavelength range used, this expression gives the length of the transverse spectrum produced in the chamber space.

Taking as typical numerical values $\sin I = 0.5$, $t = 100$ mm, $\delta n = 0.008$ (the spectral range $0.48\,\mu$ to $0.65\,\mu$ for BK7), we find a value of about 0.1 mm. This is clearly another reason in favor of restricting the spectral range. Alternatively, we shall see in Section V,C that both transverse chromatic aberration and distortion as given by Eqs. (42–44) can to some extent be corrected by suitable modifications to the camera lenses, although there is bound to be some residual variation in depth through the liquid.

When considering angular tolerances on positioning of the windows, we note first that a tilt of a window will cause an apparent lateral displacement of the tracks which will vary across the field, as can be seen by differentiating Eq. (41) with respect to I; we find that a window tilt δI gives an error

$$\delta\varepsilon = \frac{t}{n}\left\{\frac{\cos^3 I' - \cos^3 I}{\cos^2 I \cos^3 I'}\right\}\delta I, \tag{46}$$

or to a sufficient approximation,

$$\delta\varepsilon \sim \frac{3t(n^2 - 1)}{2n^3}\sin^2 I\,\delta I. \tag{47}$$

This equation can be used for tolerancing the angular setting of the main chamber window with respect to the camera axes, since it gives the error in the expected value of ε, and this can be set equal to ρ, the displacement tolerance of Section IV,A.

Second, in the case of the windows on the vacuum chamber, the windows in the different camera beams must be parallel to each other to a tolerance given by the condition that the differences between the values of Δ from Eq. (40) for all windows must be less than ρ; this is clearly a much more stringent tolerance and is likely to be only a few minutes of arc. Of course, it is possible that the reconstruction programs can be arranged to allow for such optical displacements between the camera axes, but it would seem better to avoid them in the first instance.

E. CONCENTRIC OR "FISH-EYE" WINDOWS

The very large chambers at present under construction have a volume and shape such that it is generally agreed that it would be impracticable to photograph them through large flat windows; this is partly because the lost volumes (see Section III) would be too large, partly because the required field angles would introduce very large aberrations at the windows (Section IV,D), and partly because the cost would be too great; one estimate obtained in 1966 was about $100,000 for a window about 3 meter diameter and 30 cm thick.

These requirements of shape and size together with the possibility of Scotchlite retrodirective bright field illumination have led to the adoption of windows with concentric spherical surfaces, the so-called "fish-eye" windows; these have their common center of curvature at the entrance pupil of the camera lens and they project into the chamber liquid, as in Fig. 35. It is obviously desirable to have the camera lenses at room temperature,

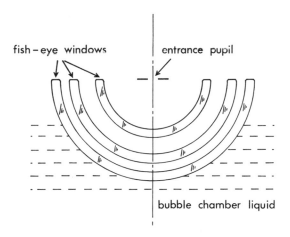

FIG. 35. Fish-eye array.

and there are problems in arranging the temperature transition from, say, 26°K to room temperature. Usually three concentric windows are proposed, as in the figure, but at the time of writing there is some uncertainty about the best thermal conditions for the intermediate window and whether it should have a heat reflecting coating. The fish-eye window principle eliminates the distortion and transverse chromatic aberration inherent in flat windows and it also solves the problems of stray reflected light, since it can easily be shown that the only rays which can be reflected from any fish-eye surface into the entrance pupil are those which actually have come from the pupil. On the other hand, the windows themselves and the concave liquid interface contribute significantly to the total refractive power of the lens and to its field curvature, so that the lens design must be modified to allow for the fish-eyes.

Obvious problems of centering and clamping arise, but no tested designs are at present available.

V. Photography

In this section, we discuss the general optical conditions relating to photography of a bubble chamber, reserving discussion of camera mechanisms and auxiliary data for Section VII. The principal points of interest are resolution, depth of focus, choice of film, and choice of camera lens. These are partly bound up with the choice of film format, which is to a considerable extent a question of economics; this is best discussed in Section VII since the actual size of film is governed partly by the auxiliary data to be printed and the method of camera drive. In this section, we discuss the film format only to the extent that it is affected by the optimum magnification.

A. DEPTH OF FOCUS

If as usual we assume that the bubbles are too small to be resolved, we find they form images which, in the absence of the degrading effect of the photographic emulsion, have the well known Airy pattern (see, e.g., Born and Wolf, 1959). The light intensity in the image is given by

$$(2J_1(q)/q)^2, \tag{48}$$

where

$$q = (2\pi/\lambda)nu\eta ; \tag{49}$$

η is the distance in the image plane from the geometrical image point; u is the (small) semiangle of the cone of rays forming the image, i.e. the convergence angle; and n is the refractive index of the medium in which the image is formed. The same expression gives the image projected back into the object space provided the quantity nu is chosen appropriately. The expression on the right of Eq. (48) is normalized to unity at $q = 0$. The effect of a change of focus is to produce a spread and change in this diffraction pattern until with large amounts of defocusing the image is roughly a uniform disk, as would be predicted by geometrical optics, but the immediate effect of a small focal shift is to decrease the intensity in the central maximum without appreciably broadening it. In fact, the intensity at the center is given by the expression

$$(\sin p/p)^2, \tag{50}$$

where

$$p = (\pi/2\lambda)nu^2z, \tag{51}$$

and z is the change in focus. As before, this is applicable to the object or image space by suitable choice of n and u.

The maximum of defocusing which is reasonable is that which causes the central intensity to drop to about 40% of its in-focus value; from Eqs. (50) and (51), we find the corresponding focal range is

$$z = \pm \frac{\lambda}{nu^2}. \tag{52}$$

Frequently half this range is quoted, corresponding to a drop to 80% of the central intensity. The form of the diffraction pattern image has been calculated for all planes near focus and the results are given graphically by, e.g., Born and Wolf (1959); from these results may be judged the degradation of the image at the limits of the focal range, but the effect of the photographic emulsion is to smooth out and hide the diffraction effects, so that the full extent and more of the focal range given by Eq. (52) can be used. This equation is used, of course, by putting z equal to half the chamber depth and finding the convergence angle u in the liquid.

As noted in Section III,B,1, the bubbles scatter more light into the camera lenses from tracks nearer the cameras; some compensation for this effect can be achieved by setting the best focal plane further from the cameras than the median plane of the chamber, so that the function of Eq. (50) has its maximum further out. However, such optimization can only be done experimentally, using the particular emulsion, lenses, and exposure conditions to be expected in the actual chamber.

Having found the convergence angle in the object space, we can substitute in Eqs. (48) and (49) to find the size of the bubble image; the first zero of the Bessel function is given by $q = 3.83$, so that the diameter at half intensity (the half-width) of the bubble image is approximately

$$0.5\lambda/nu, \tag{53}$$

in object or image space according to the choice of n and u.

B. Magnification and Choice of Film

The next question, the choice of magnification, is inevitably to be considered together with the choice of the type of photographic emulsion. Leaving aside for the moment the fact that film comes in standard widths and it is desirable to fill the width of the film, we note the following points: (a) the diffraction image of a bubble should be comparable with the point spread function of the emulsion[3] so that resolution of adjoining tracks is

---

[3] The point spread function is the image produced on the emulsion by an infinitely narrow concentration of light, or in practice by contact-printing through a pinhole a few microns in diameter. There is a corresponding definition for the line spread function.

not limited by the emulsion; (b) the random movements in the emulsion due to processing should correspond to ρ, the maximum permissible distortion in the chamber (see Section IV,A); (c) distortions contributing to ρ should, when demagnified, correspond to the limit of accuracy of the measuring machine to be used. This is illustrated in Fig. 36, which shows distances in the chamber plotted against u', the convergence angle in the

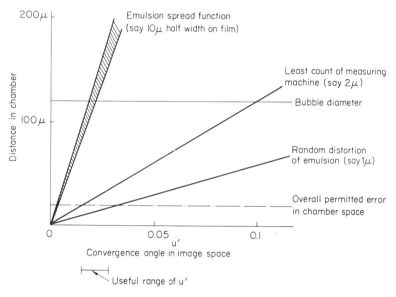

FIG. 36. Factors affecting choice of magnification; the graph shows the magnitudes in chamber space of different factors as a function of the convergence angle in image space. The convergence angle in object space was taken as 1/600.

image space; the demagnification is u/u', and we can regard u, now referring to object space, as already fixed by considerations of focal depth. The size of a bubble image in chamber space is then represented by a horizontal line, as is the overall distortion ρ; the film spread function, the precision of the measuring process, and the emulsion distortion are constant in image space and are therefore represented by the sloping lines in chamber space. Clearly, it is desirable to use a magnification corresponding to a value of u' equal to or less than that at the intersection of the bubble image size and the film spread function. The smaller the demagnification, i.e., the larger the image, beyond this point the better off we shall be, but it is clear that if we use a much smaller value of u', we shall merely be magnifying up bubble images far beyond the emulsion resolution limit and gaining very little; in fact, we begin to lose in exposure, since the flux in a bubble image is spread over a larger area. Thus, the useful region is that denoted by the marker in Fig. 35.

The above argument ignores the strong economic reasons for using as small a picture as possible, because the cost of film is an appreciable proportion of the cost of running a bubble chamber and this cost must increase as the inverse square of u'. A small picture is also desirable for convenience in film handling, camera design, measuring machine design, and film storage!

The above analysis is in fact too simplified because the emulsion spread function and the diffraction pattern image interact in a complicated, non-linear fashion and the finite graininess of the emulsion contributes appreciably to the form of the track image. A detailed experimental study of emulsions from the point of view of their suitability for bubble chamber photography was reported by Welford (1962). In this study, a narrow illuminated slit was photographed at demagnification $\frac{1}{10}$ with convergence angles over a wide range; the line spread function was measured at various exposures and with defocusing. The general conclusions were that the focal range is represented approximately by Eq. (52), but that emulsion grain tends to blur fine differences due to slight changes in focus. In the many different emulsions tested, there were only slight differences in speed; it was even found that some finer grain emulsions, which are classed as of only medium speed, were actually faster under these conditions than coarser grained "fast" emulsions. Two films, one supplied by Ilford Ltd. and having the general properties of their PanF emulsion but with only blue sensitivity, and one supplied by Kodak Ltd., and having similar properties, were found to be particularly good. These both gave a spread function about $17\,\mu$ wide with peak density 1.0; the Ilford film is now in extensive use at CERN. It should be explained that both these emulsions were produced experimentally and the lack of color sensitization was specified in order to cut down the wavelength range of the light used; as previously explained, this is desirable for several reasons. Other films frequently used for bubble chamber work are: Special Dacomatic #2 for dark field and Microfile for bright field illumination. Also Linagraph Shellburst film is recommended. (All these films are manufactured by the Eastman Kodak Company.)

Emulsion distortion was also reported on in the same paper. Linear distortion due to changes in humidity and temperature can be quite large but this is easily accounted for in the measuring process. There remains a random distortion presumably due to processing in which small areas of the emulsion shift about in different directions. Over distances of 1 to 2 mm these movements appeared to have an rms value of about $1\,\mu$, provided the film is brought to humidity and temperature equilibrium. This applies to thin emulsions ($\sim 10\,\mu$ thick); thicker emulsions, the faster emulsions according to the usual speed scales, might distort worse.

A tinted (gray) film base is often used to decrease halation and, in the tests mentioned before, film on gray base was found to give a slightly narrower spread function than clear base film. However, the preference now seems to be for clear base film because the slightly higher background transmission improves the signal to noise ratio in high speed measuring devices such as flying-spot digitizers.

C. Choice of Camera Lens

The subject of camera lenses can be discussed from two viewpoints. We may suppose that a specification for a lens is to be drafted, so that a suitable lens can be designed and made; or, alternatively, we may choose among existing lens types. In the first approach, there are several essentials in which the ideal bubble chamber lens differs from available commercial lenses. Because of the large depth of focus, it will need to work at a relative aperture of $f/20$ or smaller, but, on the other hand, a wide field angle is desirable. We have already stated that $\pm 30°$ is the maximum practicable; this is based on experience of testing lenses designed for angles up to $\pm 50°$. The speed of a lens falls off towards the edge of the field as $\cos^4\beta$, where β is the field angle, for extended objects; although some lenses have been designed with a more uniform exposure over the field, this has been achieved mainly by introducing strong barrel distortion. It is difficult to get really good aberration correction beyond $30°$, even with a lens stopped down to $f/20$, and the extreme field angle imposes very stringent requirements on film flatness. Also distortions due to the chamber windows become very large at angles beyond $30°$ (see Section IV,D), and this is a great inconvenience in scanning. On the other hand, a field angle of $\pm 30°$ permits stereo angles up to $30°$ and is thus enough for any requirements so far stated by bubble chamber physicists.

The small aperture and limited wavelength range means that it should be possible to achieve close to Rayleigh limit correction of aberrations, with the exception of distortion. Ideally, the distortion ought to be corrected taking account of the thicknesses of the windows and of half the chamber depth, so that straight tracks at the midplane of the chamber are photographed straight (Belonogov et al., 1963), but even when this is done there will be considerable distortion at other depths. Equation (41) shows that with hydrogen in a total thickness of 40 cm this would be about 2.5 mm at the front and back of the chamber for a 30° field angle; the corresponding figures for helium and propane are about 0.5 mm and 4 mm. These correspond to quite large displacements on the film at the usual demagnification, so that provided the lens distortion is actually known it is not important that it be reduced precisely to zero at the midplane or anywhere else.

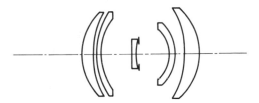

FIG. 37. The Tropel lens. This has a semifield angle of 30° and focal length of 154 mm. Its image quality is stated to be diffraction-limited at apertures of $f/16$ or smaller.

As final points about the ideal lens, we note that it should have its entrance pupil as near to the front component as possible, so that only a small window is needed in the outer casing of the bubble chamber; its mounting should be of nonmagnetic material to avoid stresses from the magnetic field.

No details are available about the specially designed lens mentioned by Belonogov. For the Brookhaven 80 in. hydrogen chamber, lenses were specially designed and made by Tropel Inc. (see Fig. 37); these have focal

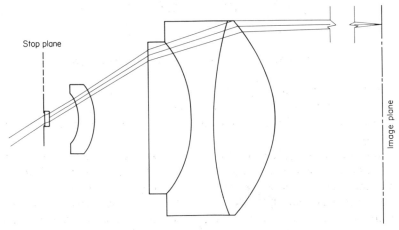

FIG. 38. Inverted telephoto lens with telecentric stop for 32 in. helium chamber. The film plane is 180 mm from the last surface and the focal length is 100 mm.

length 154 mm, relative aperture $f/16$, and semifield angle 30°. A lens designed and made at Imperial College for a 32 in. helium chamber is shown in Fig. 38; this has focal length of 100 mm, relative aperture $f/20$, semifield angle 30°. The unusual feature of this lens is that it has a telecentric aperture stop, i.e. the principal rays in the image space are all parallel to the optical axis, so that the effects of nonflatness of the film are minimized.

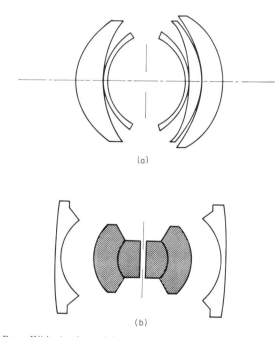

FIG. 39. (a) Ross Wide-Angle aerial survey lens, (b) Schneider Super-Angulon lens.

The aperture stop is actually right at the front of the lens, so that only a small vacuum tank window is needed. There is a strong negative telephoto effect, since the back focal distance is 180 mm, nearly twice the equivalent focal length.

Among commercial lenses which have been used are the Ross Wide-Angle lens (Fig. 39a), an aerial survey lens designed for a field angle of ±45°, and the Schneider Super-Angulon (Fig. 39b), a wide angle lens intended for press photography, etc. Such commercial lenses are designed with small residual distortion when used to photograph objects in air, the residuals being of order 100 μ at the focal plane; thus graph a of Fig. 40 shows the distortion of a Schneider Super-Angulon, the ordinates being the radial displacement of the image point from the ideal position. However, 100 to 200 mm thickness of windows and more of chamber liquid between the object (track) and the lens causes pincushion distortion, as can be seen from Eq. (41); the result of this could be as in graph b of Fig. 40, which shows the effect of a total window thickness of 200 mm with demagnification 1/12.5.

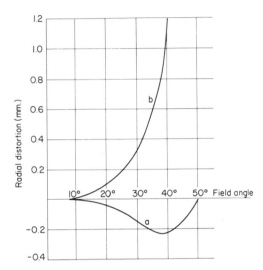

FIG. 40. Distortion of 90 mm Schneider Super-Angulon lens (radial displacement of image point) as a function of field angle; (a) the lens with demagnification 12.5; (b) as (a) but with 200 mm thick glass plate, refractive index 1.52, in object space. (Data for (a) kindly supplied by J. Schneider and Co., Kreuznach.)

It can be shown that if the demagnification is $1/m$ the distorting effect of a glass thickness t on the object side is exactly canceled by a thickness t/m on the image side; this device has been used to remove some of the window distortion on the Rutherford Laboratory 1.5 meter hydrogen chamber; it was found that, over the 30° semifield used, the astigmatism and transverse chromatic aberration of the Ross Wide-Angle lenses used were improved by putting 15 mm thick glass plates between the lens and film, thus also partly canceling the distorting effect of the main chamber windows.

In discussing lens aberrations, we have to distinguish between design aberrations, i.e. the computed aberrations of the lens design on paper and the aberrations of a given lens as actually made; the differences arise from manufacturing errors such as inhomogeneous glass, faulty centering of components, errors of figure on lens surfaces, etc. For the present purposes, distortion appears to be the aberration which is most seriously affected by this effect; the difference between design distortion and distortion in the finished lens has been variously called asymmetrical distortion, random distortion, differential distortion, and tangential distortion. It may occur as a variation of the radial distortion function along different azimuths but, in addition, the image points may be displaced tangentially, i.e. at right angles to the radius in the field plane. In either case, the distortion function is no longer symmetrical about the lens axis; in fact, the lens cannot be said to have an axis of symmetry in the strict sense at all.

Very little information is available about actual measurements of asymmetrical distortion. Hall (1962) reported measurements on 15 Wild 6 in. Aviogon lenses, a high quality lens intended for precision aerial survey work. The mean asymmetric distortion at the film plane over the whole field was "less than 0.01 mm," but values up to 0.02 mm were found in places; the effect does not seem to be much less near the center of the field and Hall found values up to 0.01 mm within a 30° semifield angle. The design distortion of these lenses is only about $10\,\mu$. Rhodes (1962) reported asymmetries up to 0.01 mm on an unspecified lens. According to Hart (1963), Bureau of Standards tests on the Tropel lens (Fig. 37) showed asymmetries of up to $5\,\mu$, the maximum design distortion being of order $5\,\mu$.

Asymmetrical distortion can be divided into two components. The first is that due to the resultant prism or wedge due to errors in centering and edging the lens components; the effect of this is to produce an additional curvature all over the field, i.e. if there were no design distortion all straight lines in a certain direction would be uniformly curved because of the prismatic spectrum line curvature effect. The other component is more irregular and rapidly varying and it may be due to some or all of the following causes: irregular figure of the optical surfaces and inhomogeneity, thermal gradients, stress birefringence in the glass. Asymmetrical distortion effects of a few microns correspond to deviations at the lens components of a few seconds of arc at the focal lengths we are concerned with, and this is below ordinary lens manufacturing tolerances. It seems, therefore, that if we wish to avoid systematic measuring errors due to asymmetric lens distortions, an individual calibration process is needed for each camera lens or else the lenses must be made to much closer tolerances than is usual. In view of the results above for the Wild lenses, which would presumably have been made with special consideration for distortion, it seems doubtful whether present manufacturing techniques could be relied on to reduce asymmetry to below $5\,\mu$.

The calibration process envisaged by some laboratories involves the photography of an accurately ruled grid. This would permit the construction of a two way table of corrections to be applied to a point anywhere in the field, as illustrated schematically in Fig. 41; the grid is photographed on film and from the measurements a set of correction vectors is obtained that show to a suitable scale how any point must be displaced for it to obtain its position corrected for distortion. Clearly, the symmetrical design distortion can be included in this process. In principle, this can be done without a

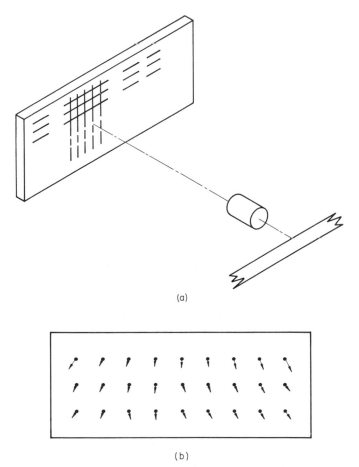

(a)

(b)

FIG. 41. Calibrating a camera lens; (a) photographing the grid, (b) the matrix of correction vectors (in practice, the origins would be chosen to make the mean correction vector zero).

special calibration process, simply making use of the fiducial marks on the chamber windows; but in practice these fiducials may be spaced too far apart to show in sufficient detail the asymmetric distortion. This has been done for the camera lenses of the 1.5-meter Rutherford laboratory chamber.

The latest chambers under construction call for very wide-angle lenses, with fields up to ±70° from the axis, so that the full benefit of the wide view possible with fish-eye windows and Scotchlite illumination can be obtained. These chambers will possibly also be expanded in a fully resonant mode, so that multiple expansions take place within a single accelerator cycle; this implies that a close approach to telecentricity in the camera lens is essential, because there may not be time between successive exposures to flatten the film sufficiently to ensure no distortion at wide field.

Other requirements besides telecentricity include a rather small front diameter, to permit the use of small diameter ring flash tubes for Scotchlite illumination, and diffraction limited correction of aberrations, so that high resolving film can be used at great demagnification. Such a lens naturally tends to be very asymmetric with respect to the aperture stop, most of the power being behind the stop, and this gives strong barrel distortion and transverse chromatic aberration.

In a lens design evolved for the Argonne 12 ft hydrogen chamber, it was decided to limit the wavelength range to 500 Å in order to ease the transverse color problem, and to permit a large amount of barrel distortion. The latter

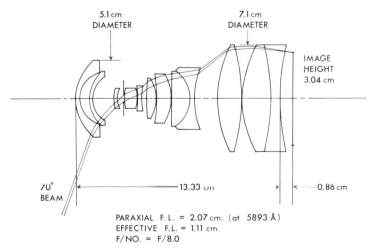

FIG. 42. Telecentric lens with 140° field for Argonne 12 ft chamber. The lens has a (paraxial) equivalent focal length of 2 cm and a relative aperture F/8.

decision was taken because, in a chamber of roughly square shape, the distribution of tracks is such that approximately equal information is found per unit solid angle in any direction, and so it would be sensible to have a distortion function such that equal angles in object space are mapped as equal distances on the image plane. If the distortion is not constrained in a telecentric design, this is roughly the shape obtained. On the other hand, if the distortion were corrected, i.e., the tangent of the field angle mapped linearly in the image plane, too much space would be devoted to the outer parts of the field and the center, where most interactions occur, would be unduly compressed.

Figure 42 shows the Argonne design, carried out by M. J. Buzawa of Tropel, Inc. As shown, it covers a circular field 60 mm in diameter, i.e., it is intended for 70 mm perforated film. The aberrations are diffraction-limit corrected, with the exception of distortion, which rises to 50 % at the edge of the field. The maximum departure from the telecentric condition is at the edge of the field, where the principal ray is inclined to the axis by 5°.

VI. Light Sources

The kind of light source to be used is dictated by exposure time, which must be not longer than 100 to 200 μsec; the total light energy, which is such that of the order of 100 to 1000 J must be dissipated; and the requirements of accurate triggering and a repetition rate of 30 to 60 per minute for days on end. Some form of xenon flashtube is the only source at present available which fulfills these requirements.[4] The exposure time is chosen to be short compared to the delay after the beam and also to be short enough to prevent bubble growth and turbulence from blurring the exposure. The required light energy follows from the order of magnitude calculation outlined in the next section.

A. ORDER OF MAGNITUDE CALCULATION OF LIGHT ENERGY

We define the following symbols:

J = electrical energy dissipated in the flashtube per flash, joules.

η = efficiency of flashtube, i.e. ratio of useful light energy obtained to total energy dissipated.

Ω = solid angle over which the light is collected by the condenser or precondenser, steradians.

---

[4] For bright field illumination, less light power is needed but a flashtube is still very convenient.

A = area of bubble chamber window illuminated by the tube, cm^2.
r = radius of bubble, cm.
R = distance from bubble to camera lens, cm.
$G(\alpha)$ = scattering function of bubble.
a = radius of camera lens pupil, cm.
l = image side conjugate distance of camera lens, cm.

The energy per unit incident on a bubble is then

$$\frac{J\eta}{A}\frac{\Omega}{4\pi} \tag{54}$$

and the scattered energy entering the camera lens is

$$\frac{J\eta}{A}\frac{\Omega}{4\pi} G(\alpha)\left(\frac{r}{R}\right)^2 \pi a^2 ; \tag{55}$$

this energy is distributed over the bubble image on the emulsion, and we assume as an approximation that this is a uniform patch of diameter equal to the radius of the first dark ring in the Airy pattern (Eqs. (48) and (49)). The energy density in this patch is therefore (Welford, 1962)

$$\frac{1}{0.36\pi}\frac{J\eta}{A}\Omega G(\alpha)\left(\frac{r}{R}\right)^2\frac{a^4}{\lambda^2 l^2}. \tag{56}$$

It has been found by Zweig et al. (1958) that an energy density of $10^{-8}\,J\,cm^{-2}$ of white light on medium speed panchromatic emulsion produces a density of about 0.4, so that the expression in Eq. (56) must be equated to this to find the required value of J. All the quantities in this expression, except η, are determined by the geometry of the optical system; the value usually taken is about 0.01, which allows for colored filters to produce roughly monochromatic light.

The above applies, of course, to dark field illumination; in the bright field, the energy density at the emulsion is given simply by

$$\frac{J\eta\Omega}{4\pi A}\left(\frac{l}{R}\right)^2, \tag{57}$$

provided that the camera lens takes in all the source image.

B. TYPES OF FLASHTUBE AND TRIGGERING CIRCUITS

Flashtubes for bubble chambers need a longer life, faster repetition rate, and greater light output than those ordinarily made for most other purposes.

To secure these qualities, the tubes are usually made in fused silica and an improved triggering mode is adopted. In the ordinary method of triggering, the tube is permanently connected to the high voltage supply and the flash is triggered by a pulse applied to an auxiliary electrode. Tubes used under these conditions have a useful life of only a few thousand flashes, presumably due to erosion of the electrodes and tube walls by field emission. In an improved system originated by S. R. Borenstein, the high voltage supply is switched on only at the instant of triggering; this has resulted in a life of hundreds of thousands of flashes for a variety of different tubes. One realization of this system was described by Yamamoto and Sims (1963). A block diagram of the system is shown in Fig. 43; the resistance R, typically several megohms, keeps both electrodes at the same potential when the system is quiescent; the initiating pulse both closes the switch S and triggers the flashtube; S may be a spark gap or an ignitron.

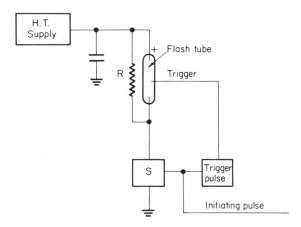

FIG. 43. Method of running a flashtube with no high voltage (H.T.) on electrodes in quiescent period.

Conventional sealed-off flashtubes have been used on most bubble chambers; Fig. 44 shows a few designs. Apart from the triggering method just described, the other important factor in securing long life and reliability seems to be adequate cooling. A different approach to the flashtube problem was described by Früngel *et al.* (1963); they estimated that about 1000 to 2000 J per tube would be needed for the CERN 2 meter hydrogen chamber and they describe a demounted tube that is sealed with O rings and has tungsten-thorium electrodes.

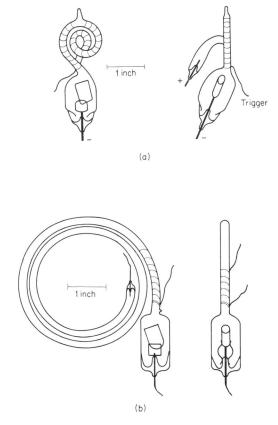

(a)

(b)

FIG. 44. Xenon flashtubes made by P.T.W. Ltd., Wiesbaden: (a) a quasi point source, (b) ring source for imaging around a camera lens aperture.

VII. Cameras

It would not be practicable to go into mechanical details of camera mechanisms in this section but we indicate the main points which are peculiar to bubble chambers and need special consideration in design. These are, briefly, the width and length of film, the length of wind-on, the accuracy of flatness needed in the film gate, the need for auxiliary data channels, the overall precision of alignment of the cameras relative to the chamber, and the complication that the mechanisms sometimes have to operate in a strong magnetic field.

A. FILM SIZE AND FRAME FORMAT

The actual frame size depends on the magnification (Section V,B), but, in addition, there are auxiliary data to be put on each exposure and there is the question whether to use perforated or plain film; this last depends to some extent on the continent in which the chamber is situated, because it appears that the saving in cost due to using unperforated film is considerable in Europe, whereas in the U.S.A. it is no more expensive to use a larger width of *standard*, perforated film. It is obvious that sprocketed film greatly simplifies the camera mechanism, and the vacuum film holding gates used in measuring equipment can be made to take perforated film, so the choice has to be made between cost and convenience. The length of film per spool for large chambers is generally 300 meters (or 1000 ft); shorter lengths would need too frequent film changing during the chamber run, but it is often the custom to cut the film for scanning and measuring.

As an example of a film format, Fig. 45 shows the layout of film from the Rutherford Laboratory 1.5 meter hydrogen chamber. The film is 35 mm unperforated on clear base. The bubble tracks and fiducial marks on the windows are indicated schematically. The eight-sided line round the frame is contact printed on in the camera, i.e. it is a camera based fiducial to which camera lens distortion measurements can be referred. The data photographed in the data box indicate frame number, time, magnet current, and

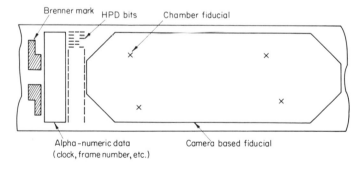

FIG. 45. Layout of film for Rutherford Laboratory 1.5 meter hydrogen chamber.

any other information which it is desired to add. The "Brenner marks" are used as indicators for automatic frame counting devices in scanning and measuring equipment. The "HPD bits" are binary digits containing the frame number and other information; they are intended to be scanned by a flying spot digitizer as an absolute check on the frame number. The data box proper, the Brenner marks, and the HPD bits are all set up together at some distance from the cameras and photographed through auxiliary lenses.

In the Brookhaven system, binary digits are printed along the film edge at one side of the chamber picture (Fig. 46); they are read "on the fly" as the film is wound through measuring equipment.

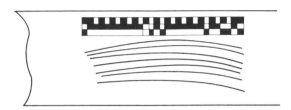

FIG. 46. HPD bits on film as used at Brookhaven; the bits are read as the film is wound through the measuring apparatus.

In most chambers, the three or four separate stereo views of the chamber are taken on separate film rolls, but, in the Berkeley 72 in. hydrogen chamber, the camera forms a single unit taking the three views on a single roll of film.

Whatever system is adopted, some care is needed to ensure correct handing and orientation of data with respect to the chamber image, bearing in mind that at some stages the alpha-numeric characters have to be read in projection devices.

B. CAMERA MECHANISM

Because of the need for accuracy in the reconstruction, the cameras are usually arranged so that the lenses, and in most cases the film gates also, are all rigidly attached to a single plate, the lens plate, which is then attached to the chamber vacuum tank. This lens plate can be calibrated and will keep three or four cameras in the same relative positions. The winding-on mechanism, film spools, and feed and take-up mechanisms can then be mounted in separate light casings which can be loaded in the darkroom and quickly interchanged.

Figure 47 shows sections through film gates; in (a), the backing plate is of metal and the film is sucked flat against it by a grid of holes a few hundred microns in diameter; in (b), the vacuum is applied through the gaps along the side and the backing plate can then be of glass, so that it is possible to

FIG. 47. Vacuum film gates for cameras: (a) sucking through backing plate, (b) sucking around edges of backing plate.

contact print fiducial marks, etc., through it. It seems essential to use suction to hold the film flat enough; the system used in several aerial survey cameras, in which the film is pressed flat against a "register glass" on the emulsion side, entraps air between the glass and the emulsion and causes flatness errors of several microns.

The winding-on operation presents no difficulties with perforated film, and standard mechanisms can be used. With unperforated film the most powerful drive system seems to be the vacuum capstan (Fig. 48); such a

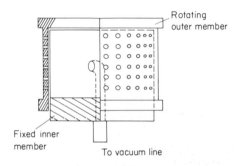

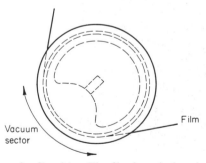

FIG. 48. Vacuum capstan for film drive. The film is sucked against the outer component only over the sector of the inner component to which the vacuum is led.

capstan, about 5 cm in diameter, can pull 35 mm film with a kilogram or so tension before slipping. The length wound on can be metered by means of a cam driven by the film, which itself actuates microswitches. The take-up film spool must have a steady torque applied to it and, in order to prevent the formation of loose loops of film between it and the drive mechanism, a tensioning mechanism is sometimes used; similar arrangements might be envisaged on the feed side, so that a schematic of a camera mechanism would be as in Fig. 49. The power for the wind-on and torque mechanisms is usually derived from electric motors with magnetic clutches, but these have to be placed at some distance from the cameras to avoid the field of the chamber magnet. Similarly, bearings and other moving parts should be nonmagnetic. Printed circuit motors are probably suitable for operation in the stray field of most chambers but they require elaborate power supplies.

The following facilities are desirable in running the cameras: independent operation of any combination of the cameras; triggering pulses to simulate those from the chamber, available with a range of time intervals; indication of the operation of the wind-on of each camera, driven from the film; indication of film breakage; approximate metering of film length.

C. Test Strip Cameras and Direct Viewing Systems

It is very desirable to have facilities for rapid photography and for direct viewing of the tracks, both in the lengthy stages of commissioning a chamber

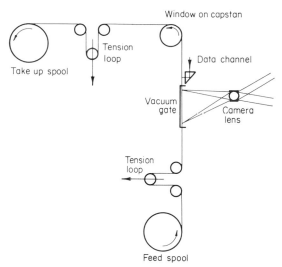

Fig. 49. Schematic of camera.

and for routine checks during a long experiment, since the interval between photographing an event and seeing the processed negative may ordinarily be several hours. It is easier to provide facilities on larger chambers because there is more free space at the camera end of the chamber. The ideal is to have an extra port which can be used either for direct visual inspection or for photography; it should be situated at a point from which a good part of the chamber can be seen in dark field, preferably at a scattering angle not too different from that used at the main cameras.

It is quite possible to see tracks directly; in fact it is a good rule that anything which can be photographed at $f/10$ or a larger f ratio with an exposure less than 0.1 sec can be seen. However, it helps to know roughly where to focus the eye. If the geometry of the chamber is such that it is not possible to bring the eye to a port, then a periscope system can be used; Fig. 50 shows the principle of such a system, giving unit magnification, which can be taken around corners with mirrors as desired. The eyepiece used at the viewing end should have an illuminated graticule so that the eye can accommodate on the image of the midplane of the chamber.

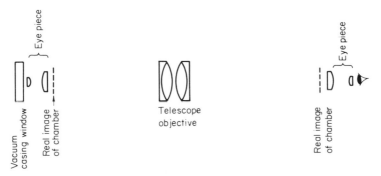

FIG. 50. Periscope optical system. The axis can be turned as desired by means of prisms or mirrors.

The test strip camera should ideally use the same film as the ordinary cameras, so that track quality and exposure can be assessed; it may even be incorporated as part of one of the main cameras, the image being diverted onto the test strip film by means of a mirror. Alternatively, a Land Polaroid camera may be used; this has the disadvantage of an inconvenient format for most chambers, but, on the other hand the result is available in a few seconds. The best material to use is P-N 55, a cut-film pack which has high speed and yields a negative on film with a resolution equal to or better than that of the emulsions used for ordinary bubble chamber photography.

VIII. The Optical Constants

In order to be able to carry out the geometrical reconstruction of the position in space of an event, we have to know the relative positions of the cameras, their magnifications and distortions, the positions of the chamber windows relative to the cameras, and the thicknesses and refractive indices of the windows. These data are known collectively as the optical constants.

If we leave aside the thicknesses and refractive indices, we find the optical constants fall into two groups, those relating to the cameras and those relating to the chamber. It would appear that up to the time of writing, not much attention has been paid to the problems of determining these constants, but with the larger chambers coming into operation, the matter is being taken more seriously. There are, broadly speaking, two possible approaches; one is to make use of an elaboration of the process outlined in Section V,C and, by photographing a test grid simultaneously with all cameras, to obtain a correlation between points on the film planes and rays in the object space. The camera array can then be used to photograph the chamber as a completely calibrated stereo camera system.

The second approach consists in finding, by a conventional surveying process, the locations of the chamber windows relative to fixed points outside the chamber and relating these points to the camera lens "axes."

It is now becoming clear that it is necessary to measure and take account of the symmetrical and asymmetrical distortions of wide field camera lenses, so that in practice a combination of both systems would be used, providing perhaps some useful overdetermination in the optical constants.

The chamber fiducial marks are ruled on the inner surfaces of the window, or windows if the illumination system requires two windows; the marks on the side remote from the cameras provide a useful check on the refractive index of the chamber liquid but those on the camera side window are of most use in the reconstruction. The choice of the arrangement of these marks depends very much on the film measuring system but certain principles can be stated: front and rear marks should appear the same size on the film, no front and rear marks should overlap or nearly overlap on any view, and the arrangement of the marks should be sufficiently asymmetrical and irregular to ensure that measurements of the relative positions of the images of any three marks will identify them unambiguously; the last condition also ensures that there is no doubt about the orientation of the window.

In addition to the chamber fiducials, it is desirable to have some kind of camera based fiducial marks; these are printed on the film in known positions relative to each camera lens and from an elementary point of view they may be regarded as giving the locations of the points at which the camera lens axes intersect the film planes. If we take into account the possibility of asymmetric camera lens distortions, the lenses cannot be said to have axes at all; the camera based fiducials then serve to define coordinate systems in each film plane relative to which the distortion calibration can be made.

We now describe in some detail the process of calibrating the camera array as it has been carried out on some chambers, including the 1.5 meter hydrogen chamber of the Rutherford Laboratory. The lens plate carries the three camera lenses and film gates; it also has three holes which can take an alignment telescope, and these holes, together with those for the camera lenses, are machined on a jig borer at known distances and with their axes perpendicular to a machined flat surface. The camera array is set up opposite the "grid," a piece of $1\frac{1}{2}$ in. thick plate glass which is ruled on a jig borer in 5 cm squares; it also has crosses ruled on it at positions corresponding to the axes of the camera lens holes and the alignment telescope holes. By means of the alignment telescope, which can also function as an auto-collimator, the grid is set parallel to the lens plate, with its crosses opposite the corresponding holes in the lens plate; its distance is set by steel tape to correspond roughly with one of the chamber windows and several exposures are made on all three cameras simultaneously. The grid is then moved a distance parallel to the lens axes approximately equal to the chamber depth; this distance ($2d$, say) is measured with a stick micrometer. Another series of exposures is then made.

The positions of the images of the grid intersections are then determined with reference to a coordinate system (x, y) in each film plane; the origin and axes of each system can be chosen arbitrarily and are fixed and reproduced by means of the camera based fiducials. Similarly, rectangular axes are taken in each grid position, as in Fig. 51. Thus, the measurements at

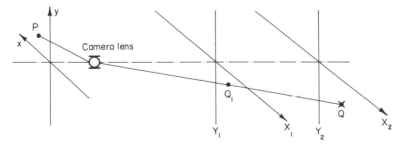

FIG. 51. Principle of camera calibration.

first determine, for each camera lens, two correlations between points $P(x, y)$ on the film and points $Q(X, Y)$ in the further grid position or $Q_1(X_1, Y_1)$ in the nearer position, and each of these may be expressed by a suitable double power series or interpolation table. Now let $P(x, y)$ on the film correspond to $Q(X, Y)$ in the further grid position; by means of the interpolation table we find that $P(x, y)$ also corresponds to $Q_1(X_1, Y_1)$ in the nearer position, where Q_1 is not in general a point on the grid. Then Q and Q_1 determine a line in the object space of the lens, the coordinates of this line being expressible in terms of the axes for either grid position.

In this way, we have the coordinates of the ray in object space corresponding to any point on any of the three film planes; the ray is given with respect to a coordinate system rigidly fixed with respect to the lens plate; the position of this system is known with respect to the fiducial surface and alignment telescope holes. In this process, the symmetrical and asymmetrical lens distortions are both automatically taken into account.

In principle, this calibration is all that is needed to locate exactly whatever is photographed by the camera array, but in practice it may be desirable to make measurements by theodolite of the chamber fiducial marks to provide a check. Also, depending on mechanical details, either chamber or camera may be regarded as being dimensionally more reliable, and if both sets of measurements are available the geometry program can be suitably weighted.

ACKNOWLEDGMENT

The author would like to acknowledge advice and assistance received from C. C. Butler, R. B. Palmer, A. G. Prodell, C. R. Richardson, R. P. Shutt and several others.

REFERENCES

ANDROULAKIS, J. G., et al. (1963). Nucl. Instr. Methods 20, 100.
BELONOGOV, A. V., et al. (1963). Nucl. Instr. Methods 20, 103.
BORN, M., and WOLF, E. (1959). "Principles of Optics," Pergamon, Oxford.
BOUGON, M. and TAMOSAITIS, A. (1966). Private communication.
BRADNER, H. (1960). Ann. Rev. Nucl. Sci. 10, 109.
CAMPBELL, N. P., and PLESS, I. A. (1956). Rev. Sci. Instr. 27, 875.
CATALÁN, L. A. (1962). J. Opt. Soc. Am. 52, 437.
DAVIS, G. E. (1955). J. Opt. Soc. Am. 45, 572.
FIRTH, D. R. (1963). Rev. Sci. Instr. 34, 1393.
FRÜNGEL, F., KÖHLER, F., and REINHARD, H. P. (1963). Appl. Opt. 2, 1017.
HALL, R. (1962). Photogrammetric Rec. 4, 141.
HART, E. L. (1963). Private communication.
JONES, G. O. (1956). "Glass." Methuen, London.
NIKITIN, S. YA. (1963). Nucl. Instr. Methods 20, 95.

PALMER, R. B. (1963). Private communication.

POWELL, W. M., OSWALD, L., GRIFFIN, G., and SWARTZ, F. (1963). *Rev. Sci. Instr.* **34**, 1426.

REITMEYER, F. O., and DEEG, E. W. (1963). *Appl. Opt.* **2**, 999.

REITMEYER, F. O. (1962). Private communication.

RHODES, C. B. (1962). *Photogrammetric Rec.* **4**, 147.

ROSIN, S. (1963). *Appl. Opt.* **2**, 1003.

SHUTT, R. P. (1963). *Nucl. Instr. Methods* **20**, 71.

THETFORD, A. (1964). *Opt. Acta* **11**, 113.

VAN DE HULST, H. C. (1957). "Light Scattering by Small Particles." Wiley, New York.

WARD, J. H., and THOMPSON, B. J. (1967). *J. Opt. Soc. Am.* **57**, 274.

WELFORD, W. T. (1962). *J. Phot. Sci.* **10**, 243.

WELFORD, W. T. (1963a). *Appl. Opt.* **2**, 981.

WELFORD, W. T. (1963b). *Appl. Opt.* **2**, 1037.

WELFORD, W. T. (1966). *Appl. Optics* **5**, 872.

YAMAMOTO, S. S., and SIMS, W. P. (1963). *Appl. Opt.* **2**, 997.

ZWEIG, H. J., HIGGINS, G. P., and MACADAM, D. L. (1958). *J. Opt. Soc. Am.* **48**, 926.

CHAPTER VI

Spark Chambers

JAMES W. CRONIN

Palmer Physical Laboratory, Princeton University
Princeton, New Jersey

I. Introduction

In recent years, the spark chamber has become a standard tool of physicists in the pursuit of knowledge about fundamental particles. The spark chamber utilizes gas amplification processes to render visible in the form of electric sparks the primary ionization of a charged particle passing through a gaseous medium.

Today there are many different variations of spark chambers which use in one way or another the gas amplification phenomena. The early history of the development of spark chambers has been discussed in Chapter I, this volume. We emphasize again that the development of the spark chamber has been one of gradual evolution. Practicing high energy physicists were slow to adopt spark chambers even though clear demonstration of the principle existed in the literature. The explicit demonstration that spark chambers were useful tools in high energy physics was made by physicists in the United States. The early progress was discussed at a symposium held at the Argonne National Laboratory in January 1961. Since that time four different types of devices have been developed: track sampling chambers, wide gap chambers, projection chambers, and streamer chambers.

a. Track Sampling Chambers. These devices consist of a series of parallel conducting plates, spaced approximately 1 cm apart, immersed in a noble gas. When a charged particle passes through the plates, a trail of positive ions and electrons is produced. This trail becomes the nucleus of a spark discharge when a field of approximately 10 keV/cm is applied across each gap immediately after the passage of the particle. A visible spark develops at the location of the original ions, which can be photographed. The information gained about the particle trajectory is the X, Y coordinate in the plane of the gap and a Z coordinate represented by the location of the plane. In fact, a sample of the trajectory is obtained as it passes through the plane containing the spark chamber gap. Figure 1 is the original photograph taken by Fukui and Miyamoto (1959) which shows a track registered in a series of parallel gaps. The photograph was taken perpendicular to the

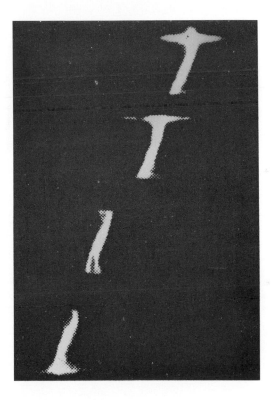

FIG. 1. Photograph taken by Fukui and Miyamoto (1959) which shows track of cosmic ray particle in spark chamber made of neon filled glass boxes.

electric field. Although the spark has the tendency to follow the trajectory, one has essentially a sample of the trajectory at a series of discrete points. If, as in Fig. 2 which shows a 200 MeV proton passing through an 18 gap spark chamber, a large number of sampling planes are placed adjacent to one another, one begins to have a coarse-resolution picture of the entire trajectory. This picture of the trajectory is poor, however, for tracks which are inclined steeply with respect to the normal to the plates.

The stimulation provided by Fukui and Miyamoto was in a somewhat different direction than they had intended. While the classic form of the spark chamber developed with metal electrodes immersed in the gas, the chambers of Fukui and Miyamoto were constructed so that neon was contained in glass boxes placed between the pulsed electrodes. The essential difference is that in the case of Fukui's chamber there was an insulating

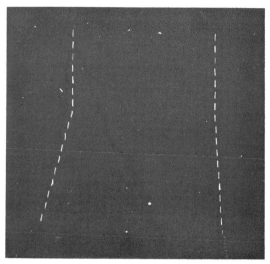

FIG. 2. 200 MeV proton passing through an 18 gap spark chamber. Notice scattering in one of the plates (Cronin and Renninger, 1960).

layer between the pulsed electrode and the gas. The energy available for the sparks is considerably less, but, on the other hand, there is less interaction between the sparks when more than one particle passes through the chamber.

b. Wide Gap Chambers. In this type of chamber, the spark itself conveys directional as well as position information. Figure 1 shows that each spark tends to lie along the trajectory of the particles. By enlarging the gap spacing to dimensions of 30 to 40 cm and applying pulsed fields of $\sim 10\,\text{keV/cm}$ across the gap, we can make the sparks follow faithfully the direction of the true trajectory up to angles of $45°$ with respect to the electric field. Such chambers were first constructed by the Russian group of Alikhanyan *et al.* (1963). Figure 3 shows a spark track obtained by the group of Bareyre *et al.* (1964) in a chamber with a 40 cm gap spacing. In this type of chamber, tracks are registered well for angles less than $45°$ to the normal.

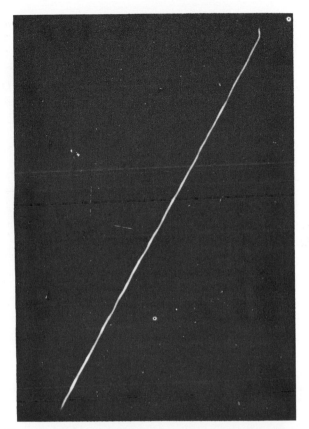

FIG. 3. Photograph of a cosmic ray track in a wide gap chamber (Bareyre, 1964).

c. Projection Chambers. If a conducting glass or wire screen electrode is used, the discharge can be viewed parallel to the electric field. Fukui and Miyamoto (1959) made photographs of tracks which passed parallel to the electrodes. The track appears well defined in the direction of the electric field, but is composed of a series of sparks which cross the gap, so that when the track is viewed perpendicular to the field, a sheet of sparks is seen with no spatial information. Figure 4 shows a projected track obtained by Pondrom (1964). In effect, the tracks are projected onto a plane perpendicular to the electric field. There has been very little application of this type of chamber up to the present time, although the properties have been well established by a number of careful studies (Charpak and Massonet, 1963; Fukui and Zacharov, 1963).

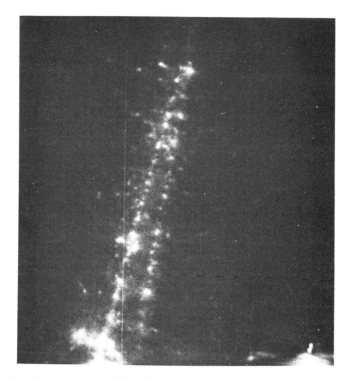

FIG. 4. Pair of cosmic ray particles registered in a projection chamber (Pondrom, 1964).

d. Streamer Chambers. Two Russian groups (Chikovani *et al.*, 1964; Dolgoshein *et al.*, 1964) have demonstrated that if a projection chamber is operated with a very short high voltage pulse, only the beginnings of the streamers localized near the original electrons left by the ionizing particles develop across the gap, instead of full sparks. Figure 5 shows a photograph obtained by Dolgoshein *et al.* (1964) for a chamber operating under these conditions. The streamers along the electric field are about 0.7 cm in length. This final type of chamber has nearly isotropic properties and can register many particles simultaneously. Up to the present, there has been little experience with these chambers in actual experiments.

Of the four types of track registration devices, we shall devote most of the discussion to the parallel plate spark chamber which is the only type to have been extensively used in high energy physics. In the future, there is every promise that this type will continue to be a prominent tool. Also, it

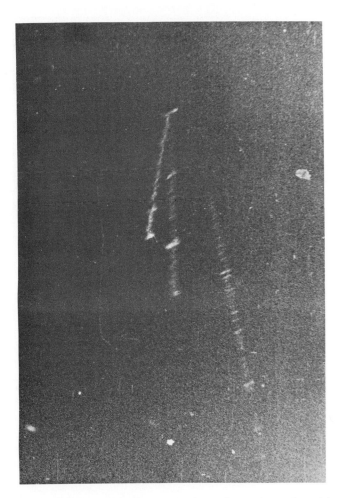

FIG. 5. Three simultaneous tracks from a cosmic ray interaction registered in a streamer chamber (Dolgoshein *et al.*, 1964).

can be expected that the wide gap spark chambers and the streamer chambers will begin to see more frequent use.

The impact of spark chambers on the progress of high energy physics has been most dramatically exemplified by the use of a 10 ton spark chamber in 1962 (Danby *et al.*, 1962) to detect high energy neutrino interactions. Countless other experiments have been made feasible because of the development of the spark chamber. In all of these experiments, the spark chambers have been used in combination with scintillation and Čerenkov counters. Ideally, the counters select a particular type of event for which one needs detailed spatial information in order to carry out the physical measurement.

A simple example is the study of elastic pion-proton scattering. The demand, with the counters, of approximate coplanarity of the events causes a selected sample to be displayed in the spark chamber. Because of the selection, the sample is enriched in elastic scatterings. The spark chambers are then used to make a fine check of the coplanarity. When the sample of pure elastic scatterings has been established, the desired physical measurement (e.g., angular distribution) can be carried out.

In the above example, the spark chamber served two distinct purposes. First, the geometrical properties of the event as registered in the spark chamber assisted in a final purification of the events. Second, a particular geometrical distribution of the purified sample was displayed by the spark chamber as the goal of the experiment. In general, it is desirable to have a triggering system which minimizes the amount of effort required for the purification. The spark chamber is being used most effectively when the trigger system selects electronically in advance a nearly pure sample.

In this regard, a crucial property of the spark chamber is its short memory time. A dc clearing field applied across the gap can remove the primary electrons which carry the information of the particle trajectory in times of the order of a few hundred nanoseconds. Thus, with particles passing through a spark chamber at a rate of 10^6/sec, an individual track can be detected by counters and registered alone in the spark chamber.

II. Basic Properties of Spark Chambers

A. THEORY OF OPERATION

We shall consider an idealized spark chamber and try to develop the elementary features of a theory of operation. Consider two parallel conducting plates with a noble gas at atmospheric pressure between them. A minimum ionizing particle passing through liberates approximately 30 ion pairs per centimeter in neon; 1 cm is a typical gap for a spark chamber. At a later time, a high voltage pulse is applied across the plates and a discharge occurs in the vicinity of the original ionization. This phenomenon is the basic process of a spark chamber.

Experience among many workers has shown that the properties of the spark chamber do not depend on the nature or material of the plates but rather on the properties of the gas. Plates have been constructed of almost all materials, including carbon and conducting wire mesh. The independence of the spark chamber property from the materials of the plates suggests that surface phenomena do not play a decisive role in the behavior of the chamber.

The theory of breakdown in gases at high pressures is not understood in all quantitative detail. The theory of Raether (1941) or of Meek and Craggs (1953) provides a convenient framework within which one can understand the fundamental properties of spark chambers. The ionization of the gas atoms by the passage of the particles provides electrons and positive ions. In the interval of time between the passage of the particle and the application of the high voltage pulse, which is usually $\sim 1\ \mu$sec, the number of primary electrons is reduced by the processes of

(a) diffusion to plates,
(b) recombination,
(c) attachment of negative ions, and
(d) externally applied dc clearing fields.

When the high voltage pulse is applied, the remaining electrons in the gas provide the origin of the discharge. The positive ions have a sufficiently low mobility so that they cannot produce any additional ionization; hence, they play no essential role in the spark formation process. In the noble gases, the thermal diffusion coefficients of electrons are of the order 10^3 cm^2/sec; so that in 10^{-6} sec, the mean square displacement of a single electron is only ~ 0.4 mm, making the loss of electrons by diffusion negligible. The probability of recombination with the positive ions is completely negligible, and in pure noble gases the probability of electron attachment is also negligible. The contamination by electro-negative gases, however, will strongly influence the lifetime of the free electrons in the gas.

When the high voltage pulse is applied to the conducting plates, the electrons begin to drift in the field. If the impressed field is sufficiently high, each electron will begin to produce additional electrons at a rate α per centimeter as it drifts towards the anode. Here α is the first Townsend coefficient; it is a property of the gas and a function of the ratio E/p, where E is the electric field and p is the pressure. Most spark chambers are operated with pressures of the order of one atmosphere. Here the "streamer" theory of spark development applies (Raether, 1941; Meek and Craggs, 1953). The essential feature of this theory is the production of an electron avalanche by electron multiplication, followed by rapid spark development when the avalanche reaches a critical size. The time scale of the avalanche development is typical of the electron mobilities in the high impressed fields. The subsequent time required for the avalanche to develop into a streamer and spark is short compared to the avalanche development time, being approximately one tenth of the total spark formation time.

This two stage development of the discharge recently was demonstrated photographically by Von Tholl (1963). Measurements of the spark formation time indicate that roughly 10^8 electrons must be accumulated in the primary avalanche (Fletcher, 1949). This result seems more or less independent of the kind of gas.

The final spark channel, which forms a conductive path across the gap by the development of streamers, will pass through the location of the initiating avalanche. Actually, in the real spark chamber gap there will develop a number of simultaneous avalanches each originating from an original electron or cluster of electrons. One has the latter situation often since an ionization event producing a δ ray gives a cluster of secondary ionized electrons in a very small space.

If the distance between the separate avalanches is sufficiently close so that space charge fields between the two avalanches are on the order of the impressed field, then a single discharge channel will pass through the centers of all the primary avalanches, resulting in a spark which tends to follow the trajectory of the particle.

Let us consider the development of an avalanche from n_0 initial electrons. We have

$$\frac{dn}{dX} = n\alpha,$$

where X is the distance through which the electron moves and n the number of electrons at that instant. The number of electrons at any distance is thus $n = n_0 \exp[\int \alpha \, dX]$. The criterion for the development of a spark is that $n \geq 10^8$ or $\ln n_0 + \int \alpha \, dX \geq 20$. We shall refer to this criterion as the Raether condition and shall use it as the principal guide in understanding qualitatively the properties of spark chambers. When the Raether condition is satisfied, we expect the spark chamber to show very good efficiency. When the condition is not satisfied, we expect the chamber to have a poor efficiency.

Figure 6 gives the value of α versus E for helium, neon, and argon, and for neon with a 1% argon admixture at atmospheric pressure. Typical values of α for 10 keV/cm are 40, 65, and 10 respectively for helium, neon, and argon.

If the condition for a spark is $\int \alpha \, dX = 20$, and we assume for the moment a sharp rise to a constant voltage for the applied pulse, we find a definite distance required for the formation of a spark, $d = 20/\alpha$. A time for the spark to form is found by replacing d by $V\tau$, where V is the drift velocity of the electrons in the applied field and τ is the spark formation time. Thus,

$$\tau \approx 20/\alpha V.$$

Fischer and Zorn (1961) have made extensive and detailed measurements of spark formation time as a function of applied voltage and plate separation. Figure 7 shows a summary of their results. They measured the time τ as a function of voltage, plate separation, and gas filling.

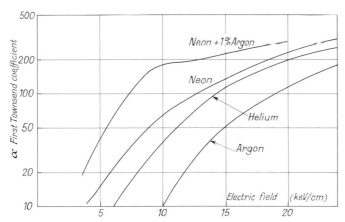

FIG. 6. Values of the first Townsend coefficient α for the noble gases (Von Engel, 1956).

The curves by Fischer and Zorn fit a form $\tau = C/\alpha V$, where they find for C the approximate values 30, 20, and 30 for helium, neon, and argon, respectively. The spark formation times for the narrow gaps are longer than those for the larger gaps except for the highest applied fields. This is the result of the fact that the distance d exceeds the gap spacing, so that the Raether condition is not fully satisfied.

One can discern from these measurements a number of qualitative features of the behavior of spark chambers. The efficiency of the spark chamber will depend on the length of the applied pulse. Several authors have observed this effect (Burnham *et al.*, 1963; Meyer, 1963). For example, Meyer studied an argon-filled chamber with a gap of 6 mm and a voltage pulse of variable length. In one experiment, he varied the length of the applied voltage pulse between 2 and 15 μsec with a resultant change in efficiency from 4 to 93%.

For a pulse of length 0.1 μsec, the thresholds for neon and argon spark chambers of 1 cm gap are estimated to be 7 and 14 kV, respectively. These

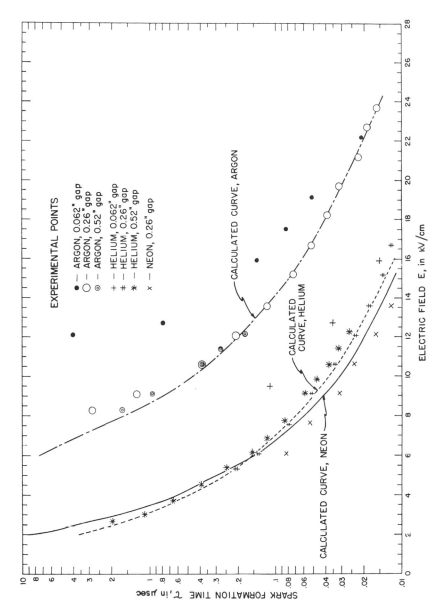

Fig. 7. Spark formation time in various gases (Fischer and Zorn, 1961).

values are in fair agreement with observations. Efficiencies for a single gap of greater than 99% are readily obtained if the length and height of the applied pulse allow the Raether condition to be satisfied.

The efficiency of a spark chamber will also depend on the rise time of the high voltage pulse. Consider as an example an argon chamber of 1 cm gap. Figure 8 shows the computed time required for 10^8 electrons to build up in the avalanche and the corresponding distance required as a function of

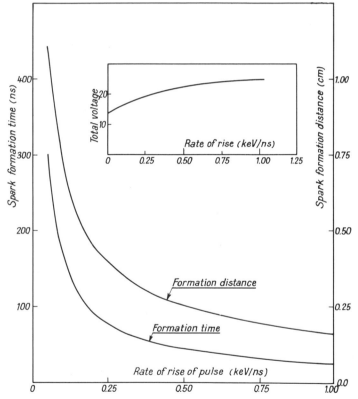

FIG. 8. Computed spark formation time and distance for argon as function of the rise time of the voltage pulse. Inset shows the voltage at which the breakdown occurs.

linear rise times of the voltage pulse. In this calculation, the values of α and V are taken to be power relations of the electric field. If the critical distance required exceeds the gap spacing, then the efficiency can be expected to be very poor. For a 0.2 cm gap chamber, a rise time of $\sim 10^6 \ V/\mu\text{sec}$ is required.

If the rise time is slower, then the electrons will be cleared from the gap before the avalanche can develop to the critical size. Observations of the dependence of efficiency on rise time have been made by a number of authors (Burnham *et al.*, 1963; Michael and Schluter, 1963).

The Raether spark criterion provides a semiquantitative understanding of the basic mechanism of the spark chamber. In subsequent sections, we shall refer to the results obtained here. It should also be remarked that the values of α given in Fig. 6 are for very pure gases, which is usually not the case for actual spark chambers. A dramatic effect results from the addition of a small amount of argon to neon. Notice in Fig. 6 the enhanced value of α when 1% argon is added to the neon. This is the Penning effect (Druyvesteyn and Penning, 1940). Metastable neon atoms produced by electron impact in the avalanche subsequently collide with argon atoms and ionize them. A study by Tsukishima (1963) has indicated that 1% argon mixed with neon at atmospheric pressure gives the lowest threshold for spark chamber operation. The author as well as many others have made this observation in a qualitative way.

B. CLEARING PROPERTIES

1. *Clearing by Electric Fields*

Let us again consider the electrons in the noble gas immediately after the passage of a single ionizing particle. We have shown that the processes of diffusion, recombination, and attachment do not significantly alter the electron population in times of order 1 μsec. If a dc field is applied between the plates, the electrons can be cleared from the gap. Figure 9 gives the drift velocities measured under various conditions by English and Hanna (1953) and Bowe (1960). In an electric field of 100 V/cm, the measured neon drift velocity is $\sim 0.3 \times 10^6$ cm/sec, so that the electrons would be cleared from a 1 cm gap in a time 3.3 μsec.

There are two polarities possible for the clearing field. If the clearing field is applied in the same direction as the high voltage pulse, the electrons will drift towards the plate which will eventually be the high voltage anode when the pulse arrives. We have previously remarked that a certain distance is required for the avalanche to develop. If g is the distance across the gap and if d is the distance required for the avalanche to develop, then the memory time of the chamber will be $t_m \approx (g - d)/V$, where V is the drift velocity of the electrons. If the clearing field is applied in a direction opposite to the applied voltage, then the electrons drift towards the plate that will eventually be the high voltage cathode, so that the electrons that are just

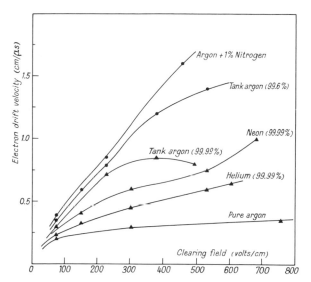

FIG. 9. Drift velocities of electrons in noble gases under various conditions of purity. The curves marked with circles were measured by English and Hanna (1953) and those with the triangles by Bowe (1960).

about to be removed from the gap will have the full width of the gap in order to develop an avalanche, hence, $t_m = g/V$. Figure 10 shows some measurements of Meyer's (1963), who used an argon chamber with a gap

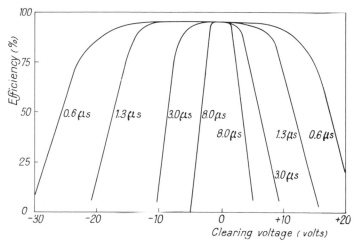

FIG. 10. Efficiency of argon chamber as a function of delay and clearing field. Note that both signs of the clearing field are used (Meyer, 1963).

spacing of 0.8 cm. The figure plots clearing field versus efficiency with time delay of the high voltage pulse as a parameter. The negative clearing voltages correspond to the clearing field being opposite to the applied high voltage pulse. As one expects for the considerations of the avalanche distance d, the clearing times are shorter for positive clearing voltages. By raising the clearing field to sufficiently large values, it is possible to reduce the memory time of the spark chamber to less than 0.1 μsec. Generally, the sensitive time is kept longer because delays in the triggering system in most practical applications have been 0.25 μsec or greater. Some authors have found, however, that neon exhibits a minimum clearing time of 0.25 μsec (Cronin and Renninger, 1960).

Many authors have measured the clearing properties of spark chambers. It is found that the detailed features of the curve depend very much on gas purity and various additive agents, such as alcohol. Also, with sealed chambers, where the gas is not continuously circulated and purified, large changes in clearing are recorded as a function of time. This fact has prompted a number of workers to provide either a flow of fresh gas or continuous purification by charcoal traps or hot calcium.

The simplest interpretation of the clearing field data is in terms of electron drift velocities. The drift velocity can be approximately computed by the equation $V = g/t_m$. Figure 11 shows the computed drift velocities from a number of workers for argon and neon and some mixtures. These drift velocities are compared with velocity curves measured in pure neon, pure argon, and argon at various stages of purity.

In general, the drift velocities implied by the data are considerably larger than those measured carefully in pure gases. A second fact to note is the wide variation observed, especially in neon. Cronin and Renninger (1960) compared spark chamber clearing characteristics at the instant of filling with fresh gas with those observed several weeks later. In addition to some structure in this inferred mobility curve, the measurements with the fresh gas are roughly in agreement with the measured drift velocity curves. Later the drift velocities increased by a factor of 3 above 100 V/cm applied field. The influence of accumulating impurities is clearly indicated. In the case of the author's work, the gas was analyzed and found free of nonnoble gas contaminants above a level of a few parts in 10^4.

Figure 12a shows the clearing field results of Culligan et al. (1961) for a 4 mm gap chamber. Here the argon was 99.99% pure and was flowed through the chambers to assure constant purity. With no clearing field, the chamber was efficient for 30 μsec. The drift velocities which correspond to these curves were among those plotted in Fig. 11 and are too large by a factor of 5.

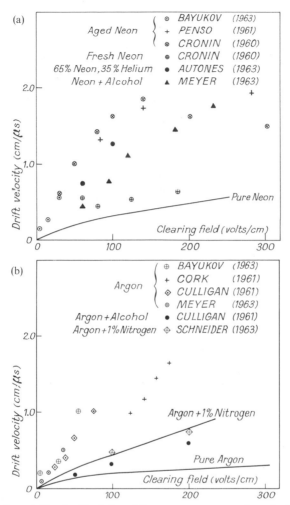

FIG. 11. Electron drift velocities inferred from measurements of spark chamber clearing time. Reference is given in the figure to the sources of the measurements. Solid lines represent direct measurement of drift velocity. (a) Neon, (b) Argon.

Figure 12b shows the result of addition of 38 mm Hg partial pressure of alcohol. The alcohol eliminates the 5% residual efficiency at long times, probably because the alcohol de-excites metastable states produced at the time of particle passage. Alcohol reduces the sensitive time with no clearing field to about 7 μsec. Also, it has a profound effect on the drift velocities, reducing them by a factor of 4.

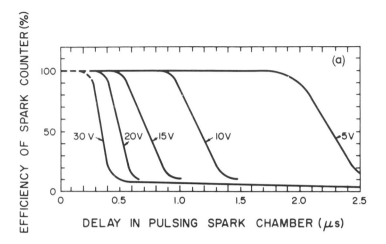

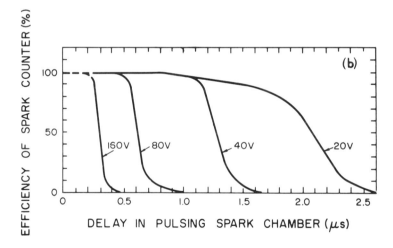

FIG. 12. (a) Efficiency of a 4 mm gap argon filled chamber as a function of delay and clearing
field. (b) Same curves for argon saturated with alcohol (Culligan *et al.*, 1961).

There is little understanding of many of the details discussed in the above
paragraphs. The essential conclusion is that only the qualitative details of
clearing phenomena are reproducible. It does seem that it is possible to
produce as short a sensitive time as one requires just by application of the
clearing field.

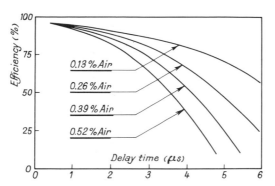

FIG. 13. Effect of air contamination in a neon filled spark chamber (Burnham and Thompson, 1964).

2. *Clearing by Electron Attachment*

Sealed spark chambers sometimes show a deterioration in efficiency. This phenomenon is attributed to the growth of electron attaching impurities in the gas. The attachment probabilities for most substances are velocity dependent, so that the clearing field properties are also affected. Schneider

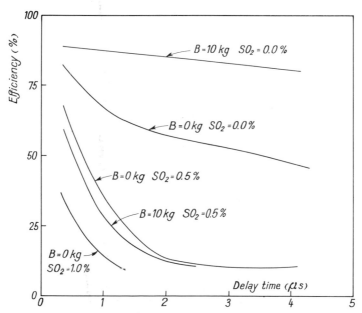

FIG. 14. Efficiency of a neon filled spark chamber gap as a function of delay and concentration of SO_2 vapor (Murphy and O'Neill, 1962).

and Höene (1963) have studied clearing field properties of argon–oxygen mixtures. They conclude that oxygen contaminations of a few percent in argon can reduce the memory time to less than 1 μsec. Figure 13 shows the results of Burnham and Thompson (1964) on the effect of small amounts of air contamination in a neon filled spark chamber.

Murphy and O'Neill (1962) have chosen SO_2 as a suitable clearing substance. They point out that initially the electrons have 6 eV energy on the average and moderate to thermal energies in about 0.3 μsec. SO_2 has an attachment probability that is very small for energies of 6 eV, large for thermal energies. This feature means that very little clearing occurs during the first 0.3 μsec, giving time for trigger logic to act. Figure 14 shows the results. The addition of 0.5% SO_2 reduces the efficiency to 10% at 2 μsec delay and only reduces the efficiency to 70% at 0.39 μsec delay. As we shall see in Section II,E, the use of chemical clearing has advantages for the use of chambers in magnetic fields.

C. DEAD TIME

Triggering the spark chamber on a second track results in the recognition of the old tracks if the second pulse arrives too soon after the first. Autonès *et al.* (1963) measured the time required for the chamber to forget a previous

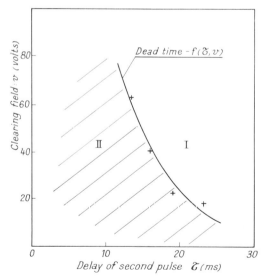

FIG. 15. Dead time of a spark chamber as a function of clearing field. In region II a second pulse causes reignition of the original track (Autonès *et al.*, 1963).

track. Figure 15 shows the time required for a chamber to recover as a function of clearing field. These particular measurements were made with a graphite plate chamber of 1 cm gap filled with a 65% neon 35% helium mixture. Figure 16 shows an exposure of the original track of Autonès *et al.* (1963) and the reignited track for a pulse 10 msec later. The film was rapidly displaced so that both tracks are visible.

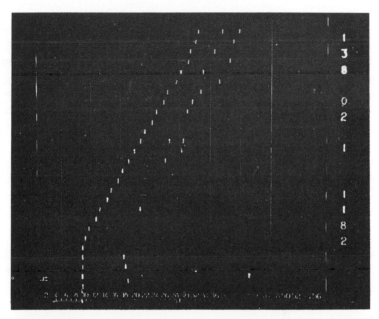

Fig. 16. Photograph showing original track and reignited track for a pulse applied 10 msec after the original pulse (Autonès *et al.*, 1963).

The mechanism which produces the relatively long dead time is not completely understood. Perhaps the field, caused by the large number of positive ions remaining after the spark discharge, traps the many free electrons released in the same discharge. The free electrons and positive ions are reduced in number by recombination, and the positive ions drift slowly in the external field. The presence of a clearing field clearly influences the recovery time, as shown by the results of Autonès *et al.* (1963). A detailed account of the theory of recovery has been given by Fukui and Miyamoto (1961).

The addition of alcohol was found to shorten the recovery time of an argon filled chamber from 4 msec to less than 1 msec (Culligan *et al.*, 1961).

The recovery time seems also to depend on the amount of energy dissipated in the spark discharge. Studies of wire spark chambers (to be discussed in Section VIII,B) for which only 0.001 J per spark is used give recovery times of the order of a few hundred μsec (Fischer et al., 1963). This short recovery time is materially assisted by application of pulsed clearing fields.

D. DETECTION OF IONIZATION AND MULTIPLE TRACKS

There has been little success in attempts to use spark chambers to measure the ionization of single particles passing through them. The essential reason is that once an avalanche develops to the point of the Raether condition there is no memory of the original number of electrons present. The only information about the original ionization is in the spark formation time. If n_0 is the original number of electrons, then $\tau = (20 - \ln n_0)/\alpha V$. If a sufficiently short pulse is applied, it may be possible to distinguish ionization by relative efficiency, but the dependence is only on the logarithm of the initial density. Beall et al. (1961) reported that when their chamber was operated at reduced applied voltage so that the efficiency was only 80% for minimum ionization, the efficiency was 90% for twice minimum ionization. Up to this date, no application known to the author has been used to detect differences in ionization by this method.

Ionization differences, when two simultaneous tracks pass through a spark chamber, have been observed by a number of authors. The problem of detection of ionization and multiple track efficiency are intimately related. In fact, most spark chambers have a common high voltage plate which serves two gaps on either side of it. In most cases, the electrical coupling time between each side is very short, so that the development of sparks on either side of the high voltage plate is similar to the development of two sparks in a single gap.

If two ionizing particles pass through a single gap, fluctuations in the spark formation time can occur, because of fluctuations in the original number of free electrons and in the avalanche development time. If n_0 is the average number of electrons produced in a gap by a minimum ionizing particle, then one expects fluctuations in spark formation time of order $\delta\tau/\tau \cong [20(n_0)^{1/2}]^{-1}$. The formula is approximately correct and agrees with more detailed calculations of Schneider (1963).

For neon gas with a 1 cm gap, $n_0 = 45$ and so $\delta\tau/\tau \cong 0.007$. However, with a gap of 0.3 cm, $n_0 = 15$ and $\delta\tau/\tau \cong 0.013$. Since the secondary processes which lead from the pregnant avalanche to the full electrical spark are very swift, such fluctuations as these can vastly alter the relative development of the two sparks. The development of a full spark lowers the voltage on the high voltage plate so that the second spark which suffers a fluctuation in its formation time does not develop fully.

The relaxation time of the high voltage on a conducting spark chamber plate following the avalanche criteria has not been measured for the noble gases, but one estimates that it is of the order of 10^{-9} sec. If fluctuations in spark formation time are greater than $\simeq 10^{-9}$ sec, the double spark efficiency of the chamber is likely to be poor. Evidently, the shortest possible formation time of the spark must be obtained to achieve good multiple track efficiency. This fact probably explains why argon generally shows poorer multiple track efficiency (Burleson *et al.*, 1962). It is obvious also that plates with a poor surface conductivity will have a higher multiple spark efficiency (Fukui and Zacharov, 1963).

Short spark formation times require high voltages and fast rise times. Michael and Schluter (1963) have done some experiments to demonstrate this phenomenon. They observed the two spark efficiencies for a track which passes through a two gap spark chamber with a common high voltage plate. The study was made with cosmic ray muons. The chamber was filled with pure neon gas and the purity was controlled so that the oxygen content was always less than a few parts in 10^4.

The high voltage pulse was applied across gaps of 0.125, 0.25, and 0.375 in. such that the same field strength of 10 kV/cm was achieved for each gap. The delay of the pulse after particle passage was 0.21 μsec. The pulse was

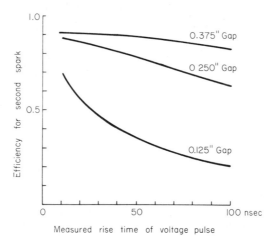

FIG. 17. Double spark efficiency of a spark chamber gap as a function of rise time of the pulse and gap spacing (Michael and Schluter, 1963).

200 μsec long, much longer than typical spark formation times. The rise time of the pulse was varied, and the single and double spark efficiencies were measured. The rise time was the time for the pulse to rise to 90% of its maximum. No clearing field was used.

In Fig. 17 a curve of efficiency for the appearance of a second spark is given. As is to be expected, there is great difficulty in achieving good double spark efficiency when the gap is 0.125 in.

It is demonstrated by these studies and the general experience of all workers in the field that the single most important parameter in spark chamber operation is the achievement of a rapid spark formation time.

Relative ionization phenomena can be made to appear by means of differences in spark formation time. Figure 18 shows a photograph of a Λ^0 decay into a proton of 1.6 times minimum ionization and a pion of minimum ionization, observed by Engels *et al.* (1962). The computed time difference to achieve the Raether condition is $\Delta\tau \cong [\ln(1.6n_0) - \ln n_0]/\alpha V$. The fractional time difference in formation is $\Delta\tau/\tau \cong 0.025$. Typical values of τ for a neon spark chamber are ~ 30 nsec, so that the time difference in the achievement of the Raether condition is of the order of 1 nsec. This time difference is sufficient to inhibit the full development of the minimum ionizing spark, so that the two sparks share the energy discharged through the chamber in some relation to the ionization. Many workers have made

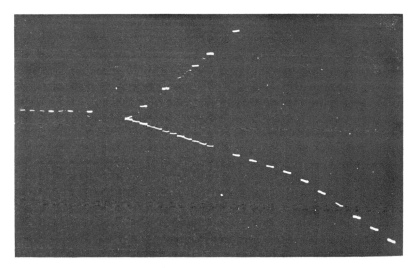

FIG. 18. Decay of a Λ^0 observed in a spark chamber. The relative efficiency of the two decay prongs is in relation to the ionization.

qualitative use of this ionization phenomenon, but it seems difficult to use it quantitatively since it depends so strongly on the characteristics of the spark chamber operation.

The multiple track efficiency for larger numbers of incident tracks has also been investigated by Faissner *et al.* (1963a) using 100 by 160 cm aluminum spark chambers. As a source of multiple particles, they used

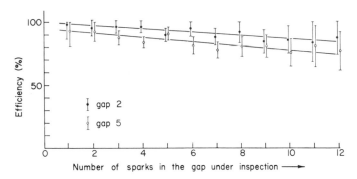

FIG. 19. Efficiency of a gap for a given spark as a function of the number of sparks in the gap (Faissner *et al.*, 1963a).

electron showers produced well upstream so that the average distance between particles was about 20 cm. Figure 19 shows the results of one of their studies for a 80% neon 20% helium mixture. The voltage was 13 kV across 1 cm and the rise time was 40 nsec. They find for widely spaced particles the efficiency of a given gap is almost independent of the number of particles which pass through. One observes that the electrical coupling time between sparks 20 cm apart will be ∼ 1 nsec which will allow a somewhat larger fluctuation in formation time without serious effects. The same group finds there is a somewhat lower efficiency when the electron showers contain particles that are less widely separated.

As well as ionization, a relative time between the passage of two particles through a spark chamber gap can produce a difference in the number of initial electrons present at the time of application of the high voltage pulse, providing a clearing field is placed on the chamber. Figure 20 shows a photograph of a 200 MeV proton which scattered to trigger the spark chamber. After 0.3 μsec, a high voltage pulse was applied. Just prior to that time, another 200 MeV proton happened to pass through, interacting in one of the plates. One can observe that the younger proton robs the energy from the track that originated the trigger. This is another manifestation of unequal sharing of electron energy based on a different number of initiating electrons. When the chamber is operated in a flux of uniformly ionizing particles, the last track through the chamber registers best. Because of this phenomenon, one finds, in fact, that the actual value of a clearing voltage is not always important, and the effective sensitive time is more nearly the time required to trigger the chamber after the detection of a particle. Ionization electrons

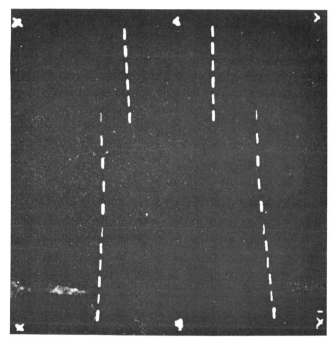

FIG. 20. More recent particle which stops and robs energy from the track that triggered the chamber.

from a particle passing prior to the desired particle are strongly discriminated against since more are cleared out at the time of firing of the chamber.

The sensitivity of the efficiency on the relative spark formation time also depends on the precision of plate spacing. Fluctuations in plate spacings produce fluctuations in the applied electric fields. In argon, for example, α varies roughly as the $\frac{7}{2}$ power and the formation time varies as $\delta\tau/\tau \approx 7\delta d/2d$ where d is the gap spacing and δd is a fluctuation in this spacing. Again, in a typical spark chamber operated with $\tau = 30$ nsec and $d = 1$ cm, a value $\delta d = 0.01$ cm produces a $\delta\iota \approx 1$ nsec. The uniformity of gaps is very

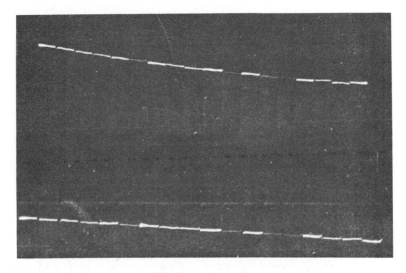

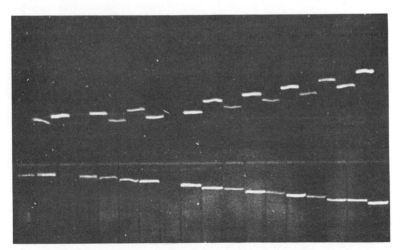

FIG. 21. (left) Track in magnetic field with 100 V/cm clearing field. The photograph shows two orthogonal views, the one at the left being perpendicular to the magnetic field. (right) Photograph taken under the same conditions except with a 0 V/cm clearing field (Overseth, 1964).

important and again these tolerances can be relaxed as the spark formation time becomes shorter.

E. Properties of Spark Chambers in Magnetic Fields

Beall *et al.* (1961) first demonstrated that spark chambers operate in magnetic fields of 15 kG impressed parallel to the plates. More recently, Platner *et al.* (1963) have shown that spark chambers will work in a pulsed axial field greater than 200 kG. In such pulsed field operation, thin plates must be made of a low conductivity material, stainless steel or phosphor-bronze, in order to prevent the destructive effects of eddy currents. When the magnetic field is placed parallel to the plates with a clearing field E, there is a drift in the primary electrons in the direction $\mathbf{E} \times \mathbf{B}$. In a vacuum, the motion of the electrons is cycloidal with a net drift along $\mathbf{E} \times \mathbf{B}$. When the electrons undergo collisions, the motion is more complicated, and there is a drift also in the direction of the electric field (Townsend, 1947). Figure 21 (left) is a photograph taken by Overseth (1964) of a spark trail in a 10% helium 90% neon filled spark chamber with a clearing field of 100 volts and a delay time of 0.4 μsec. The separation of the sparks due to the $\mathbf{E} \times \mathbf{B}$ effect is clearly indicated. Figure 21 (right) shows a photograph under the same conditions except that the clearing field is zero.

The sensitive time of the spark chamber for a given clearing field is increased in the presence of a magnetic field. Figure 22 shows the results of Burleson *et al.* (1962) for the sensitive time as a function of clearing field of a neon–helium chamber with and without magnetic field. They find, however, that with clearing fields of 250 V sensitive times less than 1 μsec can be obtained. A study of the $\mathbf{E} \times \mathbf{B}$ drift as a function of gas filling was made by Overseth (1964). He found that helium produced the smallest transverse

TABLE I

$\mathbf{E} \times \mathbf{B}$ Drift for Various Gases[a]

Gas	Clearing field (V/cm)			
	0	40	100	200
Helium	0.3	1.2	1.3	1.4
90% Neon–10% Helium	0.4	2.2	5.0	—
Argon	0.6	2.6	7.0	—

[a] Separation in millimeters between successive sparks for tracks in a 9 kG magnetic field as a function of gas and clearing field. Delay between particle passage and high voltage pulse was 200 nsec (Overseth, 1964).

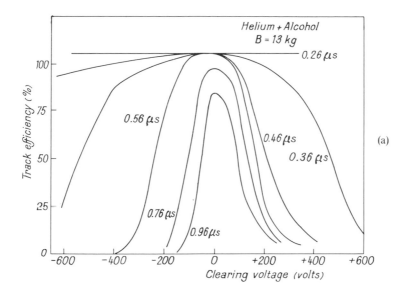

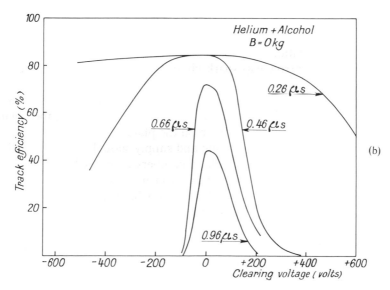

Fig. 22. (a) Dependence of the "track efficiency" on delay and clearing field with a magnetic field of 13 kG. (b) Same curves without magnetic field. "Track efficiency" is defined as the ability to recognize a track, and approximately measures the same thing as gap efficiency (Burleson *et al.*, 1962).

drift. Table I gives his results. The conditions for the experiment were HV pulse 10 kV, clearing field 100 V, rise time 20 nsec, delay time 140 nsec, and gap spacing 0.375 in.

The use of SO_2 to clear the chamber, instead of an electric field, eliminates the $\mathbf{E} \times \mathbf{B}$ effect except for small displacements which occur during the rise of the HV pulse.

III. Construction Techniques

A. GENERAL REQUIREMENTS

We have seen from our discussion of the properties of spark chambers that there are a few general requirements for spark chambers of high performance.

A mechanical design which provides a uniform and stable gap spacing is important, particularly if high gap efficiency is required. The most common fault is the nonequality of gap space on either side of a common high voltage plate. The result is alternating intensities or gap efficiency of successive sparks. Often, in a noncritical spark chamber application, this feature is not important. Practical experience argues that except in the most critical applications a variation in spacing of a few percent of the total gap width is tolerable. For narrow gap spark chambers, even this tolerance becomes quite demanding.

The electrical connections are best arranged so that a low inductance path exists between the high voltage pulses and the spark chamber plate to minimize the rise time of the voltage on the plates.

The arrangement of the gas filling and supply should be such that the gas impurities remain relatively stable. Chambers contained within gas-tight boxes with a large volume to surface ratio have been filled with gas and not changed for periods of several months. Chambers constructed so that they have a small volume to surface ratio seem to operate best with a gas flow system.

The design should avoid high fields due to sharp edges of plates and other regions of small radius of curvature. Spurious edge sparking results if attention is not given to the removal of sharp edges.

These criteria represent conditions required to have high performance spark chambers. It is also true that a number of successful experiments have been carried out with less than ideal conditions. The requirement that the efficiency be very near 100% is not always necessary. Rise times for the applied voltage pulse as slow as 0.1 μsec have been used with successful chamber operation.

Per unit volume, spark chambers represent the cheapest type of detector which has a reasonable spatial resolution. For this reason, the design of a spark chamber can be directed towards a specific experiment with the expectation that the chamber will no longer be used afterwards. Spark chambers of various geometries can be quickly built and placed in operation, particularly small units using the lucite construction techniques. Pulsing and electrical equipment can be used over again.

In the following sections, we shall describe some construction methods used in a variety of different applications of spark chambers. These are representative examples which have found common usage.

B. CHAMBERS CONSTRUCTED WITH LUCITE FRAMES

A very simple chamber construction technique consists of a sandwich of plates separated by lucite frames. The lucite frames form both the gas box and the optical windows. The edges of the plates are exposed to the air or buried inside the lucite. Meyer and Terwilliger (1961) were the first to construct such chambers. Figure 23 shows a view of the assembly of a lucite chamber. In this type of chamber, foils of aluminum 0.001 in. thick have been used for electrodes. In order to obtain flat electrodes, the foils were attached to the lucite frames under tension. This was best done by cementing with epoxy the foil to the frames at 10° C less than room temperature. The differential expansion of the lucite with respect to the aluminum places the foil under tension at room temperature. The walls of the lucite frames were 1 in. thick so that the foil was brought under even tension without wrinkling. Further stretching of the foil can be achieved by operating the chamber at elevated temperatures. A variation of this method has been used at Princeton. Foils are attached to cooled lucite frames by "double sided" tape. When warm, the foils are stretched, but the tape relaxes and the foils become loose in a few hours. If, however, the frames are immediately glued together with fairly fast setting epoxy, the tightness of the foils is maintained.

Construction of chambers with thicker self-supporting electrodes is very simple since no stretching is necessary. The thickness of the lucite frames determines the electrode spacing. Surfaces for the optical viewing of the sparks are polished. The edges of the plates are buried within the lucite or emerge to the outside air so that there is no difficulty with spurious sparking. Such chambers rarely have difficulty with discharges along the surface of the lucite. The gas is usually introduced by flowing, although Meyer and

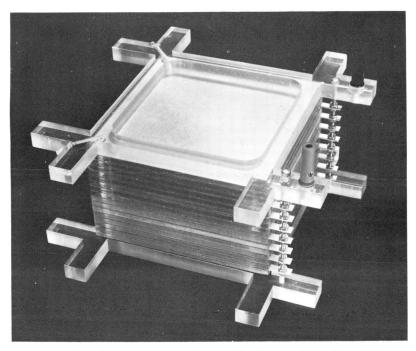

Terwilliger (1961) evacuated their chambers by placing aluminum plates at each end to support the air pressure.

The connections are made to the electrodes by tabs of the foil emerging from the lucite frames. There is no tendency of the edges to break down when exposed to air.

FIG. 23. View of construction technique used by Meyer and Terwilliger (1961).

Gas-tight lucite chambers can be filled with neon, sealed, and operated for several weeks. Small chambers of similar construction with a volume of 8 liters were built at Princeton but without such attention to gas tightness. These chambers operated satisfactorily with a gas flow of 0.02 ft^3 per hour.

Lucite chambers are simple and easy to construct. The technique has disadvantages for larger thin foil chambers. A great thickness of the frame is required to stress the foils evenly; also, the large relative coefficient of thermal expansion means that the tension on the foils and hence precision of spacing of the gaps is a strong function of the temperature.

A novel construction scheme was used by Deutsch (1961). He sliced glass battery jars with a diamond saw into square frames $\frac{3}{8}$ in. thick. The foils were then cemented to the glass frames to produce a chamber of characteristics similar to the lucite chambers.

For the construction of very large spark chambers, the gluing technique is unreliable and impractical. The spark chambers built by the Brookhaven–Columbia University Group (Danby et al., 1962) for the first high energy neutrino interaction experiment employed O-ring seals between the lucite

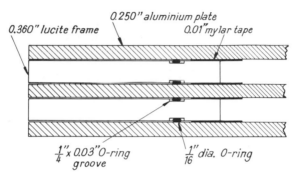

FIG. 24. Schematic view of assembly of Columbia–Brookhaven spark chamber (Schwartz, 1964).

frames and the 1 in. thick plates. The most recent Brookhaven–Columbia neutrino experiment (Schwartz, 1964) used spark chambers constructed of plates of aluminum 6 ft × 6 ft × $\frac{1}{4}$ in. The seals between the lucite frames and the plates were made with O-rings. 0.030 in. deep grooves were cut in the lucite frames. A view of the assembly is shown in Fig. 24. Soft rubber O-rings of $\frac{1}{16}$ in. diameter were placed in the grooves which were $\frac{1}{4}$ in. wide. The total compression of the O-rings was about 0.020 in., the remaining space was taken up by a 0.010 in. mylar spacer. The plates were either aluminum jig plate or ordinary $\frac{1}{4}$ in. aluminum plate. A lucite spacing disk 1 cm in diameter was glued to the center of each plate to maintain gap uniformity. The total assembly was made of groups of 93 plates clamped at each end by a 2 in. thick jig plate for stability.

C. PLATES CONTAINED WITHIN A BOX

Another common construction technique is to place the plate assembly within a gas-tight box. There are a number of advantages to such a construction. It is relatively easy to make the box gas tight so that a chamber can be filled with gas and then sealed. Windows of better optical quality than lucite can be used. Plates of various materials can be used alone or in combination with one another.

Some of the first chambers built using this construction were chambers with carbon plates for polarization analysis. We describe here a large chamber built by Beall *et al.* (1962) for the detection of the polarization of decay protons of Σ^+ hyperons. The chamber consisted of forty-nine $20 \times 24 \times \frac{1}{2}$ in. plates with a gap spacing of $\frac{1}{4}$ in. Figure 25 shows a

FIG. 25. View of construction of a spark chamber used for polarization analysis (Beall *et al.*, 1962).

photograph of this chamber. The carbon plates were sprayed with conducting silver paint to bind the surface and then were baked out. Without the silver paint, continuous sparking produced carbon dust which could become a source of spurious sparking. The plates were supported on individual steatite insulators. The plates were machined flat to ± 0.003 in. Adjustment of the nuts on the threaded rod allowed the plate spacing to be regulated. The first few plates were hollow, having stretched aluminum foil attached to rigid aluminum frames by epoxy. The edges of the foil which were exposed were painted with silver paint to smooth the sharp edges. A $\frac{1}{8}$ in. radius was placed on the edges of the plates to eliminate edge sparking.

The high voltage connections to the individual plates were made through short sections of RG/8U cable with the outer ground braid stripped away. A seal that is reasonably leak-tight can be made with an O-ring about the polyethylene insulation of the cable. The chamber was enclosed in a relatively thin gas-tight box which could not be evacuated. The chamber was filled by flushing several times the volume of argon through the box and was then sealed off.

One very important type of spark chamber construction has resulted from the development of plates of large area with thin foils. Chambers used in scattering experiments or in spectrometer experiments need only to sample a trajectory and must perturb it as little as possible. A large number of thin foil chambers have been built at Princeton University. We will describe briefly the construction of the plates for these chambers.

In order to maintain flat plates, it is necessary that the foil be under considerable tension. For plate sizes larger than 1 sq ft, lucite is an insufficiently sturdy material. 20×40 in. plates were manufactured with frames fabricated of extruded aluminum stock $\frac{1}{2} \times 1\frac{1}{4}$ in. with a $\frac{1}{4}$ in. radius placed on one side of the extrusion. The rounded edge saved machining time. Frames of the above size were assembled by bolting at the corners. The assembly was carried out on a surface plate to assure flatness. It was found necessary to straighten each piece of the frame before final machining and assembly to achieve the desired flatness.

The 0.001 in. or sometimes 0.0005 in. aluminum foil was attached with Eastman 910 cement. Prior to attachment, the foil was secured to a larger mechanical stretching frame by double sided tape. By mechanical adjustment, the foil was stretched. If the frame which is to become the final plate is to have a foil on both sides, then two stretched foils are prepared simultaneously. The plate frame with the 910 applied is placed on one stretched foil, and the second foil is then placed on top of it. The 910 sets instantly, so that the foil can be trimmed from the stretching frames immediately. The edges of the foil on the frame are covered with mylar tape to prevent breakdown at the sharp foil edge. Figure 26 shows a photograph of a thin foil chamber constructed with the above technique for use as part of a magnetic spectrometer. The hollow thin foil construction technique permits the installation of lead plates inside for electron shower detection. When the lead is placed inside in a slot in the frame, there is no concern for the flatness of the lead. In other experiments, polyethylene has been inserted inside hollow plates to serve as proton targets for incident pions.

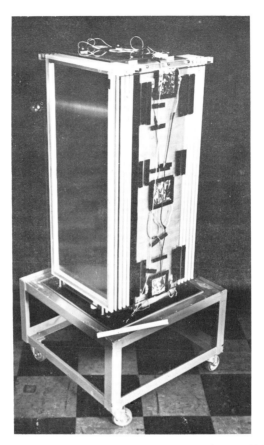

FIG. 26. View of thin foil chamber constructed at Princeton University.

D. CYLINDRICAL SPARK CHAMBERS

A number of groups have constructed chambers with a cylindrical geometry (Beall *et al.*, 1963; Wahlig *et al.*, 1962). Such a geometry proves useful in a number of experimental configurations. Figure 27 shows a cylindrical chamber built by Beall *et al.* (1963). The electrodes were made by rolling 0.010 in. aluminum foil into cylinders 18 in. long, varying in diameter from 10 to 20 in. These were supported at the ends by circular grooves milled in two polished lucite end plates. The spacing between the gaps was 0.375 ± 0.010 in. Electrical and gas connections were made through a lucite post running the length of the chambers; this post also provided a suitable

FIG. 27. Cylindrical chamber constructed by Beall *et al.* (1963).

shielding for the edges of the rolled aluminum plates. The gas seal was made by epoxy between the inner and outer plates and the lucite end windows.

IV. Triggering Techniques

A. GENERAL REQUIREMENTS FOR A SPARK CHAMBER TRIGGER SYSTEM

The simplest pulsing arrangement for a small spark chamber of capacity C_s is shown in Fig. 28a. A thyratron or spark gap is used as a switch which closes on the reception of a trigger pulse derived from the counter logic.

When the switch is closed, the charge in C immediately is shared between C and C_s, producing an applied pulse to the chamber of $V[C/(C + C_s)]$ volts. The length of the pulse is controlled simply by the parallel resistor R across the chamber. The voltage then decays with a time constant $\tau = R(C_s + C)$ giving a pulse that can be adjusted in length by the value of R.

This simple analysis is quite adequate for very small chambers, particularly test chambers which have been used to measure gas properties. As the
capacity of the chamber rises, however, series inductance in the thyratron
and conducting leads and series resistance become important. The capacity
of spark chambers with 1 cm gap is approximately 100 pF/sq ft. A typical
figure for the inductance of leads is $\sim 0.01\ \mu H/in$. Also, the effective series
resistance of the switch may be several ohms. A large chamber high voltage

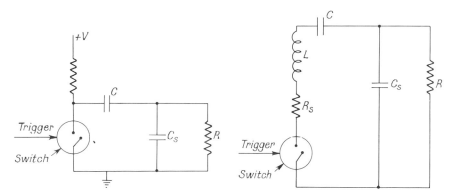

FIG. 28a. Equivalent circuit for a small   FIG. 28b. Equivalent circuit for spark
spark chamber.   chambers where series inductance is important.

plate may have a capacity of 1000 pF. To charge this to 10 kV in 10 nsec
requires a current of 1000 A. If the effective lead length is of the order of
10 in., then a series inductance of 0.1 μH might be expected. For an applied
pulse voltage of 10 kV, the maximum rate of rise of current is $di/dt = V/L$
$= 10^{11}$ A/sec. Such a current can just rise to 1000 A in 10 nsec.

We have used the above example to illustrate the importance of the series
inductance of the leads and the source when considering the rise time of the
chamber pulse. In the case where the series inductance is important, the
circuit of the spark chamber and pulsing system becomes a series resonant
circuit. We neglect, for the moment, the load resistor R. In order that a
high voltage source be used most efficiently, it should be arranged so that
the time constant $R(C_s + C)$ is long compared to the rise time, which justifies
the neglect of R. Figure 28b gives the equivalent circuit with L equal to the
total inductance around the loop; R_s, the effective resistance of the switching
device; and C and C_s, the source and spark chamber capacity, respectively.
For situations where $R_s \ll (4L/C_f)^{1/2}$, the circuit resonates with a frequency

$1/2\pi(LC_f)^{1/2}$ and the rise time of the pulse is $\sim \pi(LC_f)^{1/2}$, where C_f $= CC_s/(C + C_s) \approx C_s$ for $C \gg C_s$. For our example, $L = 0.1\,\mu\text{H}$ and $C_s = 10^3\,\text{pF}$, the rise time is 30 nsec. This result follows if $R_s \ll 20\,\Omega$. It is difficult to evaluate the effective internal resistance of the thyratron or spark gap switches. Fischer and Zorn (1962) have evaluated the effective resistance of some spark gaps and find them to be a few ohms. Note that in this particular example the voltage rises to twice the voltage $V(C/(C + C_s))$. The relation between the high voltage supply and the peak voltage on the chamber depends in detail on the circuit arrangements. If the resonant frequency of the chamber and pulsing circuit can be measured, a good estimate of the rise time can be made.

Chamber plates as large as 64 sq ft have been constructed, for which case a common high voltage plate has a capacity of $10^4\,\text{pF}$. In order that the high voltage supply be used effectively, the charging capacity per plate is usually several times the chamber capacity. A typical high voltage is 15 kV, which means that the energy in each of two sparks produced by the high voltage plate is more than 0.5 J. This amount of energy discharged across plates of 0.003 in. aluminum foil does not seem to do serious damage although small pit marks are seen. At 1 J, significant dimples develop in 0.001 in. foil (Fischer and Zorn, 1961). Excessive energy also results in a very wide spark, which tends to affect measurement accuracy.

The load resistor R is generally used to adjust the length of the pulse. If no ionizing particle has passed through the chambers, then a spurious discharge may result if the high voltage pulse is not removed in the shortest possible time consistent with high efficiency. If the rise time of the applied pulse is <50 nsec, then a time constant of 0.1 to 0.2 μsec is typical and does not give rise to extensive spurious sparking.

A number of workers (e.g. O'Neill et al., 1963) have used coaxial cable to store the discharge energy. Here a square pulse shape can be obtained if a proper termination can be made at the chamber. Such a termination can be made in the case of chambers of sufficiently low capacity or if the impedance of the driving cable is sufficiently reduced.

B. SWITCHES

1. Thyratrons

The switch which discharges the storage capacitor into the spark chamber can be either a thyratron or a spark gap. The two most important requirements of the switch are (1) that the delay time in the switch be short and (2) that the internal impedance of the switch be very small.

In the first few years of spark chamber use, the most common switch element was the 5C22 hydrogen thyratron. Many workers, including the author, continue to use thyratrons for spark chamber arrangements which do not have a large capacity. When this thyratron is triggered with a fast rising positive pulse greater than 500 V, it exhibits a delay time of ~ 100 nsec. This delay time can be further reduced to about 80 nsec if the grid is given a positive bias just below the point of free running of the thyratron. Setting the heater voltage at 7.0 to 7.5 V instead of 6.3 V also shortens the delay time of the thyratron.

The intrinsic impedance of the thyratron is difficult to measure. For low duty cycle operation such as the spark chamber application, no precautions need to be taken to prevent overcurrents. Once the thyratron fires, the rate of rise of the current is controlled to a large extent by the inductance of the thyratron itself and the external circuit. We have found as a rule that 1 thyratron will conveniently drive 1500 pF with a 15 kV plate voltage. Three 5C22 thyratrons have been used to trigger a $0.012\,\mu$F spark chamber (Autonès et al., 1963). Under these circumstances, great care in providing uniform parallel gaps was required to obtain a high efficiency in all the gaps, since longer spark formation times are the result of slow rising pulses.

Experiments have been operated with 10 thyratrons triggered simultaneously. Experience has been that, on the average, a thyratron will serve for $\sim 5 \times 10^5$ pulses. The symptoms of deterioration are excessive delay in triggering, free running, and poor rise time.

2. Spark Gaps

When one has a spark chamber system of high capacity, spark gaps are more desirable for the trigger element than are thyratrons, since they have a very low internal impedance and can pass large amounts of current. Also, the breakdown time of the spark gap can be made as short as 10 nsec after an applied trigger pulse. The shorter triggering delay allows higher clearing fields. Thus the sensitive time of the spark chamber can be shortened and the instantaneous rate of particles passing through the chamber can be augmented.

Figure 29a shows a typical spark gap, used by a large number of workers. The cathode rests at ground potential but is pierced by a hole which contains a fine tungsten wire needle. The needle protrudes only slightly into the gap. Normally, the gap withstands the voltage across it. However, when a negative trigger pulse is applied to the needle, electrons from the corona discharge produce a space charge disturbance of the electric field which allows avalanches to grow. The amount of time required for the avalanche to grow is characteristic of the time required for breakdown. The discharge is also accelerated by ultraviolet light which is released in the corona discharge. In fact, it seems that ultraviolet light produced by the trigger electrode serves the same purpose as the avalanche so that part of the time required for an avalanche to grow to a critical size is bypassed.

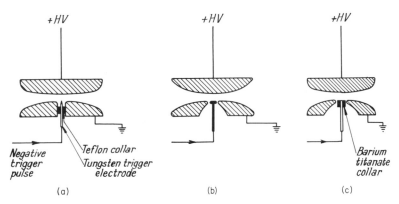

FIG. 29. Three types of triggered spark gaps. (a) Tungsten needle trigger, (b) disk trigger pin, (c) trigger pin covered with barium titanate.

Another type of electrode has been used, with the geometry indicated in Fig. 29b. Here, the blunt pulsed electrode immediately breaks down to the cathode producing ultraviolet light and, hence, photoelectrons which lead to the rapid breakdown of the main gap.

Gaps of the type described above require trigger pulses of between 5 and 10 kV of very short duration, and the breakdown time is 10 to 20 nsec. Gaps of the type shown in Fig. 29a last for at least 10^5 pulses when discharging about 2 J of stored energy. Gaps with the blunt type of electrode last much longer since the electrode has a greater surface over which to wear.

A group at Chicago (Lavoie et al., 1964) has modified the design of the triggered gap by the addition of a barium titanate insulating sleeve about the trigger pin. This gap is shown in Fig. 29c. The high dielectric intensifies the field in the remaining air gap between the pin and the ground electrode. This intensified field allows a smaller pulse to trigger the chamber. Typical trigger pulses are in the neighborhood of 1000 V. The reduced trigger voltage in turn allows faster circuits to be used to develop the trigger pulse.

Many materials have been used for the fabrication of the electrodes. Common materials are tungsten (heavy-met), stainless steel, brass, and copper. The main item of wear is the trigger electrode. Wenzel (1964) has described a gap used at Berkeley which has been designed to eliminate excessive current drain from the trigger electrode. The unique feature of this gap (shown in Fig. 30) is the floating electrode. The recessed tungsten brush, when pulsed, produces electrons by corona. The floating electrode quickly assumes the potential of the trigger, increasing the voltage across the gap. Other electrons begin the ionization processes which cause a rapid

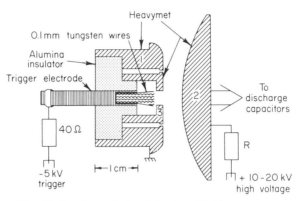

FIG. 30. Spark gap designed for long life (Wenzel, 1964).

breakdown to the floating electrode. The ultraviolet light from this break-down triggers the main gap with a 5 kV pulse; the delay time is 20 nsec and the tungsten fibers last indefinitely since they are not required to carry much current. A single spark gap such as one described above has been used to drive a capacity of 0.01 μF. This gap has pulsed several million times without failure.

Spark gaps such as those described above can either be operated in the air or at elevated pressures. Pressurizing the gaps allows the interelectrode spacing to be reduced and consequently allows a reduction in spark forma-tion time. Also, variation of pressure allows an easy adjustment of the dc standoff voltage of the gap without changing any physical dimensions.

C. TRIGGERS FOR SPARK GAPS OR THYRATRONS

A number of circuits to provide triggers have been used (e.g. Wenzel, 1964; Lavoie et al., 1964; Conversi et al., 1962; Kerns, 1963). Almost all consist of two basic stages: an EFP 60 trigger circuit to convert a positive pulse of a few volts to a current pulse of 1 A taken from the dynode, followed by an additional voltage and power gain to drive a number of spark gaps or thyratrons in parallel. The EFP 60 circuit is similar to a circuit designed by Coffin *et al.* (1958). With a 3 V positive input pulse, the output pulse has a rise time of 20 nsec and a delay of 20 nsec. The EFP 60 in this circuit is operated with plate voltages between 1200 and 2000 V. When it is operated in low duty cycle pulse operation, the tube life is very long.

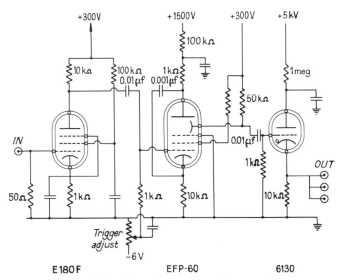

FIG. 31. Typical pulsing circuit for spark gaps or thyratrons.

The EFP 60 output can drive a 5C22 thyratron directly, but usually another stage of voltage and power gain is used. In Fig. 31, we illustrate a circuit which is designed to drive a large number of thyratrons or spark gaps. The EFP 60 is preceded by an E 180F isolation amplifier to invert a 1 V negative input from the counter logic and isolate the transistor circuits from the pulsing circuit. Following it is a 6130 thyratron operated at 3 to 5 kV with the signal taken from the cathode to drive thyratrons or from the plate to drive spark gaps. Ferrite cores on the filament leads of the thyratron isolate it from the filament transformer during the high voltage pulse. The 6130 produces a high voltage low impedance pulse which can drive ten 5C22 thyratrons or an equal number of spark gaps. The overall delay from input pulse to a 5C22 firing is ~180 nsec. For spark gaps, this figure can be reduced to about 100 nsec.

Alternatively, the EFP 60 can drive a high voltage tetrode such as a 4PR60 which produces a negative pulse to fire a spark gap. Such a hard tube pulser can provide a faster but higher impedance output which is suitable to trigger a single spark gap. This spark gap may either fire a chamber or in turn be used to fire several gaps in parallel to drive a large system of spark chambers.

Spark gaps which can operate with a small trigger pulse of ~ 1000 V can be driven by transistor circuits operated in the avalanche mode (Lavoie *et al.*, 1964). Combining the avalanche transistor circuit and the spark gaps with the barium titanate trigger electrode results in a total delay of 30 nsec between a 1 V input pulse and a 15 kV output pulse which has an output impedance of about 1 Ω.

D. COMPONENTS AND MECHANICAL ARRANGEMENTS

In most applications, the spark chambers are triggered by discharging a capacity. These condensers have a barium titanate dielectric and plane parallel geometry. Wrapped mylar insulated condensers have too much inductance and cannot provide suitable rise times. The barium titanate capacitors are available in a wide range of capacity and voltage ratings. For example, a 500 pF 20 kV condenser is $\frac{3}{4}$ in. high by 1 in. diameter.

A large variety of high voltage supplies are commercially available. A simple, inexpensive high voltage supply can be assembled from a 15 kV, 5 mA power pack which is available at a cost of $140. Very large spark chamber assemblies require large amounts of stored energy, and often require a large buffer capacitor bank if more than one trigger per accelerator pulse is used. Transport of the high voltages up to 50 kV can be accomplished with RG/8U cable. Commercial high voltage connectors can be used, or simple, reliable connections can be made from ordinary uhf connectors, banana plugs, and RG/8U cable.

To reduce the series inductance of the pulsing circuit, large short leads are required. This requirement necessitates the final high voltage switch to be located at the chamber. The triggers for the switch can be located remotely and fed by cables. If the spark chamber has thick exposed plates, the storage capacity and spark gap can be mechanically attached to the plate. Figure 25 shows an arrangement for pulsing a large chamber contained in a box. The pulsing cables are fed individually through the base plate. Below, the cables are brought to a common capacitor bank and spark gap. The length of the cables plus a small 5 Ω series resistor is used to isolate electrically each high voltage plate from the other, so that fluctuations in spark formation time between separate high voltage plates do not cause serious inefficiencies. Generally, for large high voltage plates, a common switch with separate storage capacitors for each plate is the best arrangement.

The type of load resistor used is not critical. Many workers use 2 W carbon resistors or 5 W "Koolohm" resistors. The adjustment of the value of the load resistor is usually done empirically. One wants the smallest value possible to discourage edge sparking in the absence of tracks; however, the efficiency of the chamber must not be impaired.

The clearing field can be applied to either the high voltage or the ground plate, with suitable by-pass condensers if applied to the high voltage plate.

E. INTERFERENCE FROM SPARK CHAMBERS

If no care is taken with ground returns, the spark chamber discharges will cause excessive interference with the discriminators and scalars of the electronic triggering system. A good working rule is that, when the chamber fires, every low level discriminator also fires. In many cases, this is not serious if fast-off gates can be applied to all counting electronics during the time of the expected spark discharge.

To isolate completely the spark chamber from the remaining electronics requires isolation of any part of the spark chamber pulsing system from the ground of the remaining electronics. For chambers within a box, this is relatively easy if the ground plates are not connected to the box but return directly to the pulser. Complete shielding of the spark chamber and pulsing system is required with a low impedance ground connection. No pulse currents should flow in this shield. Double-shielded cable may be required for the trigger pulses, so that the return current itself is shielded. A push-pull pulsing system has been used by D. G. Cassel and V. L. Fitch at Princeton University to reduce interference with the triggering electronics. Even with careful precautions, interference often remains and is a practical problem that must be faced with each experimental configuration.

V. Photography of Spark Chambers

A. OPTICAL SYSTEMS

The parallel plate construction of the spark chamber and the fact that the arrangement of various chambers may be complex give rise to rather difficult problems in coupling the camera to the chambers. In early applications, insufficient attention was given to effects of distortion of lenses and mirrors of the optical system. Many workers, including the author, were happy to obtain photographs in which all the sparks were clearly visible, without great attention to fiducial marks.

The parallel geometry necessitates the use of lenses, prisms, or mirrors to extract the light from the spark chamber parallel to the gap and then direct it to the camera. Figure 32 shows three schemes to accomplish this purpose that are generally used.

In Fig. 32a, a cylindrical lens is placed above the chamber and the camera a focal distance away from the lens. If the lens is planoconvex, it is best to

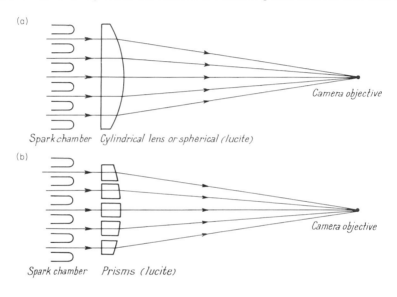

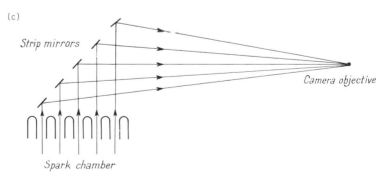

FIG. 32. (a) Optical system using cylindrical or spherical lens, (b) optical system using prisms, (c) optical system using strip mirrors.

place the plane side toward the camera to reduce spherical aberration. In any case, the use of a cylindrical lens of aperture greater than $f/4$ results in a shift of the focal length by more than 2% between the center of the lens and the edge. The use of a cylindrical lens gives rise to an unavoidable distortion on the film. The direction parallel to the axis of the lens is mapped on the film by conical projection, while the direction perpendicular to the plates is mapped on the film as an orthogonal projection. The use of a spherical lens instead of a cylindrical lens results in a complete orthogonal projection on the film, which is ideal for event measurement and reconstruction.

Spherical lenses have been made from lucite as large as 4 ft in diameter with a focal length of 15 ft. For deep chambers, the precision required for the lens is rather severe. For a 4 ft deep chamber with a gap of $\frac{3}{8}$ in. the angular aperture of the gap is 0.0018 rad. In order that the particular gap be seen clearly, the deflection by the lens must be accurate to $\pm$ 0.0004 rad, demanding a precision of the local angle of the lens to 0.0008 rad.

The use of prisms as illustrated in Fig. 32b provides another solution to this optical problem. Prisms can be machined of preshrunk lucite rather easily and the polishing procedure is not difficult. Prisms have been used for a number of very large spark chamber systems. Strip mirrors, as shown in Fig. 32c, have also been used and have the added advantage that they are adjustable although the process is obviously tedious. With such mirrors, one can simultaneously bend the light through a large angle as well as direct the light of each gap towards the camera. Front surface mirrors 6 ft in length have been used by the neutrino group at CERN (Faissner et al., 1963b). Care in mounting the mirrors must be taken to avoid twisting. Bowing of the mirrors in the plane of the gap is generally less serious if a good arrangement of fiducial marks is available.

Both the prisms and the strip mirrors have the difficulty of the unavoidable astigmatism of the mapped film image. In large systems, even with a good spherical lens, it is difficult to maintain linearity when large mirrors are involved in the optical system. The need for fiducial marks is essential.

Chambers with thin foil plates are generally of sufficient reflectivity that they can be operated without a lens. The sparks are observed by the multiply reflected image. The action of the multiple reflection is similar to that of a cylindrical lens so that one has an orthogonal projection perpendicular to the gaps and a conical projection parallel to the gaps. Sparks from tracks which lie at angles to the plates are distorted by this method and appear wider than their natural width.

In many experiments, spark chambers have been arranged in peculiar geometries and have been distributed over large distances. These various views are often brought together on a single film by a system of mirrors. Although these systems provide all the information in a compact way, the subsequent analysis is often complicated. Further, because of the myriad mirrors on frames that can possibly distort, the hope of maintaining a stable

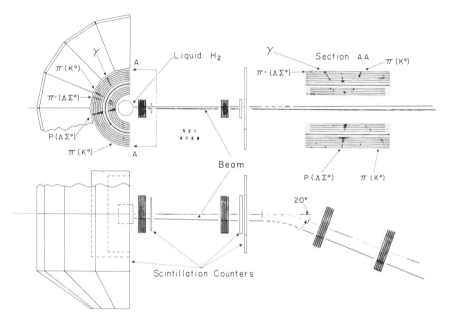

FIG. 33. View of production of $\Sigma^0 + K^0$ with decay of Σ^0 to $\Lambda^0 + \gamma$. The unique feature is photography of the cylindrical chamber by multiple reflections (Wenzel, 1964).

optical system is often lost. These problems can be largely circumvented by the placement of sufficient fiducials to enable a complete event reconstruction to be made without knowledge of mirror or camera position. It is also of great importance to provide an optical system and film format consistent with ease of measurement and interpretation of events on a measuring or scanning table. This last consideration is altered if automatic scanning of the film is envisaged.

Most chambers are viewed with a 90° stereo pair of cameras. The use of only two cameras has an intrinsic ambiguity in the case of multiple tracks. The spark tracks in most cases have sufficient character (e.g. fluctuation of intensity of sparks) so that there is no practical ambiguity. The only situation which might be dangerous is in the use of a single gap chamber as a hodoscope to mark the trajectories of passing particles.

Small angle stereo pictures can be provided with a tilted mirror below the chamber so that one sees both the direct image of the spark and its reflected image. The separation of the spark and its reflection is a measure of the depth of the spark in the chamber.

For cylindrical chambers, a spherical lens or mirror is required. Depth information is obtained by a ring of tilted mirrors beneath the chambers as is shown in Fig. 27. The cylindrical geometry also allows, by means of conical mirrors, a reduction of the size of the image. This technique was used by an M.I.T. group (Frisch, 1964) to enclose totally a large cylindrical chamber in a magnetic field and then extract the optical information through a small hole in the magnet. At Berkeley, a semicylindrical chamber has been viewed by multiple reflection along an edge as well as at the end. Straight tracks viewed through the edge appear to be sections of hyperbolas. Figure 33 shows a reassembled view of a Berkeley experiment in which a cylindrical chamber is photographed by multiple reflections.

Chambers for hodoscopic purposes have been constructed of wire mesh so that they can be viewed parallel to the electric field. Here the spark appears as a dot, and this two-dimensional information, coupled with the location of the chamber plane, determines a coordinate on the trajectory of the sampled track.

B. Photography

The intensity of the light released from the spark can be adjusted easily by the amount of energy discharged through the spark. The real width of the spark also depends to a large extent on the energy of the spark. Figures 21a and 21b were taken with an average energy of 0.01 Joules per spark, a lens aperture of $f/8$, and Tri-X film. Figure 34 was taken with $f/8$, Tri-X film, and a spark energy of 0.25 J per spark. In the latter example, the width of the sparks appears as great as the length. Precision work with spark chambers requires thin sparks. Sparks of uniform intensity can be obtained if the gap spacing is uniform. By reduction of the amount of energy contained in the sparks, thin sparks can be obtained without the danger of loss of efficiency due to undeveloped sparks.

Most of the demands on the camera lens and film occur because of the large size of spark chambers generally used in high energy physics experiments. The depth of focus is often required to be as great as 6 ft. For a large system, a demagnification of as much as 100 is required. With a precision of better than 0.01 in. usually obtainable, the requirement of accuracy and stability of the film is ～2.5 microns. These requirements are not dissimilar to those of bubble chamber photography. In addition to the above, a wide angular aperture for the camera lens is often desirable to make the large optical system more compact. A good system of fiducial marks can help overcome wide angle distortions.

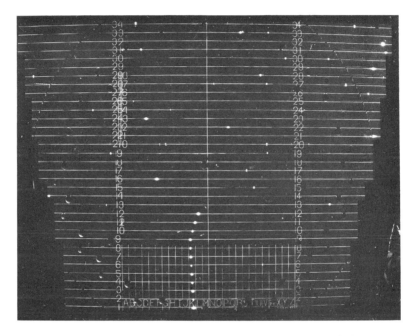

FIG. 34. View of recoil proton in spark chamber of Eandi *et al.* (1964). The large amount of energy discharged into each spark produces a large width.

Generally, panchromatic films are desirable since the spark light from neon or helium filled chambers is strong in the red. For large demagnifications, a film of fine resolution is desired. Films with a sharp knee in their exposure curve, like Kodak Shellburst, can be used to advantage to suppress edge sparks and other faint background sparks. Shellburst worked very well in a spectrometer system (Christenson *et al.*, 1964a) to provide sharp thin tracks of uniform exposure under conditions of high demagnification. Films with a more linear exposure curve are generally desirable, however, because fluctuations in spark brightness with multiple tracks are expected with wide ranges of ionization. Kodak Plus-X has been used with chambers which have a wide fluctuation in spark intensity. Both the above films have speeds ~ 150 A.S.A. and work well with 0.04 J sparks at an $f/8$ aperture.

Conventional parallel plate chambers can be pulsed every 20 msec, so that it is possible to obtain more than 10 pictures per pulse from a 400 msec burst of the accelerator. Commercial 35 mm cameras can be obtained which can be pulse advanced with a dead time of 40 to 50 msec for a cost of $4000. A camera of five times that speed is available at a higher cost. The acquisition of data at these high rates photographically chokes most analysis systems quickly. Such rates require automatic data handling in any case. There are a number of filmless methods of extracting data from spark chambers, which will be discussed in Section VIII.

Brief mention must also be made of the problem of illumination of the fiducial marks when many photographs are desired each pulse. Generally, the fiducial marks consist of lines engraved on lucite reticles. The lucite reticles are illuminated with xenon flash lamps which may be pulsed as often as every 20 msec. The amount of energy used by these lamps is often greater than the energy required to operate the spark chambers.

VI. Considerations of Accuracy

A. Location of Trajectory from Spark Positions

Some of the earliest investigations of triggered spark counters were concerned with the accuracy of the location of the trajectory. Henning (1957), using parallel plate spark counters filled with argon and alcohol vapor, found that the scatter of the coordinates of an individual spark projected on a plane was given principally by a Gaussian distribution of width 0.8 mm.

There are a number of factors to be considered in the determination of the trajectory location accuracy. First is the relative displacement of individual sparks from a least squares fit line when a high energy particle passes through a series of plates. There is the question of the absolute relation of the straight line to the actual trajectory of the particle. A further consideration is the location of the sparks in space with respect to fiducial lines which serve as reference to other chambers if one is dealing with a multichamber system. The latter problem involves questions of mechanical stability and quality of the optics.

The position of the electron avalanches when they reach the critical size determines the discharge path of the spark that will be visible. These positions are determined by diffusion of the original electrons from their point of production and by their motion in clearing fields. Also, there is a minimum distance of motion along the field lines which is required for the development of the critical avalanche. All of the above-mentioned effects cause a displacement of the spark position from the original trajectory.

For tracks that pass through the chamber parallel to the electric field, only the lateral diffusion of the primary electrons is important. For tracks which pass through at angles to the electric field, the displacements of the primary electrons by the clearing field and by the avalanche development are clearly important. One redeeming feature is that these displacements are equal and opposite on each side of the high voltage plate. Thus much of the deviation of the spark from the trajectory is coherent and cancels when the average position of a spark pair is taken. There remains a net displacement which depends on diffusion of the primary electrons and fluctuations in the number and positions of those primary electrons which succeed in forming avalanches.

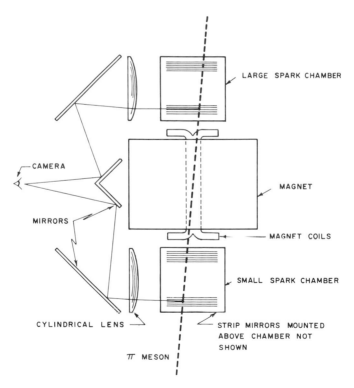

FIG. 35. Schematic view of a spark chamber spectrometer (Christenson et al., 1964a).

A large number of studies of spark chamber accuracy have been made (e.g. Rutherglen and Patterson, 1961; Mikhailov *et al.*, 1961; Burnham *et al.*, 1963; Christenson *et al.*, 1964a). The general results for gaps of 1 cm or less are agreed on by all workers. For tracks which pass within 15° to the normal to the plates, the projected standard deviation of the individual

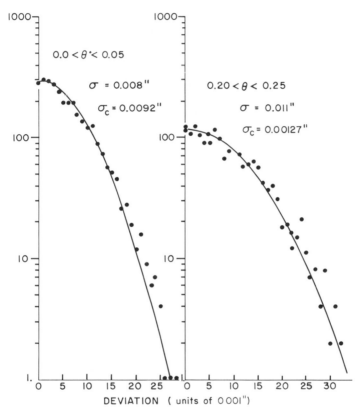

FIG. 36. Spatial distributions of deviations of sparks from a best fit straight line (Christenson *et al.*, 1964a).

spark from the true trajectory is found to be about 0.2 mm for neon filled spark chambers. Helium, because of fewer primary electrons and greater diffusion gives somewhat less precision. For tracks at larger angles to the normal, all workers have found an increase in the spark fluctuations. Many have demonstrated that if one measures the spark at the proper location in the gap the coherent displacements can be removed. For example, Rutherglen and Patterson (1961) find that, without a clearing field in a 6 mm gap chamber, the best measurement point is a distance 0.2d from the negative high voltage electrode, where d is the gap space. Such specific prescriptions clearly depend on operating conditions of the chamber. The same authors find for normal tracks and no clearing field an increase in standard deviation from 0.25 to 0.4 mm when the pulse delay is changed from 0.25 to 1.6 μsec.

A careful study of spark location accuracy was made by Christenson et al. (1964a). The studies were made in connection with the exploration of properties of a pair of spark chamber spectrometers. They studied the distribution of individual and paired sparks in thin foil spectrometers. The spark chambers were filled with a 90% neon 10% helium mixture and pulsed 300 nsec after the particle passage. 1000 pF capacitors charged to 15 kV were switched across each high voltage plate giving 0.05 J sparks. A 100 Ω load resistor was placed in parallel with each gap. Figure 35 shows a schematic view of one of the spectrometers used in this study. The demagnification for these spectrometers was about 80 and the photographs were taken with Kodak Shellburst film. The measurements on the film were made with an X–Y digitizer of $\pm 1\,\mu$ least count on the film. The position of each spark was recorded at the center of the gap. The coordinates were reconstructed in space and the projected distributions plotted. Figure 36 shows the spatial distribution of deviations of individual sparks from least squares fit lines to the side view track segments. The dark lines are Gaussian fits to the distribution. The two graphs show the results for tracks normal to the plates and for tracks inclined at a small angle. The distribution of the sparks fits a Gaussian very well, with some tendency to develop a tail at large deviations. The distributions also show the expected larger error when an inclined track appears.

The widths of the distributions can probably be reduced by measurement at some point other than the center of the spark to improve the accuracy. An alternate method, however, is to pair the sparks of a common electrode and take as the location of the trajectory the average position of the pair. This method has the advantage of averaging the spark displacements due to clearing fields, slow rise times, and $\mathbf{E} \times \mathbf{B}$ drifts. Since these displacements are always equal and opposite, their effect is canceled in the average. Figure 37 shows the results which compare single and paired spark accuracy as a function of angle. The paired sparks give a nearly uniform accuracy up to an angle of 30°, while the single spark deviations rise rapidly.

The deviations found actually are due to three sources; intrinsic statistical spark jitter, measurement error, and reconstruction error. Unfolding of the measurement error, which can be estimated, from the distribution leaves a

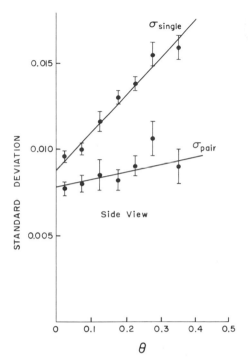

FIG. 37. Standard deviations of sparks from a best fit line as a function of angle (in radians) with respect to the normal to the plates (Christenson *et al.*, 1964a).

single spark standard deviation for normal tracks of ± 0.007 in. or 0.18 mm. This represents an upper limit to the true spark jitter for these particular chambers. If the diffusion of a single electron were responsible, one would expect 0.4 mm for the rms deviation. The smaller measured value is due to the fact that many electrons participate in the development of the avalanches and the rms deviation is therefore reduced.

B. OTHER FACTORS WHICH INFLUENCE ACCURACY

It is rare that the intrinsic spark jitter about the true trajectory is the limiting factor in the determination of the achievable accuracy. One must consider the effect of measurement accuracy, optical distortions, multiple scattering, and, in the case of multichamber experiments, the accuracy of placement of the chambers. In an experiment of Christenson *et al.* (1964a), spark chamber spectrometers were employed. As an example of other accuracy considerations which depend on the particular experiments, we discuss briefly the features of these spectrometers. The two spectrometers were placed at equal angles, each to measure the vector momenta of one of the decay pions of K^0 mesons. From these data, the mass and direction of

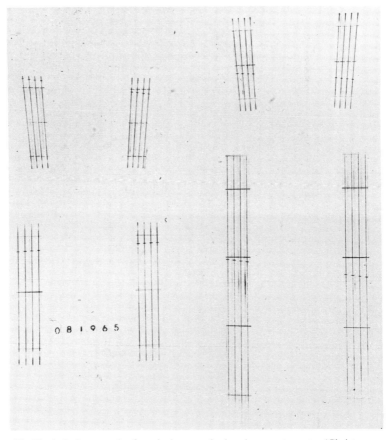

FIG. 38. Typical photograph of tracks in a spark chamber spectrometer (Christenson *et al.*, 1964a).

the K^0's could be computed. The momentum resolution of the spectrometers was 1.4% for 500 MeV/c pions with a 160 kG-in. magnetic field. This resolution was controlled entirely by multiple scattering. The mass resolution of the K^0 was Gaussian with a 4 MeV standard deviation and the angular resolution of the computed K^0 direction was 3×10^{-3} rad.

Careful attention was given to fiducials in the spectrometers. For each spark chamber lucite reticles were installed inside the gas box on all four sides of the plate structure. The fiducial plates were scribed on the inner surface facing the spark chamber plates. The accuracy of scribing was 0.001 in. The front and top fiducials are observed in the photograph shown in Fig. 38. The vertical lines were carefully centered in the gaps and serve by intersecting a spark to give a precise location on the spark to measure. The back and bottom fiducials (which are identical to front and top) were only illuminated periodically during operation. The horizontal lines at the front and back or the top and bottom provide a means to relate the slope and position of a light ray passing through the optical system to the camera. Thus, the observation of the position of a spark on the film with respect to the fiducials gives the slope and position of a line on which the spark lies. The intersection of two such lines from the top and side views gives the spark location. This fiducial arrangement allows the reconstruction of the sparks in space independent of the refraction of light in the cylindrical lenses and windows. It was not necessary to know the camera position nor was it necessary to require that the mirrors be completely flat. The reconstruction could be accomplished independent of the external optical system.

The same fiducial marks also served as primary references for surveying the relative positions of the chambers. Good mechanical stability was necessary for mounting the individual chambers, but the stability of the remaining optical system and the flatness of the mirrors were not quite so critical since optical shifts are selfcalibrating by photographing all four fiducial plates simultaneously. The spectrometers were used in two separate experiments over the course of nine months. It was found during this time there were discernable changes in the apparent position of the camera, but with the fiducial system the precision of the measurements was unimpaired.

VII. Applications

A. GENERAL

The use of spark chambers can be divided into two broad categories. First, a hodoscopic application which samples particle trajectories with the least possible interference to the particle. The definition of an incoming beam direction or a trajectory in a magnetic field to measure momentum are examples of the hodoscopic use. Second is the application of spark chambers to observe detailed processes which involve the interaction of particles in the plates themselves for production of reactions or the identification of particles. Some examples are the detection of nucleon polarization, the separation of muons and pions by mean interaction length, and the detection of neutrino interactions.

Successful application requires a triggering arrangement which selects the desired events with high efficiency while rejecting all undesirable events. The spark chamber technique loses a great deal of its attractiveness in experiments where a reasonably selective trigger is not available. Some workers have conceived of operating spark chambers with a very loose triggering system. The search for the desired or interesting events is then made on the scanning table. In the opinion of the author, this has not been a particularly successful application of the spark chamber technique. In the following parts of this section, several specific applications are discussed.

B. DETECTION OF PROTON POLARIZATION

The earliest experiments carried out using spark chambers involved carbon plates for the detection of polarization. We describe here an experiment conducted by Beall et al. (1962) to measure the polarization of protons from the decay of $\Sigma^+ \rightarrow p + \pi^0$. A unique trigger could be supplied for the production of a Σ^+ by the reaction $\pi^+ + p \rightarrow \Sigma^+ + K^+$. The observation of a K^+ uniquely specified the production of a Σ^+. In addition to a K^+, the trigger also required a decay proton to enter the large carbon plate chamber. Figure 39 shows a view of the apparatus. Figure 25 shows the detail of the carbon plate chamber. The desired event satisfied the trigger conditions and also scattered in one of the carbon plates of the spark chamber. It was impossible to include this last requirement for the event in the triggering criteria and maintain a large solid angle for proton decays. Thus, the final criterion is found by scanning the pictures of which about 1 in 50 gives a useful scatter. The polarization of the proton is found from the azimuthal asymmetry of the carbon scattering.

This experiment uses both the hodoscopic and interaction modes of spark chambers simultaneously. Foil chambers mark the path of the decay proton before it scatters and other thin foil chambers mark the path of the K^+. These directions allow one to reconstruct the event completely since the incoming beam momentum was known.

A large number of experiments have been carried out using polarization analysis. Among these were a measurement of the Λ^0 decay proton helicity (Cronin and Overseth, 1963) and measurements of recoil polarization in pion–nucleon scattering (Autonès et al., 1963; Eandi et al., 1964).

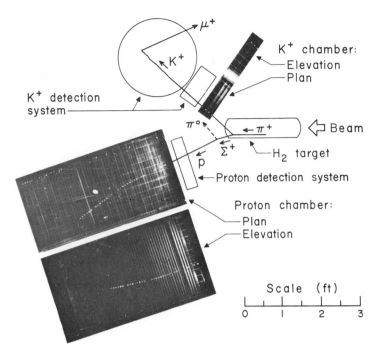

FIG. 39. Schematic arrangement of an experiment to measure polarization of Σ^+ decay proton (Beall *et al.*, 1961).

C. SCATTERING EXPERIMENTS

Scattering experiments use thin hodoscopic chambers surrounding a liquid hydrogen target. A typical arrangement for the study of $\pi^\pm + p \rightarrow \pi^\pm + p$ angular distributions between 2 and 5 BeV/c has been used by Bleuler *et al.* (1963) and is shown in Fig. 40. The two small chambers in the beam, separated by 24 in., defined the incident direction to an accuracy of 0.001 rad. The chambers that surround the target detect the scattered and recoil particles, when triggered by two counters at either side of the beam which demand a rough coplanarity. By a system of 13 mirrors, all 9 chambers are brought onto a single 35 mm frame. The accuracy of measurement of the forward scattered pion angle was 0.002 rad for the diffraction scattered pions and 0.006 rad for particles scattered into the side chambers. The authors point out the importance of accurate kinematic measurements to separate high energy elastic scattering from inelastic scattering.

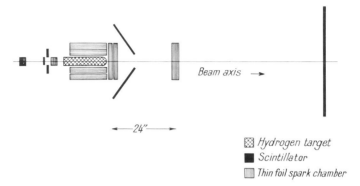

⊠ *Hydrogen target*
■ *Scintillator*
▥ *Thin foil spark chamber*

FIG. 40. View of pion–proton scattering apparatus (Bleuler *et al.*, 1963).

Cylindrical chambers have been used by a number of groups for elastic scattering. Here, the liquid hydrogen target is inserted into the center of a cylindrical chamber. Figure 41 shows a schematic view of a large cylindrical scattering arrangement built by the Berkeley group (Beall *et al.*, 1963). The large half-cylinder chambers have carbon scattering plates for polarization determination and iron plates for range determination. An added feature in this arrangement is a momentum measurement for each incident beam track, obtained by placing a thin foil spark chamber on either side of the final bending magnet.

This application brings up the general problem of the operation of spark chambers in intense beams. The electronic logic, cable lengths, and photo-

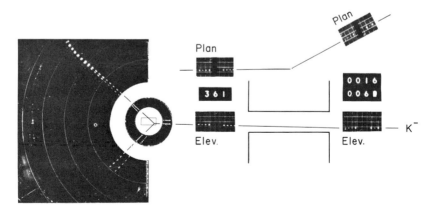

FIG. 41. Schematic view of large scattering apparatus using cylindrical spark chambers (Beall *et al.*, 1963).

multiplier delays used to trigger the chambers usually require 200 to 300 nsec. Clearing fields can be applied to remove old tracks; however, the efficiency does not drop sharply with delay of the firing, so that the chamber, fully efficient at 300 nsec, has some efficiency for tracks of age 800 nsec. The Berkeley group arranged the electronics so that beam tracks which preceded the desired track by less than 500 nsec anticoincided the entire trigger system. Older tracks, because of the clearing field, produced no sparks. The effective sensitive time of the chamber was thus the delay time of the applied trigger pulse. With this arrangement, the spark chambers in the beam could operate successfully in a flux of 4×10^5 particles per second with no serious contamination of background tracks.

Spark chambers used for scattering experiments allow a large solid angle to be covered and at the same time give detailed information for each event. These features are very useful for the study of scatterings which have very low cross sections. A muon–proton scattering experiment employing very large spark chambers was carried out by a Rochester–Columbia–Brookhaven group (Cool et al., 1964). Also, there have been a number of proposals to use spark chamber detectors for the study of electron–positron interactions with colliding beams.

It should be pointed out that the use of spark chambers to study scattering processes always has the disadvantage that the triggering system and the geometry of the experimental arrangement require solid angle corrections. These corrections are not simple to calculate, since they generally depend on the position of the event as well as on the scattering angle.

D. Neutrino Experiments

The recognition of the value of spark chambers gave great impetus to the design of practical experiments to detect high energy neutrinos. With the Brookhaven A.G.S. or the CERN PS, neutrinos from pion decay passing through a thick shield can produce between 0.2 and 2 events per ton of detector per day, depending on the production of the pion beam by an internal or external beam. The spark chamber proved to be a simple detector which could easily be made quite massive. A report on plans for a neutrino experiment was given by a Columbia–Brookhaven group in 1960 (Lederman et al., 1960). By 1962, the experiment was complete with the important discovery that there exist two types of neutrinos v_μ and v_e (Danby et al., 1962).

The first Brookhaven chambers were made of 4 ft × 4 ft × 1 in. aluminum plate using lucite frames for gap spacers, gas container, and viewing window. Prisms were used as the optical elements to direct the light to the cameras. Figure 42 shows a view of these chambers. The total assembly weighed 10 tons. The heavy aluminum plates served not only as a target for neutrino interactions but also as an analyzer for the nature of the interaction products. Electrons could be identified by their shower characteristics. Muons could be separated from pions by the observed mean interaction

FIG. 42. View of chambers used in the Brookhaven–Columbia neutrino experiment. Professor Schwartz stands at the side for scale.

length in many cases. The evidence that v_μ and v_e were different types of neutrinos was based on the fact that no electron producing events were seen.

In the Brookhaven experiment and the subsequent CERN experiment (Faissner et al., 1963a), the chambers were triggered by scintillation counters. The beam was dumped on the pion producing target with the shortest possible duration so that the total "on" time of the apparatus was very brief. This was done to reduce the probability of cosmic ray background. The second Brookhaven experiment, which has been running during the preparation of this manuscript, uses no counters at all. The external beam of the A.G.S. is extracted from the machine and placed on the pion target in 2.5 μsec. The chamber operates with no clearing field during the 2.5 μsec spill. After the beam has passed through the chamber, the high voltage is pulsed. The neon is continuously purified so that the memory time is sufficiently long. The great advantage of this method of triggering is that no biases are introduced because of the arrangement of counters. The applied high voltage pulse is sufficiently short so that very little spurious sparking takes place if no event is present.

E. Spectrometer Experiments

A number of experiments have been completed which use hodoscopic spark chambers and magnetic fields to form a momentum spectrometer (Keefe et al., 1963; Bleuler et al., 1963). Figure 35 shows a schematic diagram of one of a pair of spectrometers built by Christenson et al. (1964a). The accuracy of these chambers has been previously discussed. The two chambers were constructed of 0.001 in. foil plates. Each chamber has two banks of plates for track delineation, separated by 16 in. The magnet is a Brookhaven A.G.S. steering magnet which has a very uniform field. The momentum resolution of the system was found to be limited only by multiple scattering and was 0.7% for 600 MeV/c particles for an integrated field of 300 kG-in. These spectrometers used in pairs were employed in experiments designed to study dipion mass spectra, K_2^0 regeneration, and K_2^0 decay (Christenson et al., 1964b). In the latter experiment, a violation of CP invariance in K_2^0 decay was discovered.

Thin foil spark chambers used in conjunction with deflection magnets make very satisfactory high momentum spectrometers. The separation of the chambers and the magnet simplifies the optics and allows magnets with very homogeneous fields to be used. While such conditions are not essential for acquiring a given accuracy, they do facilitate its attainment. With a sufficient lever arm, the angle of deflection can be determined to an accuracy limited only by multiple scattering. The amount of multiple scattering material can be made quite small. Only 0.02 gm of aluminum need be inserted at each point where the track is sampled. If the path in the magnetic field is filled with helium, the multiple scattering error due to the spark chamber plates is $\Delta p/p \cong 0.04/BL$ where BL is the value of the integrated magnetic field in kilogauss-meters. The error due to multiple scattering is independent of momentum for relativistic particles. The above figure is a lower limit since, in general, thin windows, etc., must be added to the flight path.

F. RARE DECAY MODES

Spark chambers have been of great value in the observation and measurement of rates of rare decay modes. Here one exploits the selectivity of a spark chamber counting system to yield a highly enriched sample of events containing the rare one sought. A search for $\mu \rightarrow e + \gamma$ has been carried out by a number of authors (Parker *et al.*, 1964). The use of spark chambers allowed the upper limit on the branching ratio $(\mu \rightarrow e + \gamma)/(\mu \rightarrow e + \nu + \bar{\nu})$ to be reduced from 10^{-6}, obtained with counting techniques, to 10^{-8}. The principal contribution of the spark chambers in this experiment was the colinearity check on the γ ray and electron provided by the spark chambers. A Columbia group has also measured the rate of $\pi^+ \rightarrow \pi^0 + e^+ + \nu$ (Bartlett *et al.*, 1964) with the assistance of the spark chamber. This rate is $\sim 10^{-8}$ of the normal decay $\pi^+ \rightarrow \mu^+ + \nu$. This experiment was also completed without spark chambers, so that they do not always provide the unique tool that makes a particular experiment possible.

G. SPARK CHAMBERS IN MAGNETIC FIELDS

A great number of workers have placed spark chambers in magnetic fields. Some have placed chambers in conventional steering magnets and used various optical schemes such as small strip mirrors or gratings to extract the view in the plane perpendicular to the magnetic field (see e.g. Lande *et al.*, 1963). Other workers have built special magnets with a hole in the pole piece so that a direct view along the magnetic field can be obtained in a manner similar to a bubble chamber (Burleson *et al.*, 1963; O'Neill *et al.*, 1963). Some very beautiful photographs have been taken with these arrangements, an example of which is shown in Fig. 43.

Up to the present, the number of experiments that have been completed by spark chambers placed in magnetic fields has been relatively few. The general condition which requires the use of the magnetic field is the need

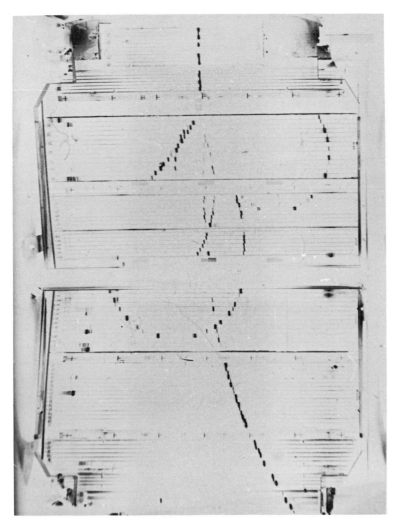

FIG. 43. Photograph of associated production event in spark chambers immersed in a magnetic field, $\pi^- + p \to \Sigma^0 + K^0$, $\Sigma^0 \to \Lambda^0 + \gamma$. One can see the γ ray convert on the right (Burleson *et al.*, 1963).

to perform momentum analysis for tracks distributed over a large solid angle. The detailed analysis of an associated production requires a large solid angle covered by the magnetic field. Conventional track sampling chambers being nonisotropic devices do not have a good resolution for

FIG. 44. View of $K^- + p \to K^0 + n$ event in a CERN magnetic spark chamber (Astbury *et al.*, 1964).

tracks which make steep angles, so that the precision of measurement depends very much on the direction of the tracks.

Thus, examples for the most effective use of spark chambers placed in magnetic fields have been cases in which the general direction of the particles has been normal to the plates and cases in which the particles have suffered rather small deflections over long flight paths. We describe briefly an experiment by a group at CERN (Astbury *et al.*, 1964) who measured the reaction $K^- + p \rightarrow \overline{K^0} + n$. Their spark chambers completely filled a volume $60 \times 67 \times 180$ cm in a magnetic field of 10 kG. At one end of the assembly, a hydrogen target was placed. The target was surrounded by a lead-lined anticoincidence counter system, to trigger the chamber on neutral final states without γ rays. The K^- beam was 10 BeV/c so that each K_1^0 decay produced two 5 BeV/c pions. Figure 44 shows an event which is an example of the charge exchange reaction.

The authors point out that it is absolutely necessary to see the decay vertex in order to make a proper fit to the event at the high energy. The location of the vertex is difficult to determine by extrapolation because of the very small opening angles involved. They found with their chamber, which had a radiation length of 30 meters, that the momentum resolution for 9.5 BeV/c tracks was $\Delta p/p = 0.017$. For 9.5 BeV/c K_1^0 decays, the mass resolution of the K_1^0 found by measurement of the secondaries was ± 15 MeV. The mass of the K_1^0 is 498 MeV. The angular distribution for the charge exchange reaction was measured. Because of the high energies, all the events were very forward in the laboratory system and very small connections were required for the geometry.

Wide gap chambers and streamer chambers with isotropic properties seem to have important applications when used with magnetic fields. These will be discussed in more detail in Section IX.

H. Detection of Electrons and Photons

Detailed studies have been made of electron shower formation in heavy plate sparks chambers (Cronin *et al.*, 1962; Faissner, 1964; Kajikawa, 1963). Electrons can be easily identified by the characteristic shower phenomena. Further, the development of the shower agrees well with Monte Carlo calculations (Wilson, 1951; Crawford and Messel, 1962). It appears that by a counting of the total number of sparks in a shower, electron energies can be measured with an accuracy of about $\pm 40\%$.

A small spark chamber magnetic spectrometer was built by a University of Chicago group (Deschong *et al.*, 1964) to measure the ratio of electrons and positrons arriving at the top of the atmosphere. The apparatus consisted of a pair of thin track sampling chambers on each side of a small permanent magnet. Below was a chamber with tantalum plates for electron identification by shower formation. The entire assembly was flown by balloon to 100,000 ft. A similar balloon-borne apparatus has been built by a European group (Agrinier *et al.*, 1963). In addition to the use with electrons, these

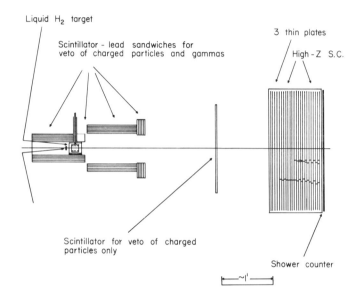

FIG. 45. Schematic view of the apparatus of Sodickson *et al.* (1964) for the measurement of $\pi^- + p \rightarrow \pi^0 + n$ at high energy.

experiments demonstrate that, by careful design, spark chamber arrangements can be made extremely light and compact.

The charge exchange cross section $\pi^- + p \rightarrow \pi^0 + n$, and more generally $\pi^- + p \rightarrow n + \pi^0 + \pi^0 \ldots$, has been investigated by several groups. The experiment of an MIT group at Brookhaven (Sodickson *et al.*, 1964) to measure the forward pion charge exchange cross section at high energies is typical. Figure 45 shows a view of the apparatus. The target is surrounded with a lead and scintillator sandwich for anticoincidence. A thin anticounter is placed downstream. The trigger consists of an incoming track plus all anticoincidences. The γ rays from the π^0 decay are detected downstream in a 12 radiation length brass spark chamber. A few thin plates are placed at the beginning. About 50% of the triggers yielded a double γ ray event. The opening angle distribution of γ rays for a given energy has a sharp minimum angle, which can be used to guarantee elastic scattering and eliminate inelastic background.

VIII. Filmless Spark Chamber Techniques

A spark chamber system is capable of recording 3×10^5 events per day at a typical accelerator, even with a dead time of 10 msec. Thus, there has been a great effort to remove photography from the data acquisition cycle and develop "filmless" spark chamber techniques. In addition, direct acquisition of data eliminates the need for complicated optical systems. The three techniques well developed at the time of writing are the acoustic spark chamber, the wire spark chamber, and the vidicon scanning system. We shall discuss each of these briefly in turn. The acoustic and wire chamber developments have been directed toward hodoscopic applications where one expects the passage of a single particle. In particular, they have been used in conjunction with magnetic fields to make accurate momentum measurements. The vidicon technique which is more related to the film technique can perhaps be oriented towards more complex events.

A. ACOUSTIC CHAMBERS

The original suggestion for acoustic chambers was made by Fulbright and Kohler (1961), and early tests indicated that spark location accuracy could be of the order of 1 mm. The work of Maglic and Kirsten (1962) showed the practicality of acoustic chambers and measured all their essential properties. Several experiments have been carried out using the acoustic technique (e.g. Cocconi *et al.*, 1964; Bardon *et al.*, 1964).

The acoustic chamber locates the position of the spark by sound ranging. Typical velocities of sound in noble gases are 0.5 mm/μsec. The spark initially produces a shock wave. The sound wave travels with ordinary velocity only after the overpressure of the gas is reduced by the attenuation of the wave. The velocity of the shock wave is larger than that of the ordinary wave, so that for a given spark energy the velocity is a function of the position of the wave. This effect is fairly well approximated by relating the distance to time by $\Delta + Vt$, where t is the time for the sonic signal to reach the detector and Δ is the shock wave correction, which is a function of the spark energy. V is the velocity of sound, which has a temperature coefficient of $\sim 0.17\%$ per °C.

The detectors used to observe the sound waves are either piezoelectric crystals or capacity transducers. The piezoelectric probes used by Bardon *et al.* (1964) are cylindrical shells of lead zirconate (Clevite Corp. No. 2020–5) 12 mm long and 3 mm o.d. The inner and outer surfaces are silver-plated, and the electrical connections are soldered to them. Care must be taken to

FIG. 46. View of acoustic chamber with probes at the four corners (Bardon *et al.*, 1964).

mount the probes so that they are decoupled from any disturbances which propagate through the frames. Figure 46 shows the probes mounted in the four corners of a single gap thin foil spark chamber. The sonic pulse received has a rise time of 1 μsec and an amplitude of several millivolts for spark energies of 0.04 J at distances of about 30 cm. The probes ring for times of order 1 msec so that one probe can register only one spark. The pulse height was found to fall as the $\frac{3}{2}$ power of the distance. Sonic chambers have been operated with sound distances up to 1 meter.

Capacity probes have been described in some detail by Foley *et al.* (1964); they have properties similar to those of the piezoelectric probes discussed in the last paragraph.

Measurement of the position of a spark requires at least two probes plus knowledge of the velocity of sound and the shock wave correction Δ. The time of flight of the sound is measured by starting an oscillator clock at the

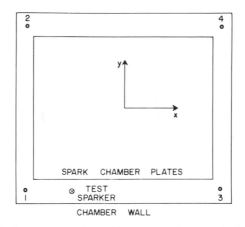

FIG. 47. Arrangement of coordinate system for acoustic chambers.

time of application of the high voltage pulse and stopping it upon receipt of the sonic pulse. Figure 47 shows the coordinate system and arrangement of probes used by Bardon *et al.* (1964). The x and y coordinates are given by

$$x = \frac{V^2}{4a}\left[\left(t_1 + \frac{\Delta}{V}\right)^2 - \left(t_3 + \frac{\Delta}{V}\right)^2\right] = \frac{V^2}{4a}\left[\left(t_2 + \frac{\Delta}{V}\right)^2 - \left(t_4 + \frac{\Delta}{V}\right)^2\right]$$

$$y = \frac{V^2}{4b}\left[\left(t_1 + \frac{\Delta}{V}\right)^2 - \left(t_2 + \frac{\Delta}{V}\right)^2\right] = \frac{V^2}{4b}\left[\left(t_3 + \frac{\Delta}{V}\right)^2 - \left(t_4 + \frac{\Delta}{V}\right)^2\right]$$

$$\frac{\Delta}{V} = \frac{1}{2}\frac{(t_4{}^2 - t_3{}^2) - (t_1{}^2 - t_2{}^2)}{(t_1 - t_2) - (t_4 - t_3)},$$

where $2a$ and $2b$ are the distances between probes 1 and 3 and probes 1 and 2, respectively. These distances as well as Δ were measured by comparison of sonic times with photographs. They can also be measured geometrically.

Bardon *et al.* (1964) also periodically used a fixed location test spark to calibrate the velocity of the sound waves in the gas. The redundancy of position measurement allows a check to assure that there were not two distinct sparks. The rms deviation between the two measurements was found to be less than 0.1 mm when a single spark occurred. The final accuracy of the spark positions thus determined was found to have an rms deviation of 0.3 mm from a fitted straight line. The determination of the accuracy was made by comparison with photographs. They also found that sparks in the chamber tilted by 20° still gave the same accuracy providing the point of origin of the sound was considered to be the negative electrode.

One great advantage of acoustic chambers is that they can be placed in a magnetic field without any need for optical viewing. The acoustic chambers described above were placed in a magnetic field to measure with great precision the spectrum of $\mu^+ \to e^+ + v + \bar{v}$. They were pulsed at a rate of 20 per second. The gas was 90% neon 10% helium which was flowed past a charcoal purifier. The efficiency was found to be 98% and dropped off if the pulse rate exceeded 20 per second.

Jones *et al.* (1964) have developed a new type of microphone in the form of a long linear strip of lead zirconate titanate. Four such microphones are mounted along the four edges of the spark chamber. With this arrangement, the sound, which is incident normally on the microphone, gives the signal indicating the spark position. Therefore the digitized times of arrival of the signals give directly the Cartesian coordinates of the spark. The authors also state that the sparks can be located with a precision of 0.3 mm, without a knowledge of the speed of sound. This type of chamber has been used in several experiments. (See e.g. Galbraith *et al.*, 1965.)

The acoustic technique is a highly accurate filmless data handling system which works well for single track experiments. The rate at which the chambers can be pulsed is limited not only by the recovery time of the spark chamber but also by the velocity of the sound. A 1 meter long chamber requires 2 msec for the sound to travel to the probes plus another millisecond for the probes to cease ringing. Thus, an event rate of order 300 per second is the absolute upper limit for acoustic chambers of that size. The rate at which the electronic digitizing circuits can handle the information may also influence this limit.

B. Digitized Wire Spark Chambers

Kreinen (1962) and Waters (1963) demonstrated the direct digitization of spark chamber information by the use of wire ground electrodes each of which threads through a magnetic core. A large number of groups have constructed such chambers. The basic sparking properties of such chambers are essentially identical to those of ordinary optical parallel plate chambers. The only difference is that far less spark energy is required to flip the cores than to produce a visible spark, so that the recovery time of the chamber can be considerably shorter. The chamber also has the advantage that the position information is recorded in the cores with essentially no delay. The cores can then be interrogated for transfer of the information to magnetic tape or directly to the computer.

As an example, we describe a test wire chamber system constructed at Brookhaven (Fischer *et al.*, 1963). They have constructed three wire planes each of which has a one dimensional resolution. Each plane consists of a 6 × 6 in. frame with a thin foil conducting plane for the high voltage pulse and a plane containing 64 parallel wires each threaded through a ferrite core for the ground electrode. The wires were 0.01 in. diameter copper and spaced at 1 mm intervals. The gap spacing was 0.25 in.

The pulse was applied to the planes and then decoupled during the spark discharge so that the energy source for the discharge was just the local capacitance to the wires. Best efficiency could be obtained with a filling of 90% neon 10% helium and 1.5% alcohol and was better than 99.5%. Another study was made of the number of wires which participate in the discharge. The average number of wires participating in the discharge was found to vary approximately linearly with the capacity of discharge and quadratically with the voltage. For a discharge energy of 0.001 J, an average of 1.5 wires was involved. If after the discharge a pulsed clearing field was applied, the recovery time could be made as short as a few hundred microseconds.

The spatial accuracy of the wire chambers when operated at low pulse energy is almost entirely due to the spacing of the wires. When the units are used as hodoscopes, it is important to reduce the effective thickness by using 0.005 in. aluminum wire instead of 0.01 in. copper. The individual wires reduce the spark robbing problem usually encountered in parallel plate spark chambers, and several individual tracks can be observed simultaneously.

In the development of large wire chambers, construction techniques are an important consideration. Miller and de Bruyne (1964) have used 0.005 in. diameter copper wires glued to mylar sheets and spaced 1.27 mm apart. These sheets were available commercially in 192 wire wide units of 15 ft length. Pizer (1964) has constructed wire chambers using printed circuit techniques. The wires are formed by photoetching on fiberglass circuit board. The technique is simple but results in a chamber with too much material for many applications. In a technique developed at the University of Chicago (Rey *et al.*, 1964), aluminum wires of 0.006 in. diameter are wound 24 per inch on lucite frames using a lathe. Figure 48 shows a view of one of these wire chambers.

The Chicago group has used wire chambers as rapid decision making devices. They use the switching of the core when a spark fires to that particular wire to develop a pulse in a secondary winding. This pulse

FIG. 48. Photograph of wire spark chamber plane constructed by Rey *et al.* (1964).

has typically a 10 to 20 nsec rise and is essentially independent of the length of the spark chamber pulse. They have used such a common fast read line to run through several cores simultaneously to establish a signal whose pulse height is proportional to the number of sparks. This information in turn can be used to trigger other spark chambers in the detector system.

C. Vidicon Systems

A number of vidicon systems have been used to observe and record spark chamber sparks (Anderson and Barna, 1964; Andreae *et al.*, 1964; Vernon, 1964). All the systems have a common arrangement. The images of the sparks are focused on the sensitive photoconductive surface of a vidicon. This surface can retain the images for times ~ 0.1 sec. A scanning electron beam, precisely controlled by an oscillator, sweeps in a programmed manner appropriate to the particular spark chamber format and records the position of the sparks on magnetic tape. The two questions of importance here in comparing this with other techniques are resolution and stability. For a standard 1 in. vidicon (General Electrodynamic Corporation 7325), the resolution on the face seems to be about 0.5×10^{-3} in. or about 1 part per 1000 of the tube face. The stability of the sweep system has to be checked by fixed illuminated fiducials.

A complete operating system has been constructed by Andreae *et al.* (1964). It can scan a parallel plate spark chamber with 12 gaps and can record a maximum of 2 sparks per gap. The clock frequency is such that the position of the spark in each gap can be digitized to 1 part in 1024 along the 50 μsec sweep. Each gap is scanned twice and the total scanning and storing time is 12 msec. A dead time of 36 msec is required to erase the event and the maximum rate of events is 20 per second or several per accelerator pulse. This system was used with success in an experiment to study recoil proton polarization in pion–nucleon scattering at Berkeley in the spring of 1964.

D. Other Filmless Recording Methods

We mention briefly here other filmless techniques that have been shown to be feasible. Charpak (1962) has constructed a chamber whose ground plate was an electric delay line. The time of arrival of the ground signal at the end of the delay line is related to the spark position.

More recently, Charpak *et al.* (1963) have developed a method which measures the difference between two branches of the spark current returning to ground. If two return paths are made at each end of the chamber, the difference in the two currents is roughly proportional to the displacement of the spark from the center of the chamber. If the two ground returns pass through a common ferrite core in opposite sense, a signal picked up by a secondary winding is proportional to the current difference. The sensitivity of the method can be made less than 1 mm. It is important to point out that the position information is immediate and the possibility exists that this information in turn can be used to trigger other chambers.

It has been suggested that magnetostrictive readout for wire chambers could be used (Giannelli, 1964). Perez-Mendez and Phab (1964) have carried out actual tests of the technique. They place a thin nickel ribbon magnetized to a suitable bias level in close proximity to the chamber wires so that the magnetic field of the wire carrying the spark current is coupled to the nickel ribbon. The magnetic field pulse of the spark current produces a local elongation by magnetostriction which propagates with the velocity of sound along the ribbon. If the ribbon is laid perpendicular to the wires, the time for the signal to propagate to the end of the ribbon is related to the particular wire which carried the spark current. The velocity of sound in the ribbon is about 5 mm/μsec and the maximum sensitivity for a reasonable detection coil is about ± 0.1 mm which is ample to decide which wire produced the pulse. Combination of this method with the current division method of Charpak may lead to a device with both x and y resolution.

IX. Developments of Other Types of Chambers

A. WIDE GAP SPARK CHAMBERS

It has been observed by many that there is a tendency under certain conditions for the spark discharges to follow the trajectory of the particle rather than the electric field. Although this effect takes place with small gaps, those chambers with larger gaps have demonstrated the effect more reliably. Figure 1, the photograph taken by Fukui and Miyamoto (1959), shows very clearly the slanted sparks. The properties of chambers with larger gaps have been pursued actively by Russian physicists since 1960 (Tyapkin, 1960).

Let us return to the discussion of the development of avalanches. In principle, each electron produced by the primary ionization initiates one avalanche. The avalanche consists of a spherical ball of electrons some tenths of a millimeter in diameter. (See, for example, Fletcher, 1949.) The critical condition for the passage to the streamer stage occurs when the avalanche contains $\sim 10^8$ electrons. At this stage, the electric field at the surface of the electron cloud is approximately equal to the applied field. Figure 49 shows a schematic view of a line of avalanches that have reached the critical stage. The net field direction between the negative ball of electrons and the positive ions left behind the following avalanche is inclined towards the direction of the original track. If the density of avalanches is sufficiently great, the streamer growth will occur along the line of avalanches and the final spark channel will be localized along the particle trajectory. If the avalanches are too widely spaced, the streamers will develop along the impressed field lines and the discharge will spread laterally over the entire projection of the track.

In the case of small gaps, the initial displacement of the primary electrons is often comparable to the width of the gap, so that little angular information remains since many of the electrons have been cleared from the gap.

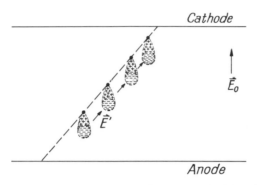

FIG. 49. Schematic view of avalanches that have reached the critical size.

Thus, one expects with narrow gap chambers that the tendency of the spark to follow the gap will be destroyed by slow rising pulses and large clearing fields. A quantitative study of these effects was made by Burnham *et al.* (1963) with the above conclusions.

When the gap spacing between the plates is extended to larger values, the spark discharge follows the trajectory very accurately. Chambers with gaps greater than 20 cm were constructed by Alikhanyan *et al.* (1963). They showed very dramatically that the tracks were accurately represented by the single spark up to angles of 45°, and that the tracks even show proper curvature in a magnetic field. This type of chamber is generally built with four lucite walls and sealed at either end by a conducting electrode. The electric field required to develop rapid avalanches is about 10 kV/in. so that voltages of hundreds of kilovolts are required for the large gaps. These voltages are supplied by Marx generators. This type of pulser essentially charges a bank of condensers in parallel and discharges them in series by means of spark gaps. Such generators with output voltages as high as 450 kV have been constructed.

Garron *et al.* (1964) have made very careful studies of the properties of wide gap chambers with particular attention to accuracy. Figure 50 shows a schematic view of their arrangement to study the properties of the chamber. The Marx generator with 15 stages produced an output of 450 kV, and the pulse duration which was chosen by the shunting resistor across the chamber was usually about 50 nsec. No special efforts were necessary to obtain a very sharp rise time since the chamber worked very well with the pulser as it was. For the wide gap chambers, the requirement of a very fast rise is not so necessary since there is ample space for the avalanche to develop, unlike the narrow gap chambers. Of course, a slower rising high voltage pulse will produce a greater displacement of the spark.

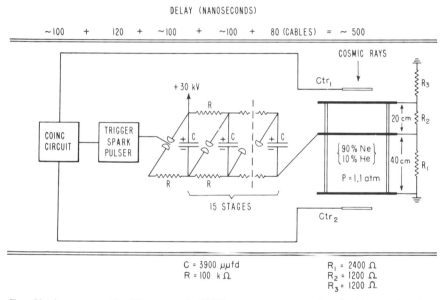

DELAY (NANOSECONDS)

~100   +   120   +   ~100   +   ~100   +   80 (CABLES)   =   ~ 500

C = 3900 μμfd R_1 = 2400 Ω
R = 100 kΩ R_2 = 1200 Ω
                       R_3 = 1200 Ω

FIG. 50. Arrangement by Garron et al. (1964) to measure properties of wide gap chambers.

A typical track in these chambers was shown in Fig. 3. The brightness and width of the track can be adjusted by the value of the shunting resistance. The range of widths is variable between 0.5 and 1.5 mm. For angles between 0 and 20°, the intensity of simple tracks is quite uniform, but, for tracks at angles greater than 20°, the intensity rapidly decreases. The maximum angle for which the discharge forms a single channel is 45°; for larger angles, many fine streamers develop.

Garron et al. (1964) found that the sensitive time of the chamber was a strong function of the gas purity. A few hours after a chamber was filled with pure neon or 90% neon 10% helium mixtures, the sensitive time was approximately 5 μsec. Immediately after the filling, the sensitive time was four times as long. Figure 51 shows the appearance of tracks as a function of delay time. Here two sections of a 40 cm chamber were driven by the same high voltage plate. The difference in intensity at 0 delay is due to a different gas purity in the two chambers. The track in the bottom chamber appears more erratic as the delay is increased. After a delay of 5 μsec, the

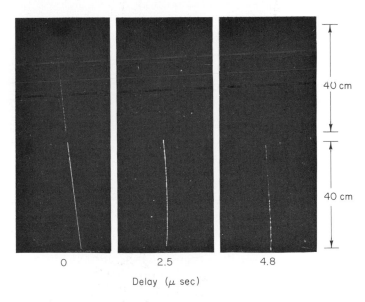

Fig. 51. Appearance of tracks in a wide gap chamber as a function of delay time (Garron et al., 1964).

tracks become very unstable. The effective sensitive time in a beam of particles is probably less than 5 μsec, since a young track having more primary electrons will develop into a spark channel more rapidly and therefore dominate the discharge. With the gas sealed in the chamber, the conditions for operation changed in a very few days, the sensitive time becoming shorter and the quality of the tracks becoming poorer. This condition could be remedied only by the increase of the shunt resistor. To permit operating with stable conditions over a long time, a gas flow system is probably required.

Garron et al. (1964) also tested chemical clearing with $\frac{1}{4}\%$ SO_2. The sensitive time was reduced by a factor of 3, but the quality of the tracks at the minimum delay of 0.5 μsec was also affected. The use of clearing fields is impractical for the wide gap chamber because the drift velocities of electrons vary as the square root of the applied field. The field necessary to clear the chamber rapidly would be near breakdown. Also, effective electrical clearing would cause serious displacements of the track.

By a comparison of the displacement of tracks at an angle between two chambers, the displacement due to the avalanche formation distance as well as clearing fields was measured. Garron *et al.* find for a 22 kV/cm pulsed field a 0.3 cm displacement of the spark from the trajectory. The corresponding value for a 4.5 kV/cm field is 0.5 cm. The fact that the lower field produces the greater drift demonstrates that the avalanche distance is shorter with the larger field. The drift of the spark due to the high voltage pulse can be compensated by a dc clearing field in the opposite direction. At a 500 nsec delay of the high voltage pulse, a 100 V/cm clearing field just compensates the avalanche drift.

Very careful studies of the accuracy of wide gap chambers have been made. By measurement of 40 points along the spark, Garron *et al.* (1964) found that the average deviation from a straight line was 0.06 mm for 90% neon 10% helium. Pure helium gives poorer results, as would be expected. The rms curvature of the straight tracks for the 40 cm chamber was found to be $\pm 0.5 \times 10^{-4} \, \text{cm}^{-1}$ for a magnetic field of 13 kG. This rms curvature represents a maximum detectable momentum of 80 BeV/c for a 40 cm track.

Tracks which are produced in regions of electric field inhomogeneity show significant distortions because of the variation in distance required to form the critical avalanche. With the wide gap, the distortion of the electric field near the edge of the electrodes is significant. Tracks at a distance less than 25 cm from the edge show distortions considerably larger than the fluctuation, $0.5 \times 10^{-4} \, \text{cm}^{-1}$, of the radius of curvature for straight tracks. By the insertion of a multiplate shielding condenser, the distortion can be reduced to less than $\pm 0.5 \times 10^{-4} \, \text{cm}^{-1}$ within 8 cm of the physical extremity of the chamber. If, however, a grounded electrode, a magnet pole piece for example, is brought near to the edge of the guard condenser, the closest distance for significant distortion is about 25 cm.

Garron *et al.* (1964) made tests of the accuracy of momentum measurement by the use of two chambers, one on top of the other. Comparison of the radii of curvature measured in the two systems enabled them to determine the accuracy. Figure 52 shows a number of tracks with the measured momenta listed below. The precision of measurement of the curvature was found to be essentially that predicted by studies of the tracks without magnetic field. Thus 1 BeV/c momenta can be measured to an accuracy of

±1.4% for a 35 cm path (the distortion of the ends not being included) in a 13.3 kG field. The principal limitation of the accuracy was the small random displacement of the track from the true trajectory. The length could have been increased to 80 cm before the multiple scattering error would have equaled the spark scatter error. Other potential sources of error are the coherent distortions of the entire track due to inhomogeneous

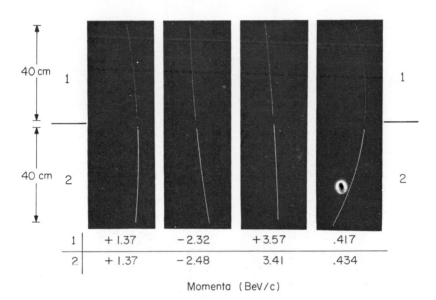

1	+ 1.37	− 2.32	+ 3.57	.417
2	+ 1.37	− 2.48	3.41	.434

Momenta (BeV/c)

FIG. 52. Comparison of radii of curvature of a track passing through two successive chambers (Garron *et al.*, 1964).

fields. Typical lateral displacements in the direction $\mathbf{E} \times \mathbf{B}$ are of the order of 0.15 cm for an 11 kV/cm field. These displacements do not affect the accuracy as long as $\mathbf{E}$ and $\mathbf{B}$ are sufficiently homogeneous, and furthermore they can be canceled by a suitable electric clearing field.

One of the very attractive features of this type of chamber is the accuracy of the momentum measurement with a very short length of magnetic field. If the position accuracy of the narrow gap chambers is assumed to be ±0.02 cm, the accuracy with which a wide gap chamber can measure momentum in a given length of magnetic field exceeds by at least a factor of 3 the accuracy obtainable with narrow gap chambers. The angular range for which effective measurements can be made is roughly the same for the two chambers. The small gap chamber has the advantage of a shorter sensitive time and relative insensitivity to field inhomogeneity. The fraction of useful volume of magnetic field with the wide gap chamber will be considerably less since a great deal of space is utilized in making the electric field uniform.

The efficiency for multiple tracks is not well known. During their studies, Garron *et al.* (1964) noticed unaccountable fluctuations in brightness when multiple tracks occurred. It is not certain that some tracks are not visible

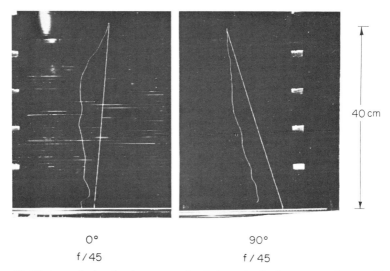

0°   90°

f /45   f / 45

40 cm

Fɪɢ. 53. Photograph showing in extreme detail the path of a low energy electron (Garron *et al.*, 1964).

at a given lens aperture. To facilitate study of multiple tracks generally, photographs were taken with two lens apertures, $f/45$ and $f/16$. For all types of spark chambers, the efficiency is a function of the photography since multiple sparks can show a continuous range of intensities. If high efficiency is desired, a photographic system of wide dynamic range is required. At the time of writing, no definitive tests of multispark efficiency have been made.

The Russian group of Lyubimov and Pavlovsky (1964) have studied the sensitivity of the wide gap chamber to ionization. They have demonstrated that under certain circumstances the wide gap chamber shows sparks of different luminosity for particles of different ionization. Also, they showed that when the chamber is operated with conditions close to being inefficient, the tracks have a granular structure which is evidenced by fluctuating intensity. They find that the number of fluctuations per unit length is nearly proportional to the ionization.

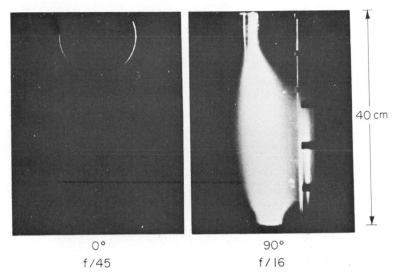

FIG. 54. Photograph showing electron deflected through 180°. The view taken parallel to the magnetic field with a larger aperture shows how the track is completed by diffuse streamers.

The fine detail possible with these chambers is remarkable. Figure 53 shows a low energy electron in addition to the main track. Figure 54 shows a track that makes a 180° bend emerging again from the top of the chamber. Although the current path is completed by diffuse streamers, the form of the track is clearly indicated. Similarly, one expects that neutral Λ^0 or K^0 decays in the interior of the chamber will be sufficiently well defined to provide useful measurements even though the discharges will be completed by diffuse streamers.

B. PROJECTION CHAMBERS

When one of the electrodes of an ordinary chamber is transparent, one can view the sparks parallel to the electric field. The electrodes can be made transparent by means of conducting glass or wire mesh. When a track passes roughly parallel to the plates, one sees many sparks which originate from the electrons left along the path of the particle. Fukui and Miyamoto (1959) discussed this mode of operation in their original paper. A track viewed in the projection mode was shown in Fig. 4.

Fukui and Zacharov (1963) argue that the property of good multiple track efficiency requires electrodes of low conductivity. They have constructed chambers with glass electrodes coated with SnO_2 on the outside surface. The gap spacing was typically ~1 cm. The glass insulator limits the build-up of the discharge, the only energy available being that of the electrostatic field. Such a chamber can register a large number of simultaneous tracks and as a consequence operate in a high instantaneous flux. The clearing time, however, is rather long, being a few μsec in length, when an electric clearing field is applied. It is difficult to measure accurately the multitrack efficiency. Although it is true that a single track passing through parallel to the gap may produce 100 sparks, it is not clear that 100 tracks passing perpendicular to the gap would produce 100 sparks. When chambers are operated in a projection mode so that the particles are distributed along the gap, a good projection of the track is obtained, even if the efficiency for an individual electron is only 25%. As a matter of fact, the number of sparks observed is significantly less than the number of electrons liberated by ionization. Whether this condition is due to several electrons coalescing into a single avalanche or just an inefficiency is not well known.

For given operating conditions, the number of sparks per unit length is related to the ionization of the particle and shows promise of being quantitatively useful (Fukui and Zacharov, 1963). The placement of such chambers in a magnetic field through which collimated particles pass is a promising application. There are no distortions due to electron drift since the electric and magnetic fields are parallel to one another and perpendicular to the path of the particle.

This type of chamber does not produce much light since the energy is limited. Thus, photography cannot be made with great depth of field. For the pure projection use, however, one essentially focuses on a plane, and a large aperture can be used. No careful studies have been made on the accuracy available with the projection chamber.

Charpak and Massonet (1963) have made extensive studies of projection chambers with both small and large gaps (6 cm). The chambers were constructed with wire mesh electrodes, and the authors found that it was difficult to arrive at stable operating conditions until iodine vapor (0.2 mm) was added to the ordinary neon–helium gas mixture. With the iodine, the breakdown potential is considerably lowered and the whole time scale of the discharge development changes. Ultimately, the electron multiplication comes from ionization of the iodine in collisions with excited noble gas atoms. Applied pulses of ~2 kV/cm and 0.5 to 10 μsec in length must be used. The dynamic resistance of this kind of discharge does not immediately consume all of the available energy.

Such projection chambers have a very good multiple track efficiency and can operate in the presence of very high rates. One very distinctive feature is the very short recovery time. The chamber can be pulsed at a rate of 10^4 per second without reignition of old sparks. With a very low electric field, the pulse energy is small and again the light levels are very low.

C. Streamer Chambers

The achievement of an isotropic gas discharge device has been a goal sought after for many years. The basic idea is to have the electrons liberated by ionization produce visible light within the immediate region of their production. Fukui et al. (1960) and Lederman et al. (1961) have attempted to build R.F. chambers. After the passage of the particle, a pulsed R.F. field agitates the electrons, and, hopefully, by this method sufficient luminous energy can be developed. These methods have failed to produce a useful device.

Damped oscillations have been employed by Cavalleri et al. (1962) to produce visible tracks of α particles in neon gas. The tracks were bright enough to photograph only in the view parallel to the electric field, although they were visible to the dark-adapted eye perpendicular to the field.

Recently Chikovani et al. (1963) observed with projection chambers that, when the applied pulse was shortened, the detailed structure of the streamers revealed not only the projection of the track but also the depth. The depth information comes from the fact that early in the streamer growth, the most luminous part of the discharge is located at the point where the critical avalanche has developed. Using two cameras with a small stereo angle, Chikovani et al. were able to localize the depth of the luminous centers to an accuracy of a few millimeters. In fact, a side view of the streamers reveals the path of the particle by nodes in the streamer columns.

By application of pulses even shorter, two Russian groups (Chikovani et al., 1964; Dolgoshein et al., 1964) were able to limit the growth of the streamers to only a few millimeters, and the centers of these streamers can be located to within a millimeter. Figure 5 in the introduction to this chapter shows a view perpendicular to the electric field of the chamber of Dolgoshein et al. (1964). Here the streamers are limited to a length of 7 mm. The view obtained parallel to the field has a considerably greater intensity, and one can continue to obtain the depth information by using two small angle stereo cameras. Chikovani et al. (1964) have constructed very large chambers which have been operated in magnetic fields. Figure 55 shows the two stereo views of a very large cosmic ray shower. Chikovani et al. state that

the light intensity parallel to the field is sufficient to photograph with an
aperture of $f/5.6$ and film speeds of $\sim$A.S.A. 1000.

The construction of the streamer chambers is very simple. For example,
the chambers of Chikovani *et al.* are constructed of a glass box $100 \times 60 \times 19$ cm. The electrodes consist of 0.1 mm copper wires spaced rather
widely apart. The boxes are filled with neon. To obtain a very short pulse,

FIG. 55. Photograph showing two stereo views of a very large cosmic ray shower in a large
streamer chamber (Chikovani *et al.* (1964)).

a shunting spark gap is placed across the electrodes outside the box. Adjustment of the spacing of this gap controls the duration of the pulse. For
chambers of these dimensions, a pulse of about 50 nsec in length and 200
kV in amplitude is sufficient to produce streamers several millimeters long.
The control on the pulse length is required to be quite accurate in order to
maintain the proper streamer length. It is clear that great care must be given
to the details of pulsing to obtain stable performance. Recently, Gygi and
Schneider (1964) have studied in detail the properties of Marx generators
and have constructed a pulser which can deliver a pulse 10^{-8} sec long with
an amplitude of 200 kV.

The present streamer chambers have the capacity of registering tracks in
all directions and can record many tracks since the energy density which
produces the illumination comes from the energy stored in the electric field.
It remains to study carefully the effects of field inhomogeneities, the long
term stability of operation, the clearing properties, and the accuracy of
trajectory location.

X. Concluding Remarks

In a book of this type, one is naturally inclined to discuss in more detail
those parts of the subject that are firmly established. Thus, we have devoted
most of the discussion to the parallel plate sampling spark chambers.

Between the time these words are set down on paper and the time of publication of this book one can expect enormous developments in the newer forms of spark discharge or streamer devices. These newer devices show promise of an isotropic response, the lack of which is a definite shortcoming of the parallel plate spark chambers.

Nevertheless, the parallel plate sampling chamber has been applied with immediate success to a wide variety of experiments. Now it can be viewed as a standard research tool along with scintillation counters, bubble chambers, emulsions, etc. It is not likely to be replaced in the near future. These chambers are inexpensive to construct and reliable to operate. Their properties complement nicely the properties of electronic detectors, providing added detailed visual information even with high rates of particles passing through. It is fortunate that the electrons in the noble gas can be made to drift 1 cm in a time less than that required by the photomultipliers and electronics to make the logical decision to pulse the chamber. Thus the limitation on the smallest sensitive time obtainable with the spark chamber is always controlled by the exterior electronics and is not a fundamental limitation of the chamber itself.

With a few exceptions, the most successful applications of spark chambers have been those using a highly selective trigger and recording a total number of events which was not too large. The need to have a small number of events is by no means a fundamental limitation; it stems only from the lack of data handling capacity. An attack on this problem is being made on two fronts; first by the filmless techniques which we have discussed in Section VIII and second by automatic film reading techniques which will be discussed in Chapter III, Volume 2. Since the spark chamber by nature yields fewer bits of information, these data handling problems are more readily solved for the spark chamber than for the bubble chamber.

It was the author's good fortune to have had the opportunity to participate in some of the very early applications of the spark chamber. It is no confession to speak of the pleasure of being able to build such a simple device which can view the spatial activities of the elementary particles over such a large volume. The author is certain that there are many others who have also sat up late at night in the laboratory watching cosmic rays pass through a newly completed spark chamber.

ACKNOWLEDGMENTS

The author would like to thank the many people who gave their permission to use figures or photographs from their published works. Generous assistance in preparation of the manuscript was given by the Laboratoire de Physique Corpusculaire à Haute Energie, Centre d'Études Nucléaires de Saclay, France.

REFERENCES

AGRINIER, B., KOECHLIN, Y., PARLIER, B., and GATZ, P. (1963). *J. Phys. Radium* **24**, 312.

ALIKHANYAN, A. I., ASATIANI, T. L., MATEVESIAN, E. M., and SHAUKHATUNIAN, R. O. (1963). *Phys. Letters* **4**, 295.

ANDERSON, H. L., and BARNA, A. (1964). *Rev. Sci. Instr.* **35**, 492.

ANDREAE, S., KERNS, Q. A., KINSTEN, F. A., MACK, D. A., NUNAMAKER, T. A., and PEREZ-MENDEZ, V. (1964). *IRE Trans. Nucl. Sci.* **NS11**, 317.

ASTBURY, P., *et al.* (1964). *Proc. Intern. Conf. High Energy Phys. Dubna, USSR, 1964.*

AUTONÈS, P., BAREYRE, P., GAILLARD, J. M., ROBERT, G., and SEIGE, R. (1963). *Nucl. Instr. Methods* **24**, 418.

BARDON, M., LEE, J., NORTON, P., PEOPLES, J., and SACHS, A. M. (1964). *Proc. Informal Meeting Filmless Spark Chamber Tech. and Assoc. Computer Use,* CERN Rept. 64–30, p. 41.

BAREYRE, P. (1964). Centre d'Etudes Nucléaires de Saclay, private communication.

BARTLETT, D., DEVONS, S., MEYER, S. L., and ROSEN, J. L. (1964). *Phys. Rev.* **136**, B1452.

BAYUKOV, YU. D., LEKSIN, G. A., SUCHKOV, D. A., and TELENKOV, V. V. (1963). *Nucl. Instr. Methods* **20**, 198.

BEALL, E. F., CORK, B., MURPHY, P. G., and WENZEL, W. A. (1961). *Nuovo Cimento* **20**, 502.

BEALL, E. F., CORK, B., KEEFE, D., MURPHY, P. G., and WENZEL, W. A. (1962). *Phys. Rev. Letters* **8**, 75.

BEALL, E. F., *et al.* (1963). *Nucl. Instr. Methods* **20**, 205.

BLEULER, E., *et al.* (1963). *Nucl. Instr. Methods* **20**, 208.

BOWE, J. G. (1960). *Phys. Rev.* **117**, 1411.

BURLESON, G. R., ROBERTS, A., and ROMANOWSKI, T. A. (1962). *In* "Nuclear Electronics," Vol. I, p. 247. Intern. Atomic Energy Agency, Vienna.

BURLESON, G. R., *et al.* (1963). *Nucl. Instr. Methods* **20**, 180.

BURNHAM, J. U., and THOMPSON, M. G. (1964). *J. Sci. Instr.* **41**, 108.

BURNHAM, J. U., RODGERS, I. W., THOMPSON, M. G., and WOLFENDALE, A. W. (1963). *J. Sci. Instr.* **40**, 296.

CAVALLERI, C., GATTI, E., and REDAELLI, G. (1962). *Nuovo Cimento* **25**, 1282.

CHARPAK, G. (1962). *Nucl. Instr. Methods* **15**, 318.

CHARPAK, G., and MASSONET, L. (1963). *Rev. Sci. Instr.* **34**, 664.

CHARPAK, G., FAVIER, J., and MASSONET, L. (1963). *Nucl. Instr. Methods* **24**, 501.

CHIKOVANI, G. E., MIKHAILOV, V. A., and ROINISHVILI, V. N. (1963). *Phys. Letters* **6**, 254.

CHIKOVANI, G. E., ROINISHVILI, V. N., and MIKHAILOV, V. A. (1964). *Nucl. Instr. Methods* **29**, 261.

CHRISTENSON, J. H., CLARK, A. R., and CRONIN, J. W. (1964a). *IRE Trans. Nucl. Sci.* **NS11**, 310.

CHRISTENSON, J. H., CRONIN, J. W., FITCH, V. L., and TURLAY, R. (1964b). *Phys. Rev. Letters* **13**, 138.

COCCONI, G., *et al.* (1964). *Proc. Informal Meeting Filmless Spark Chamber Tech. and Assoc. Computer Use,* CERN Rept. 64–30, p. 183.

COFFIN, T., GARWIN, R. L., PENMAN, S., LEDERMAN, L. M., and SACHS, A. M. (1958). *Phys. Rev.* **109**, 973.

CONVERSI, M., DI LELLA, L., and TOLLER, M. (1962). *Rev. Sci. Instr.* **33**, 777.

COOL, R., *et al.* (1965). *Phys. Rev. Letters* **14**, 724.

CRAWFORD, D. F., and MESSEL, H. (1962). *Phys. Rev.* **128**, 2352.

CRONIN, J. W., and OVERSETH, O. E. (1963). *Phys. Rev.* **129**, 1795.

CRONIN, J. W., and RENNINGER, G. (1960). *Proc. Intern. Conf. Instrumentation for High Energy Phys.*, *Berkeley, 1960*, p. 271. Wiley (Interscience), New York.

CRONIN, J. W., ENGELS, E., PYKA, M., and ROTH, R. (1962). *Rev. Sci. Instr.* **33**, 946.

CULLIGAN, G., HARTINGS, D., and LIPMAN, N. H. (1961). CERN Rept. 61–65. Unpublished.

DANBY, G., *et al.* (1962). *Phys. Rev. Letters* **9**, 460.

DESCHONG, J. A., DANIELS, R. E., HILDEBRAND, R., and MEYER, P. (1964). *Rev. Sci. Instr.* **35**, 1035.

DEUTSCH, M. (1961). Mass. Inst. Technol., private communication.

DOLGOSHEIN, B. A., RODIONOV, B. U., and LUCHKOV, B. I. (1964). *Nucl. Instr. Methods* **29**, 270.

DRUYVESTEYN, M. J., and PENNING, F. M. (1940). *Rev. Mod. Phys.* **12**, 87.

EANDI, R. D., DEVLIN, T. J., KENNY, R. W., MCMANIGAL, P. G., and MOYER, B. J. (1964). *Phys. Rev.* **136**, B536.

ENGELS, E., ROTH, R., CRONIN, J. W., and PYKA, M. (1962). *IRE Trans. Nucl. Sci.* **NS9**, 256.

ENGLISH, W. H., and HANNA, G. C. (1953). *Can. J. Phys.* **31**, 768.

FAISSNER, H. (1964). *Proc. Intern. Conf. High Energy Phys.*, *Dubna, USSR, 1964*.

FAISSNER, H., FERRERO, F., GHANI, A., KRIERREN, F., NOVEY, T. B., and REINHARZ, M. (1963a). *Nucl. Instr. Method* **20**, 151.

FAISSNER, H., *et al.* (1963b). *Proc. Intern. Conf. Elementary Particles, Sienna, 1963*, Vol. I, p. 546. Ital. Phys. Soc., Bologna.

FISCHER, J., and ZORN, G. T. (1961). *Rev. Sci. Instr.* **32**, 499.

FISCHER, J., and ZORN, G. T. (1962). *IRE Trans. Nucl. Sci.* **NS9**, 261.

FISCHER, J., COLLINS, G. B., and HIGINBOTHAM, W. A. (1963). *Proc. Intern. Symp. Nucl. Electron., Paris* p. 57.

FLETCHER, R. C. (1949). *Phys. Rev.* **76**, 1501.

FOLEY, K. J., *et al.* (1964). *Proc. Informal Meeting Filmless Spark Chamber Tech. and Assoc. Computer Use,* CERN Rept. 64–30, p. 237.

FRISCH, D. (1964). Mass. Inst. of Technol., private communication.

FUKUI, S., and MIYAMOTO, S. (1959). *Nuovo Cimento* **11**, 113.

FUKUI, S., and MIYAMOTO, S. (1961). *J. Phys. Soc. Japan* **16**, 2574.

FUKUI, S., and ZACHAROV, B. (1963). *Nucl. Instr. Methods* **23**, 24.

FUKUI, S., HAYAKAWA, S., TSUKISHIMA, T., and NUKUSHINA, H. (1960). *Proc. Intern. Conf. Instrumentation for High Energy Phys.*, *Berkeley, 1960*, p. 267. Wiley (Interscience), New York.

FULBRIGHT, H. W., and KOHLER, D. (1961). Univ. of Rochester Rept. NYO-9540. Unpublished.

GALBRAITH, W., MANNING, G., TAYLOR, A. E., ASTBURY, A., LIPMAN, N. H., and WALKER, T. G. (1965). *Phys. Rev. Letters* **14**, 383.

GARRON, J. P., GROSSMAN, D., and STRAUCH, K. (1965). *Rev. Sci. Instr.* **36**, 264.

GIANNELI, G. (1964). *Proc. Informal Meeting Filmless Spark Chamber Tech. and Assoc. Computer Use,* CERN Rept. 64–30, p. 325.

GYGI, E., and SCHNEIDER, F. (1964). "A Nanosecond Pulse Generator of 200 kV Amplitude," CERN Rept. 64–46.

HENNING, P. G. (1957). *Atomkernenergie* **2**, 81.

JONES, B. D., MALOS, J., GALBRAITH, W., and MANNING, G. (1964). *Nucl. Instr. Methods* **29**, 115.

KAJIKAWA, R. (1963). *J. Phys. Soc. Japan,* **18**, 1365.

KEEFE, D., KERTH, L. T., NOBLE, C. M., THREASHER, J. J., and WENZEL, W. A. (1963). *Nucl. Instr. Methods* **20**, 171.

KERNS, Q. (1963). Lawrence Radiation Lab. Rept. UCRL–10887. Unpublished.

KREINEN, F. (1962). *Nucl. Instr. Methods* **16**, 262.

LANDE, K., MANN, A. K., and WHITE, D. H. (1963). *Nucl. Instr. Methods* **20**, 193.

LAVOIE, L., PARKER, S., REY, C., and SCHWARTZ, D. M. (1964). *Rev. Sci. Instr.* **35**, 1597.

LEDERMAN, L., SCHWARTZ, M., and GAILLARD, J. M. (1960). *Proc. Intern. Conf. Instrumentation for High Energy Phys., Berkeley, 1960*, p. 201. Wiley (Interscience), New York.

LEDERMAN, L. M., GIORDMAINE, J., and STRELZOFF, A. (1961). *Rev. Sci. Instr.* **32**, 525.

LYUBIMOV, V. A., and PAVLOVSKY, F. A. (1964). *Nucl. Instr. Methods* **27**, 346.

MAGLIC, B., and KIRSTEN, F. (1962). *Nucl. Instr. Methods* **17**, 49.

MEEK, J. M., and CRAGGS, J. D. (1953). "Electrical Breakdown of Gases," Oxford Univ. Press (Clarendon), London and New York.

MEYER, M. A. (1963). *Nucl. Instr. Methods* **23**, 283.

MEYER, D. I., and TERWILLIGER, K. M. (1961). *Rev. Sci. Instr.* **32**, 512.

MICHAEL, D. N., and SCHLUTER, R. A. (1963). Argonne Natl. Lab., Internal Rept. DNM/RAS-1. Unpublished.

MIKHAILOV, V., ROINISCHIVLI, V. N., and CHICOVANI, G. E. (1961). *Pribory i Tekhn. Eksperim.* **1**, 39.

MILLER, D., and DE BRUYNE, P. (1964). *Proc. Informal Meeting Filmless Spark Chamber Tech. and Assoc. Computer Use,* CERN Rept. 64–30, p. 123.

MURPHY, F. V., Jr., and O'NEILL, G. K. (1962). *Nuovo Cimento, Suppl.* **26**, 286.

O'NEILL, G. K., MURPHY, F. V., Jr., WRIGHT, K., and YOUNT, D. (1963). *Nucl. Instr. Methods* **20**, 176.

OVERSETH, O. E. (1964). Univ. of Michigan, Ann Arbor, Michigan, private communication.

PARKER, S., ANDERSON, H. L., and REY, C. (1964). *Phys. Rev.* **133**, B768.

PEREZ-MENDEZ, V., and PHAB, J. M. (1964). Lawrence Radiation Lab., Rept. UCRL 11620. Unpublished.

PIZER, H. I. (1964). *Proc. Informal Meeting Filmless Spark Chamber Tech. and Assoc. Computer Use,* CERN Rept. 64–30, p. 111.

PLATNER, E. D., ORR, J. R., MASEK, G. E., and WILLIAMS, R. W. (1963). *Nucl. Instr. Methods* **20**, 505.

PONDROM, L. G. (1964). Univ. of Wisconsin, Madison, Wisconsin, private communication.

RAETHER, H. (1941). *Z. Physik* **117**, 37.

REY, C., PARKER, S., SHERWOOD, B., and SCHWARTZ, D. (1964). Enrico Fermi Inst. Rept. EFINS 384 (*Nucl. Instr. Methods.* To be published).

RUTHERGLEN, J. G., and PATTERSON, J. M. (1961). *Rev. Sci. Instr.* **32**, 519.

SCHNEIDER, F. (1963). "Multi-Spark Efficiency of the Spark Chamber," CERN Internal Rept. AR/Int. GS 63–9. Unpublished.

SCHNEIDER, F., and HÖENE, K. H. (1963), *Nucl. Instr. Methods* **20**, 152.

SCHWARTZ, M. (1964). Columbia Univ., New York, private communication.

SODICKSON, L., WAHLIG, M., MANNELLI, I., FRISCH, D., and FACKLER, O. (1964). *Phys. Rev. Letters* **12**, 485.

TOWNSEND, J. (1947). "Electrons in Gases," p. 20. Hutchinson's, London.

TSUKISHIMA, T. (1963). *J. Phys. Soc. Japan* **18**, 558.

TYAPKIN, A. A. (1960). *Proc. Intern. Conf. Instrumentation for High Energy Phys., Berkeley, 1960*, p. 270. Wiley (Interscience), New York.

VERNON, W. (1964). *Proc. Informal Meeting Filmless Spark Chamber Tech. and Assoc. Computer Use,* CERN Rept. 64–30, p. 57.

VON ENGEL, A. (1956). *In* "Handbuch der Physik," Vol. 21, p. 504, Springer, Berlin.

VON THOLL, H. (1963). *Z. Naturforsch.* **18a**, 587.

WAHLIG, M. A., BUFFINGTON, A., FRISCH, D. H., HILL, D. A., and SODICKSON, L. (1962). *Rev. Sci. Instr.* **33**, 539.

WATERS, J. R. (1963). *Nucl. Instr. Methods* **20**, 168.

WENZEL, W. A. (1964). *Ann. Rev. Nucl. Sci.* **14**, 205.

WILSON, R. R. (1951). *Phys. Rev.* **86**, 261.

BIBLIOGRAPHY

Listed below are a few general references and conference proceedings which contain a large amount of information on spark chambers, and complete list of references.

Proc. Intern. Conf. Instrumentation for High Energy Phys., Berkeley, California, 1960. Wiley (Interscience), New York.

Spark Chamber Symp., Argonne Natl. Lab., February, 1961. [*Rev. Sci. Instr.* **32**, 480 (1961)].

"Instrumentation for High Energy Physics"; *Proc. Conf. Instrumentation for High Energy Phys., 1962.* (F. J. M. Farley, ed.). [*Nucl. Instr. Methods* **20** (1963)].

Proc. Informal Meeting Filmless Spark Chamber Tech. and Assoc. Computer Use (G. R. Macleod and B. Maglic, eds.). CERN Rept. 64–30 (June 1964).

CHARPAK, G., MASSONNET, L., and FAVIER, J. "The development of spark chamber techniques." [*Prog. Nucl. Tech. and Instrumentation* **1**, 321–384 (1965)].

WENZEL, W. A. (1964). *Ann. Rev. Nucl. Sci.* **14**, 205.

Author Index

Numbers in parentheses are reference numbers and are included to assist in locating references in which authors' names are not mentioned in the text. Numbers in italics refer to the pages on which the references are listed.

A

Achermann, A. H., 147, *151*
Adair, R. K., 146, *151, 155*
Adelson, H. E., 148, *151*
Agrintier, B., 382, *402*
Ahmadzadeh, A., 44, *57*
Ainutdinov, M. S., 147, *151*
Aleksandrov, Yu. A., *151*
Alikhanian, A. I., 184, *230*, 318, 391, *402*
Allard, C., 147, *151*
Alston, M. H., 150, *151*
Alvarez, L. W., 148, *151*
Alyea, E. D., Jr., 187, 194, *230, 231*
Amiot, P., 147, *151*
Anderson, E. W., 15, 16, *16*
Anderson, H. L., 378, 389, *402, 404*
Andreae, S., 389, *402*
Androvlakis, J. G., 146, *151*, 273, *312*
Annis, A., 217, *230*
Argan, P. E., 41, 50, *57*, 190, 215, *230*
Asatiani, T. L., 318, 391, *402*
Askar'Yan, C. A., 50, *57*
Astbury, A., 386, *403*
Astbury, P., 380, 381, 386, *402*
Aubert, B., 218, 219, *230*
Autonés, P., 334, 335, 354, 372, *402*

B

Badier, J., 147, *151*
Baglin, C., 218, *230*
Balandin, M. P., 183, *230*
Bamberger, J. A., 146, *152*
Bardon, M., 383, 384, 385, 386, *402*
Bareyre, P., 318, 319, 334, 335, 354, 372, *402*
Barkov, L. M., 194, *230, 231*
Barmin, V. V., 217, *232*
Barna, A., 149, *152, 389, 402*
Barrera, F., 148, *152*
Bartlett, D., 378, *402*
Bartlett, M. S., 210, *230*
Bassi, P., 149, *152*, 189, 192, *230*
Bayukov, Yu. D., 331, *402*
Beall, E. F., 336, 342, 348, 350, 351, 372, 373, 374, *402*
Behr, L., 210, 219, 222, 223, *230*
Bella, F., 11, *16*
Belonogov, A. V., 147, *152*, 258, 259, 294, *312*
Bergmann, W. H., 194, *230*
Bertanza, L., 190, *230*
Birmingham, B. W., 148, *154*
Biswas, N. N., 44, *57*, 136, *144*
Blanpied, W. A., 107, *145*
Bleuler, E., 373, 374, 377, *402*
Blevins, M. E., 149, *153, 154*
Blewett, J. P., 5, *17*
Blinov, G. A., 41, *57*, 189, 215, *230, 231*
Bloch, M., 149, *152, 153, 154*, 162, 175, 219, *230*
Blokhiniseva, T. D., 147, *152*
Blondet, R., 147, *154*

407

Subject Index

415